POWER

BY HOWARD FAST

POWER

A NOVEL BY

HOWARD FAST

DOUBLEDAY & COMPANY, INC., GARDEN CITY, NEW YORK, 1962

8 13.52

F26p

All of the characters in this book are fictitious, and any resem-
blance to actual persons, living or dead, is purely coincidental.

44038

Oct. 1962

To the memory of my mother and father,
Ida and Barney Fast.

PART I

In 1920, I was working for the New York *Daily Mail*, I had the world licked and rated, I was cynical and certain of myself, and I was probably as unpleasant and arrogant as a kid of twenty-two can be. I believed that I was good-looking, I kept count of the women who went in and out of my life, and since I had served two years with the A.E.F., I considered my score of experience to be fairly complete.

This is in the way of identification, and it will do for the time being. This is not a story about myself but about Benjamin R. Holt, and while I have pieced together in my mind all the events and incidents that go toward the recollection of him, my own view of myself is less clear and less pressing. I would like to see myself as Oscar Smith saw me on that May morning in 1920, when he called me into his office, but the time is too long ago and too much has changed. Oscar Smith, the managing editor of the *Daily Mail*, was then in his late fifties, white-haired, tired, his voice flat and dry, very much the kind of newspaperman that the time and circumstances produced. He has been dead these many years now, remembered by a few people, myself among them. I remember his tolerance and his knowledge of kids like myself, and his slight smile when I played the cock of the walk, and the trace of amusement in his voice when he asked me how I would like to cover a war.

"You're kidding!" I said to him.

He looked at me over the top of his glasses, put a match to the dirty black pipe that was a part of his face, and shook his head.

"You sending me to Russia? That's the only war worth looking at."

"Not Russia. West Virginia."

"Joke. I'm laughing."

"I don't joke, Al," he said softly. "I got no sense of humor."

"There's no war in West Virginia."

"There will be. Maybe a small war, but I want you to work on it. If you do all right, it could be that we'll send you to Russia. Who knows? Anyway, I want you to go down to Hogan County in West Virginia and look around a little and then get yourself an interview with a fellow called Benjamin R. Holt."

"I never heard of him."

"I think you will."

"Who is he?"

Oscar Smith looked at me for a moment, coolly and thoughtfully. I suppose he could have said that the world and this city in particular was filled with young punks who worked on newspapers and believed that the world belonged to them; but he didn't have to be specific. His expression said the same thing, and then he told me about Benjamin Holt.

"He's the new president of the International Miners Union."

"Oh?"

2

"What do you know about coal mining?"

"Not a damn thing."

"It doesn't matter," he sighed. "Draw your expense money and take a sleeper tonight."

"How long do I stay there?"

"As long as you have to."

To me, then, he was an old man with notions, and I decided that twenty-four hours would satisfy his notions. That evening, I left New York for Clinton, in West Virginia.

2

I stood at the station and watched the train jerk to a start, pick up speed, shunt away from me, and then crawl into a green valley cleft, as narrow and dark in the morning shadow as the gateway to hell. It is an old, lonely, beautiful and nostalgic sound, the tearing, straining motion of a steam locomotive getting under way, and the memory of it is as passionate and lost as the memory of a place like Clinton then, a dirty, ugly town in the bottom of a valley the angels made and the devils captured, but gentle now at half past five in the morning, full of spring mist, with the sun hitting the mountainsides in a blaze of springtime glory and leaving the valley bottom full of mystery and shadow.

I was all alone at the station after the single bag of mail had been hefted and taken away by a man in blue overalls. If history was at the point of being made here, then Oscar Smith was singular in his perception of the fact. I waited there at the station a few minutes, to see whether any place could actually be as silent and empty as this one; then I picked up my bag and walked across the street, past the little station building, to the main business section of Clinton.

There was one long street of stores, a hotel, and a dirty red brick, three-story office building facing the railroad station. In back of this, a twisting dirt road clawed at the mountainside, and there were the dwelling places of the

3

town, rectangular, one-story boxes, six homes in each box, six entrances, red brick and tin roof, ten, twenty—perhaps fifty of them here and down into the end of the narrow valley. Up where the homes were, some windows flickered with light; the sun caught the top row of houses.

The Acropolis Cafe was in the process of opening, a short man with a black mustache sweeping the sidewalk in front of the place. I named him Nick and greeted him, and he looked me up and down with no pleasure and told me that it would be twenty minutes before he had coffee ready. I said I would wait.

Coffee took a half hour, because he was not in a hurry and whenever he looked at me he told me plainly that he was in no hurry and that he did not like me. Finally, he served me with coffee, fried eggs, and bread, and then he leaned on the counter and watched me eat and hated me.

"You come in on the train?" he asked me finally.

"That's right. I'm a reporter from the New York *Daily Mail.*"

"A reporter?"

I nodded, and he stopped hating me and told me how rotten business was, and how it used to be at this time in the morning, every seat at the counter filled, himself cooking and a man to help him and a girl to serve the counter.

"Now," he said, "business stinks, only there ain't business. There is nothing. When coal ain't mined here, there is nothing! Nothing! It is dead and it stinks dead."

"No coal being mined?" I asked.

"None!"

"There must be something else people do in a place like this."

"Nothing."

"What's the hotel like?" I asked him. He was a Greek. Then, in those days, there was a Greek restaurant more or less like this one in half the towns in America. Maybe in all the towns in America; I hadn't been to all of them by a long

4

count, and this was the first one in West Virginia and my first time in West Virginia too.

"The hotel stinks," he said. "What do you expect in a place like this?"

I finished eating, paid forty cents for the breakfast, and asked his opinion about trouble. I made some stupid remark about the possibilities of a war, and he looked at me the way he had looked at me when he first saw me, a look full of hatred and distrust.

"Guys like you," he said, "they make me sick."

Then a baby began to cry from the back of the cafe. He dismissed me from his mind and his world, and went to the back of the store. I picked up my suitcase to leave, but paused to watch him open the door that led into a room behind his place. Through the open door, I caught a glimpse of the room, just a glimpse but enough to see that the room was filled with women and children sleeping side by side on the floor.

"The son of a bitch keeps a harem there," I said to myself, and I walked out.

3

Years later, I repeated this story to Ben Holt, and I made no attempt to spare myself or depict myself as anything else but what I was. He nodded and said that it figured and was more or less what might have been expected in the way of my thoughts.

"Why?"

"Because," he said, "you knew nothing. It wasn't that you were ignorant as sin, but you wallowed in your ignorance. You loved it."

"I was a kid with the limitations of a kid."

"What's a kid? Twenty-two years old? Is that your definition of a kid? You could be an old man carrying all the misery of the world at that age. What stopped you? It just happens that George Skopus, who owned that restaurant, had a heart as big as a house. He had the women and kids of five families sleeping in that back room of his, and eating out of his larder and wiping him out. And all you could think with your little mind was that he ran a harem. Six months later he closed up the restaurant. A year later he was dead. He was a saint."

"I never knew you approved of saints."

"I don't. But I don't approve of ignorant punks either," Benjamin Holt said.

But that was five years later, years after this first time I went down to West Virginia to see him and write about him.

4

The room at the Traveler's Mountainside Hotel was three dollars and dear at the price, but there was a sink in it; and I washed and shaved before I set out to find Benjamin R. Holt. As I came down into the lobby, an argument was in progress between the hotel clerk and three men. The hotel clerk was a skinny, bent man in his middle fifties. Obsequiousness had eliminated his features, his looks, his individuality. I suppose I knew what his name was then, but I have forgotten it; on the other hand, the name of the man who faced him, standing a little in front of two others, has been written down on the record as a small, hard part of the history of those times. His name was Jim Flecker, and he was the last local survivor of the famous Flecker-Curry feud that had helped to depopulate West Virginia for almost half a century.

This I learned later; now I saw a man six feet and some inches tall, lean, with a set, hollow face and an oversized underjaw that appeared to rest on the juncture of his collarbones. He had tiny blue eyes as cold as ice, and he wore the silver star of a peace officer on the flap of his left shirt pocket. He wore a large revolver in a holster on his right hip, and in his left hand he carried a double-barreled shotgun. The pockets of his brown denim pants bulged with shotgun shells. His age was somewhere between forty and fifty.

Of the two men who stood immediately behind him, his deputies, one was fat and middle-aged and the other was very young, perhaps eighteen or nineteen, with a face that reminded me of a snake. They both carried double-barreled shotguns.

As I came down the stairs, Flecker was instructing the clerk in a voice as flat as metal. He broke off what he was saying to throw his glance at me and ask me who in hell I was. The look in his tiny blue eyes made me answer quickly and respectfully. Maybe I was a smart aleck, but one thing I had learned was a decent respect for a man with a gun and a very high regard indeed for an angry man with a gun. This man was hair-trigger angry, and boiling over with the venom inside of him; so I wasted no time, but told him who I was and took out my credentials and showed them to him.

"News? You'll find news here, all right. Just stay out of the way! Stay the hell out of the way!" I nodded, and he said to the man behind the counter, "Like I told you, my patience is thin—thin as spread spit on a hot day. So just wake those sons of bitches up and get them out of their rooms and out of this hotel. And keep them out!"

"Mr. Flecker," the hotel clerk pleaded, "I can't do that, I surely can't. I work here. I don't own the hotel. The hotel is a public institution, and if I got rooms, I am obligated to rent out those rooms, I am."

"You do like I say!"

"Mr. Flecker—"

"Oh, shut your goddamn mouth!" Flecker told him. "I don't want to hear no more from you, I don't. I'll be outside for one blessed hour—no more—and then if they ain't out, I come in and drag them out and then your hotel won't never look the same, so help me God, it won't!"

"I'll do the best I can, Mr. Flecker."

"Just do what I tell you to!"

Then Flecker turned on his heel and walked out, his two deputies following him.

During the last of this exchange, a boy of thirteen or fourteen had come out of the door that led into the dining room, and now he stood staring at the hotel clerk with round, frightened eyes. The clerk motioned him over, and then said to him, quickly and quietly,

"Jemmy—you get out and find Ben Holt and tell him that there's murder going to be done unless he gets over here and puts a stop to it."

"I can't do that."

"What do you mean, you can't do that?"

"I don't know where Ben Holt is," the boy pleaded.

"The devil you don't! The very devil you don't! Now look here, boy—didn't I give you a job bussing in the dining room? Your whole family lives off that three dollars a week you bring home. There are a hundred boys in this town would give their eyeteeth for your job, and you know that. Don't you?"

"Yes, sir."

"Then do as I say! You got miner kin, and the miners know where Ben Holt is."

"I can try, but I won't find Ben Holt."

"You find him and tell him Sheriff Flecker has murder in his eyes. Tell him there's going to be murder done unless he talks to the sheriff. Go ahead now!"

The boy sucked in his breath, nodded, and ran out through the dining-room door. I went over to the counter and offered the clerk a cigarette. He accepted, and I lit his and one for myself. He thanked me and said that he wished he was a newspaperman—or anything, preferably to being a hotel clerk in this sick and dying and damned town. "Look at the situation I'm in," he said. I replied that it was no use for me to look at it, because as far as I was concerned I couldn't make head or tail of it. I knew that the sheriff wanted to kill someone, but I didn't know who.

"Upstairs, Mister—? What did you say your name was?"

"Alvin Cutter," I told him.

"Well, sir, Mr. Cutter, I got twelve operatives from the Fairlawn Detective Agency sleeping upstairs, and I'm supposed to go up to them and boot them out of their rooms and tell them that this hotel is closed to them from here on in. Now I ask you—is that reasonable?"

"Why?"

"Well, you heard Mr. Flecker, didn't you?"

Whatever else he might have said was interrupted by the sound of someone on the stairs. The hotel clerk looked up nervously, flashed a glance at me, and then sighed hopelessly. A man was coming down the stairs, followed by others. He was a short, compact man, with a bulldog face, and he wore a striped suit, pink shirt, white collar, and black tie. He and those men who had followed him down the stairs gathered around the desk, and the clerk addressed them in whispers.

I knew that something was due to happen; the air of the place was charged with what was intended to happen and what had to happen and it did happen; but I didn't want it to happen while I was trapped, so to speak, in a hotel lobby. I had seen the boy go out through the dining room, and now I took the same path, through the dining room, through the kitchen, and out of the back entrance to the hotel. There was a farmer's truck there, unloading crated live chickens; I hurried past, into an alley, and then I was on the main street, at one end of the hotel. Flecker and his two deputies were on the porch, waiting. Watching them out of the corner of my eye, I crossed the street to where the local druggist was opening his shop. There were a few people on the street now; they moved slowly, and, like myself, they watched Flecker and his deputies.

What followed happened quickly, and while my memory

of it is fairly accurate, it might be a little more exact and to the point to reprint here the news story I filed later on this same day. The story follows, just as the *Daily Mail* printed it:

Hogan County, West Virginia. May 26, 1920.

Eleven men are dead, and a twelfth lingers between life and death as a result of a gunfight in this small West Virginia town.

Today, this reporter was witness to one of the most incredible gunfights in the history of a state that is not unfamiliar with private wars. The battle that turned the quiet main street of Clinton, West Virginia, into a scene of blood and horror took place during a sixty-second interval, early this morning. But the forces that led to this showdown were growing for a much longer time.

One does not have to have pro-labor sympathies to see the situation of the coal miners in Hogan County. An hour's walk around this community, in the heart of the richest coal country in America, convinced this reporter that the coal miners in Hogan County are not to be envied. A short conversation with any one of them leads immediately to the fact that at least part of their many troubles stem from the lack of a trade union of any kind.

This is a situation Benjamin R. Holt set out to remedy when he was elected president of the International Miners Union at the beginning of this year. Stating that there could be no job security for the unionized miners in Pennsylvania and Illinois, so long as West Virginia remained an unorganized area, he personally led a force of union organizers into Hogan and Mingo counties three weeks ago. They approached the local miners with the proposal that they constitute themselves a branch of the International Miners Union.

In defense of their own interests, the mine operators here announced that any miner under suspicion of meeting with IMU organizers or of supporting their attempts to organize a union, would be immediately discharged. These discharges began the day after Benjamin Holt arrived in West Virginia, and they have continued during the three weeks since then. Today, it is estimated that at least 75 per cent of the miners in Hogan County have been locked out of the mines.

The mine operators own most of the local stores and practically all of the miners' housing. Ten days ago, they cut off the miners'

10

credit allowances at the food stores and began a program of evicting from their homes those miners who had co-operated with the union organizers. Here in Clinton, Sheriff James D. Flecker was given the responsibility of carrying out the evictions.

Sheriff Flecker, famous locally as the only survivor of the notorious Flecker-Curry feud, stated that he would uphold the law and carry out the evictions, but only if he had proof that the accused miners had actually co-operated with the organizers. When four days passed without any evictions, the coal operators charged Sheriff Flecker with deliberate refusal to carry out his duties as specified in his oath of office. They explained this attitude on the part of Flecker by the many family connections Flecker had with miners in Clinton, and demanded his resignation. When Sheriff Flecker refused to resign, the operators were forced to resort to other measures, and they brought into Clinton twelve operatives of the Fairlawn Detective Agency of Philadelphia. The operatives were skilled labor consultants, under the leadership of Jack Madison, who made a national reputation during the steel strike of last year.

Immediately upon their arrival in Clinton, the Fairlawn operatives began a program of evictions, and during the next four days, these evictions were carried forward at the rate of fifty a day. Yesterday, they attempted to evict Sheriff Flecker's brother-in-law, and they were halted by the sheriff at gunpoint. Eye-witnesses to this incident say that when one of the operatives made a gesture toward his pocket, Sheriff Flecker stated that if the operative drew his gun, he would not hesitate to shoot him dead. Whereupon, Detective Madison ordered his men to halt eviction procedures at this house. He warned Sheriff Flecker of the consequences of the sheriff's interference, to which the sheriff replied with foul and abusive language. There was a heated exchange of words, which ended with a warning by Sheriff Flecker for the operatives to leave town.

The following morning, Sheriff Flecker and two deputies, John Winslow and Steve Kennedy, all of them heavily armed with pistols and shotguns, went to the Traveler's Mountainside Hotel, where the operatives had taken rooms. Sheriff Flecker spoke to the hotel clerk and demanded that the Fairlawn operatives be locked out of their rooms and refused service at the hotel. The hotel clerk protested that such action was not in his power.

Sheriff Flecker said he would wait outside of the hotel to see personally that his orders were obeyed.

A few minutes later, the twelve Fairlawn operatives, led by Detective Madison, came down from their rooms and were informed by the hotel clerk of the circumstances. Almost immediately, Detective Madison, whose courage had not been exaggerated, led his men out of the hotel to face Sheriff Flecker and demand his rights.

In a loud, firm voice, clearly hard by this reporter, who was watching proceedings from across the street, Detective Madison denied Sheriff Flecker's authority.

"My authority is here," Sheriff Flecker answered, tapping the barrel of his shotgun.

"Not any longer," said Detective Madison, "because I have a federal warrant for your arrest!"

With that, Detective Madison reached into his jacket pocket. Subsequent inquiry seems to prove that his statement about the warrant was bluff, and Sheriff Flecker states that Madison was reaching for his pistol. The full truth will never be known, for as Detective Madison reached into his coat pocket, Sheriff Flecker fired his shotgun directly into Detective Madison's face, killing him instantly.

What happened after that took place during a few seconds, and even an eyewitness cannot give an exact account. Both of Sheriff Flecker's deputies were carrying double-barreled shotguns, and a moment after he shot Detective Madison, they opened fire on the Fairlawn operatives, who were grouped closely together. They subsequently held that the operatives had drawn guns, but when the battle was over, only three operatives had drawn their pistols and only one of the three pistols was actually discharged.

As far as I could see, at least five of the operatives were killed with Madison when the shotguns were fired, and every one of the remaining six was wounded by pellets. Sheriff Flecker dropped his shotgun and drew his pistol, as did his two deputies, and the three of them began to shoot steadily. I saw one of the deputies put his pistol to an operative's head and administer the *coup de grâce*. Sheriff Flecker shot and killed two more men. In less than a minute, all twelve Fairlawn detectives were lying on the street in their blood, as terrible a scene of carnage as this reporter ever witnessed, either in this country or overseas during the last war.

Eleven of the men, at this writing, are dead. A twelfth operative lingers between life and death in the hotel, awaiting the arrival of a physician from the next town. The single survivor has three bullet wounds in the chest, and there is not much hope that he will live.

One of Sheriff Flecker's deputies, John Winslow, was wounded in the calf of his leg.

5

After I had filed my story at the Western Union office, I walked over to the building that housed the sheriff's office and the town jail. The eleven bodies were laid out on the sidewalk in front of the building, uncovered, as ghastly a sight as you would want to see. There was a considerable crowd around the bodies, men mostly—almost all of them miners, as I learned later—and some kids, and the crowd kept shifting and changing, as if no one could bear to remain there very long.

I pushed my way into the sheriff's office, which was even more crowded than the street outside. I noticed the two deputies, one of them hobbling on a bandaged leg. Sheriff Jim Flecker sat behind his desk, listening stonily to a half-hysterical man who leaned over the desk and alternately shouted at him and pleaded with him. This man, I learned, was Max Macintosh, the mayor, and as I pushed my way toward the desk, he was shouting,

"What you don't seem to understand, Jim, is that someone is going to have to answer for this!"

"I told you I'd answer for it."

"You told me hell—you told me nothing. The state police are on their way over here. I'm the mayor. There are eleven bodies outside I'm going to have to explain! My God, man, you're not up in the hills! This ain't no feud where you can wipe out a tribe of people and notch your gun!"

"Oh, shut up!" Flecker burst out suddenly. "You make me sick!"

"Then you'll be a lot sicker," the mayor said, and then, seeing the hard look of rage beginning to gather on Flecker's face, began to plead. The least Flecker could do, he pleaded, was to get together a set of sworn depositions to the effect that the shooting was actually a case of self-defense. Some men standing behind the mayor backed him up. Flecker listened, his eyes fixed on his desk; when he glanced up, I had pushed through to the desk, and he saw me and demanded to know who in the hell I was and what in hell I was doing there.

"I'm a reporter," I said. "I told you that before."

His face was cloudy with rage and frustration and the attempt to remember how this devilish day had begun. "How did you get here so quick?" the mayor wanted to know. I told them that I had been here, and then they wanted to know whether I had filed a story.

"Of course I did. Mister, this is news—the biggest news in a long time!"

"Then you better kill that damn story and kill it quick!" Flecker roared at me.

Looking back at myself then, at the whole incident and what it began and what would flow from it—looking back at the kind of fresh and ignorant kid that I was, I can take some satisfaction from the fact that I was not afraid or intimidated, but was able to face Sheriff Jim Flecker and tell him that the story wouldn't be killed because it was already in New York and probably everywhere else in America, and that within a few hours the whole town would be swarming with reporters, and that the best thing he could do would be to talk to me as he might to a human being. I think he would have killed me if he hadn't been restrained by the mayor and the other men present; and then the mayor took me outside and said that I shouldn't mind Jim Flecker, since the state he was in was understandable and only to be expected. "This is a thing that happened," he told me, glancing

14

at the crowd around the bodies. "Great God Almighty, don't we all wish that it had never happened at all! But you put two trains on the same track and start them off at each other at eighty miles an hour, and by golly something terrible's going to happen, isn't it?"

"What I would like," I said, "is to look through the personal effects of the dead men so that I can get their names and addresses. Where are their personal effects?"

"With Jim Flecker, but for heaven's sake let that rest for a while, Mister—?"

"Cutter."

"Mr. Cutter—suppose you wait a spell, and I'll see if I can't get you what you need. Not that I'm trying to hide anything. What happened here can't be hidden. But first things first—"

He was interrupted by people who wanted to speak to him; just about everyone present wanted to speak to that poor man, from the doctor, who reported that the wounded man in the hotel had just died, making the score an even twelve, to the undertaker, to the town clerk, who had just spoken to state-police headquarters.

Then a small boy pulled at my jacket and wanted to know whether I was Mr. Cutter. When I replied that I was, he told me that he had been sent from the hotel, where a long-distance call was waiting for me.

6

Instead of telling me what a fine story I had filed, Oscar Smith, who was calling from New York, suggested that I stick to reporting the facts instead of making judgments and pronouncements.

"Well, damn it all," I began, "what kind of judgments have I been making?"

"Never mind that now. Did you interview Ben Holt?"

"Do you know what's been happening here?"

"I read your story."

"I haven't even had lunch."

He sympathized with me and suggested that I find Holt and get a story from him, and that I could send it in along with a follow-up on the gun battle. I left it at that and went down to the dining room of the hotel, where I had a sandwich and a glass of beer, and where a traveling man gave me his views on the gun battle and the rumor that the entire county would be placed under martial law, a rumor, incidentally, that had no foundation in fact. When the bus boy came to clear the dishes away, I told him who I was and said that he could earn a dollar by taking me to Ben Holt. He swore that he did not know where Ben Holt was.

The doctor who had been called in to attend the wounded man was eating lunch in the dining room, and I went over to him, introduced myself, got his name and address, and learned that the wounded man had bled to death before he arrived. "I drove twenty miles for nothing," he said with annoyance. He was one of those men with no opinions and no attitudes. From the way he spoke, one would conclude that gunfights which left twelve men dead happened at least once a week.

His name was Phelps—Tecumseh Phelps—and, like others involved in that incredible sixty-second massacre, he went down into his own tiny niche in history, indexed and cross-indexed in the files where ancient newspapers are remembered. He was fat and tired, and he told me how bad his heart was, so bad that it was a plain wonder that he went on from day to day. "I could drop dead right here," he said, "right now this minute, right here. Maybe it's a medical miracle that I don't. So you see, sonny, everything isn't as simple and clear as you'd like it to be. I killed a half a day, by golly. And who's going to pay my fee, that's what I'd like to know. The mayor? I put it to him straight, and he says he has no responsibility for the Fairlawn detectives. So then I ask him how about this deputy's leg I took a bullet out of and bandaged up. Collect from the deputy, he says. Do you

know what I collected from that deputy?" I shook my head.
"Guess," he urged me. "Go ahead and guess, sonny." I shook
my head again. "Well, fifty-five cents—won't even pay for
my lunch here. Said it was all the money he had in the world.
Can't get blood from a stone, can you? Good heavens, sonny,
this is the poorest town in the nation. Why, this town is so
poor the sparrows tell each other to avoid it. You know what
they say—nothing poorer than a miner, nothing poorer than
a miner's town. And now I got to go and take care of an
infection in Ben Holt's hand. You ever heard of Ben Holt?"

I nodded.

"I'll collect five dollars for that or I won't touch him. You
can be sure of that."

"Where is Ben Holt?" I asked, picking up his check.

"You don't have to do that, sonny."

"My pleasure."

His eyes narrowed suddenly, and he asked me what I had
in mind. He was not such a fool as he appeared to be, and I
put it straight to him that my editor in New York wanted a
personal interview with Ben Holt.

"You think he's a big man? A comer?"

"My editor seems to."

The doctor pursed his lips and nodded. "It could be.
There never was no union down here. My own opinion is
there never will be. Sure, I'll take you along to Ben Holt,
and let him bitch about it and be damned! He's at McGrady's
place up on Fenwick Crag."

7

It was a beautiful country of flat-sided mountains covered
with a mat of verdant forest, and it was clad in the pale green
of spring. It was a country that reminded me of the pictures
I had seen of the Scottish Highlands, but without the damp
and the mists; and the people who lived there were the
descendants of others who had in the beginning come from

the Scottish Highlands, bringing their own names and their place names with them. And if not for the pits and the piles of slag near them, the country would have been as wild as it ever had been; for it was bad farming country and almost no way for a man to squeeze a living out of it except to mine coal.

The doctor drove a Franklin, a good car for the mountains with its air-cooled motor—as he explained—and in it we labored up into the hills, up a dirt road past the red brick miners' houses, where the locked-out miners sat on their front steps sullenly watching us, and past other company houses naked and empty, where the Fairlawn operatives had dispossessed the tenants, down into a valley scarred with idle pits, and up again into the hills they called Fenwick Crag. This road was as bad as a cart track, and it taxed the Franklin's powers to the utmost. We were moving slowly up a sharp grade, when a man with a rifle stepped out into the road and motioned for us to halt.

He was a tall, skinny man, like so many of the men in that area, dressed in faded work pants and a cotton shirt. As cheap as the cotton pants and shirt were, they were patched all over; and he wore the badge of the miner, reddened eyes and dark lines of soot permanently engraved in his skin. He called out for us to stop, and when we did, he walked over to the car, looked at us carefully, and then said to Phelps,

"You the doctor?"

"I am. And what kind of damn nonsense is this, stopping us with that gun in your hands?"

"Who's he?" motioning with the gun at me.

"Friend of mine. He's a newspaperman, going to interview Ben Holt."

Without taking his eyes off us, he shouted for Charlie, and in a minute or so, Charlie appeared from up the road and around a bend. He gave Charlie the facts, and then continued to cover us with his rifle while Charlie, enough like him to be his brother and similarly armed, went back to get Ben Holt's opinion of the whole matter.

It was midafternoon now, the sun warm and pleasant, the little glade where the doctor had stopped the car full of the sweet smell of growing things and forest decay and the hum of insects and the pattern of insects dancing in the bars of sunlight. I wondered what would happen to me if Benjamin R. Holt had emphatic feelings against newspapermen, and considering what I had experienced of tempers and guns in West Virginia so far, I was not cheered by the thought. But from what I had learned, this was also Ben Holt's first venture into West Virginia. He had been born in eastern Pennsylvania, in a small coal town called Ringman, and he had built his union and fought his way into its command in Pennsylvania and Illinois. Conceivably, he was reasonably civilized, yet I had some uneasy moments before Charlie returned and said that it was all right and that we could go ahead.

We drove about half a mile more before the road leveled off onto a sort of cleared plateau, a space of a dozen acres with an old frame house set in the middle of it, a small cornfield, a pen of pigs, and a garden. There was also a rough pasture, where eight army-surplus tents had been pitched. Two big cook fires were going, a whole young pig roasting over one of them, and here and there around the place were at least twenty men.

Some of the men at this place were native West Virginia miners, and others were union organizers that Ben Holt had brought in with him. Even apart from the way they dressed, you could not possibly mistake the one for the other. The miners' features were etched with sadness and defeat. It was not anything of the moment, but out of their lives and the way they stood and the slow way they moved. They were stooped men, bent men. Their lives were spent working with their bodies bent and they had forgotten how to stand straight, and their heads were bent from the angry words of their wives and the rapacious appetites of their children. They were victims of a particular kind of starvation—something I learned much later—for a miner's body burns food

19

like a furnace burns coal, and what another man will fatten on, a miner will starve on. On and off through the years, I have watched working miners eat and never ceased to wonder at the enormous quantities of protein-rich food they needed for plain survival. I suppose that some of Ben Holt's organizers had been miners once, but in a different world than Hogan County.

Phelps stopped his car in front of the frame house, and we got out. Some of the men moved toward us, and then the door of the frame house opened and Ben Holt came out onto the porch. That was the first time I saw Benjamin Renwell Holt, and it was a long, long time ago, a long time before people got into the habit of opening their morning paper to see what Ben Holt had done or what he intended to do. It is possible that he had a sense of the future then. I didn't. He glanced at me with that quick, searching, half-contemptuous look that was to become so familiar to so many, and then his eyes passed by me to the doctor. For myself, I saw a big man of about thirty years—no, he was twenty-eight then—broad-shouldered, heavy, a large, square head on a bull neck, wide mouth, full lips, large, fleshy nose, and blue eyes as clear and placid as water. The expression was in the mouth, the tilt of head, the tension of the cheeks; only in moments of great anger did the eyes change. His hands were enormous, hamlike, one of them bandaged.

Even such a cursory glimpse of the man is retrospective, of necessity bolstered by hindsight. You see someone for the first time, and you see a large, heavy-fleshed man in motion, and not much more than that. His hand hurt him, and he was interested in the doctor then; pain can wall you away from anything. The doctor went inside with him, and I stood by the car and smoked a cigarette and looked around me at the headquarters that Ben Holt had made for himself in that curious West Virginia world that was half primeval wilderness and half coalpits and company towns where the miners worked and lived. This was the wilderness part of it,

with the mountains looming above us on every side, walled
in by a silence and beauty as old as the ages.

It was a big camp, the tents, piles of cut cordwood,
boxes of canned goods heaped six feet high, and behind the
frame house, four automobiles parked neatly side by side.
There was an old barn behind the house; it leaned crazily
from disuse and lack of repair. The McGradys were miners,
not farmers.

McGrady's wife and daughter were in the house; there
were no other women at the camp. The men went about
what they were doing, cooking, splitting wood, sitting around
and chewing tobacco and talking or pacing aimlessly—but
ignoring me. No one spoke to me or approached me. I
realized that there were guards all around the camp, for men
with rifles came in from the forest and other men with rifles
went out to take their places; and it moved easily if raggedly,
with no one giving orders or instructions.

In about twenty minutes, Phelps came out of the house,
Ben Holt with him, Holt's hand in a sling and with a clean
bandage on it. Holt shook hands with the doctor, and then
the doctor climbed into his car and Holt motioned a man
over to crank it. "Good luck, sonny!" the doctor shouted
at me as the motor turned over and caught. He drove off,
leaving me with Ben Holt, who said,

"The old man talks a lot, but he knows his business. This
damn hand of mine was driving me out of my mind, and
that's why you got a poor welcome, Cutter. Now we can go
inside and have a cup of coffee and talk."

8

If I sought to reconstruct that first meeting with Ben Holt
out of memory alone, it would be full of the country smell of
the old farmhouse, the late afternoon sunlight striking
through the windows, and the motions of Laura McGrady
as she brought coffee and bread and butter to us where we

sat at the table. Laura was nineteen then, finished with almost two years at normal school, tall, full-fleshed, her hair long in two thick braids, and not beautiful the way a girl is on a magazine cover, but as beautiful, I think, as any strong, handsome girl can be in the flesh and blood and movement of youth. I don't know that I fell in love with her when I saw her that first time, but I wanted her and the wanting continued, and a year later we were married.

So my own memory of meeting Ben Holt and going into the farmhouse and interviewing him is hardly to be trusted today. What I wrote at the time is plain and to the point:

Today I met Benjamin Renwell Holt, newly elected president of the International Miners Union. Our meeting took place at Mr. Holt's organizational headquarters, a mountain hide-out, the name and location of which I am pledged not to reveal. There, in an old farmhouse, surrounded by mountaineer miners enlisted as armed guards, some of them carrying rifles of Civil War vintage, Benjamin R. Holt plans and directs the organization of an industry never before organized in the state of West Virginia. Backed by a few dozen union organizers from Pennsylvania and Illinois, he has declared war on the powerful and independent coal operators of Hogan and Mingo counties. And from the looks of Mr. Holt, a dynamic, alert ex-miner himself, they have found a worthy opponent.

In the stilted newspaper language of the time, it records the moment of our meeting and something of my own impression. If it fulfills nothing of an obligation toward truth, that can be explained by the nature of what a newspaperman must write, not the subtleties of response and emotion that men exchange with each other and with their environment, but the bald declaration of a fact that can be filed and indexed into categories of facts.

I sat facing a man who was alive, alert, and so filled with a sense of his own purpose and power that it spilled out of him. He never wholly listened and never wholly inquired; he was too much with himself; but even the part of himself that he lent to another made one feel him inescapably and respond to him. All his life, he used other people and they wanted to be used by him. This is not hindsight on my part. He used me then, immediately, because I had seen the bloody gunfight in Clinton. I had come to interview him, cynical about him, with no prepared respect whatsoever, yet I found myself flattered by his attention to what I knew and what I had seen. For the most part, during the course of his life, Holt did not make friends and enemies; he chose them for whatever his purposes were at the moment, and at this moment he wanted a newspaperman. Before we finished talking, he was calling me "Al."

He wanted to know about the fight, and I told him the whole story. He made no comment until I had finished, and then he said softly,

"That stupid bastard Flecker. I hate killers! The pleasure of killing is a disease."

I hadn't thought of it that way, and I asked Holt, "Wouldn't you say his sympathies were with the miners?"

"He doesn't have any sympathies. He's an animal."

"He took your side of the fight, Mr. Holt. You'll have to admit that."

"I don't have to admit anything of the kind," Holt replied. "God save me from friends like Flecker. Murder isn't our fight. Not one bit. Nothing but trouble comes from the kind of thing Flecker did. We would have dealt with those detectives in our own good time and in our own way."

"Still you have your own armed guards, don't you? If you carry a gun, then it means that you are prepared to use it."

"Defense is one thing. Murder is something else. If everyone in this country who carried a gun used it, there'd be no one left alive. A gun is a simple thing, Al, but there's nothing simple about this situation down here in West Virginia. What do you know about coal miners, Al?"

He was calling me by my first name, and I was pleased and flattered. His voice was rich and vibrant, and already then at the age of twenty-eight, he used his voice with all the skill and command of a trained actor. At that time, I was a sharp and cynical kid, but I could not have been bought for money; if I had anything that was strong inside of me, it was some sense of integrity in my work and in what I wrote. If Ben Holt had taken any other tack, it might have turned out differently, but he left me room to summon my own annoyance as I told him that I didn't know a damn thing about miners and had never seen one before today.

"Who the hell has?" He grinned unexpectedly. "Nobody knows a damned thing about the miners except the miners. Nobody gives a damn for them except the miners. Let me tell you this—it has never been any different for five thousand years. Give or take a few centuries. That's when men began to grub in the earth and dig metal, and that's when a miner became expendable. Do you know what has changed?"

I shook my head.

"They killed them quick then. A miner was good for two years—or three. Today it averages out ten to fifteen." Laura McGrady and her mother, Sarah—the mother in her middle forties then, but dry and old, her hands gnarled with arthritis —were listening and staring at Ben Holt, who said to Mrs. McGrady, "That's right. It's an old trade, Sarah. I read every word I could ever find that was written on it." He turned to me. "I'm a miner, Al. You want to write about me, interview me—well, that's the first thing to begin with. I'm a miner. It doesn't begin with a man—it begins with the kid, he sucks it in, like the milk from a bottle, if he's lucky enough to have milk in the bottle. He goes to bed with it and he wakes up with it. Other kids wake up in the daylight. The miner's kid wakes up before the day breaks. You don't have privacy in a miner's house. He lies in bed and listens to his father dress in the darkness. The mother—well, she's been up an hour, got the stove going and the pan on the stove and into the pan whatever there is. My goodness, was there ever a miner had enough to eat for breakfast, enough to take him down into the black belly of the earth and give him strength and courage, damn all the doors to hell—was there ever enough? Now you tell me, Sarah?"

24

She had been listening to him, her daughter next to her, listening to the controlled yet passionate flow of speech that was such a strange mixture of the ordinary and the poetic; and now she shook her head and replied, "No, Ben, never enough, not nearly."

"Oh, I've seen miners that kept their bellies full for a while," he said. "Sure, Al—there have been times when Pennsylvania miners worked long enough to stock up the pantry, but not in West Virginia. These people are first cousins to hunger. They're the poorest, proudest lot in the country, so help me. Would you believe that these are the richest coal fields in the United States of America? Not to look at these lousy company towns here abouts—not by a long shot! But last year, mind you, 1919, they took seventy-nine million tons of coal out of these West Virginia fields. They undersold Pennsylvania and they undersold Illinois. Up there, most of the operators pay union wages. Down here—" He flung out his unbandaged hand in disgust. "You had a look at what's down here."

Trying to pin the conversation down to newspaper terms, I said to him, "You were elected president of the International Miners Union two months ago, Mr. Holt. I believe you're the youngest president they ever had?"

"That's right—if you count the years."

"What are your immediate goals?"

"West Virginia. That's simple enough, isn't it? How long will we have a union in the North if the operators down here undersell the Pennsylvania and Illinois operators and put them out of business?"

"Then you think you'll organize West Virginia?"

"I intend to try," he grinned. His smile was large and warm and intensely personal, and he had the knack of making you feel that it was elicited by you and directed at you in approbation and flattery.

"What would you say your chances are?"

"Worse than they were yesterday." His smile was gone now.

"In other words, that gunfight isn't to your advantage?"

"Al, how could it be?"

"Well, the dead men were your enemies, so to speak, weren't they?"

"No, they weren't my enemies, not one bit. They were cheap, hired thugs, and there's a thousand more to take their places."

"Then you would condemn Flecker's action?"

"Of course I would!" he snorted. "Do you think it can bring us anything but trouble? And let me tell you this—there's going to be trouble now, more trouble than anyone will know what to do with. But it's not trouble that the union asked for or that the miners asked for."

"Don't you see any way to solve this thing peacefully?"

He thought about that for a while before he said, "It could be solved peacefully. Any argument can. But one party's got to give up something. They want us to give up everything and get out of the state, and I guess that would make peace."

We talked for another half hour, and then he indicated that the interview was over. I had been making notes, and I told him that I would try to reflect his point of view honestly. He said that was all he asked. We shook hands, and he told me that he would have me driven back to Clinton.

9

The car was a Model T Ford that belonged to the Miners Union. I didn't know then that Laura asked to drive me back. She did a good deal of driving for them, since she knew every road and cart track in the hill country. She was a good driver too, in her second and graduating year at normal school, and had supported herself through both years driving a school bus near Charleston—the West Virginia Charleston.

For a little while, coming down from Fenwick Crag, she

was silent and attentive to her driving. The sun was low now, and the mountain road, between its walls of trees, was dark and deceptive. On my part, I began a conversation mentally half a dozen times, but whatever I thought to say became banal before I said it. I had slept poorly on the train the night before and been through a long day since then, and I was very tired. I had also been confronted with something totally new to me, met people whose existence I had been unaware of and indifferent to, and witnessed the violent death of twelve men. It added up to a good deal, and on top of that, I was sitting next to a girl I considered both beautiful and desirable. If I had known more about coal miners at that time—particularly coal miners in West Virginia—I might have reflected properly on what it means for a miner's daughter to get through secondary school and two years of normal school. But my knowledge was limited—yet not so limited that I did not have an impression, at least, of someone different from the run of nineteen-year-old girls I had known.

Down off the rutted, winding road, we came into the open valley, with the upending sweep of mountains all around us. She was able to take her eyes off the road long enough to glance at me and ask me what I thought of Ben Holt.

"I don't know—"

"Don't you have to have an opinion, if you write an interview?"

"Not necessarily. I have my questions and his answers."

"That's not enough," she said flatly. "You don't understand this place, Mr. Cutter, and you don't understand us. That's nothing you can help. You're an outsider, and you live in a world where coal miners are forgotten."

"If they were forgotten, Miss McGrady, would I be here?"

"I imagine you're here because your editor sent you here."

"Yes—he sent me."

"Not because he loves coal miners, but because he suspected that something like what happened in Clinton today might happen."

"Well, it's news," I said. "He didn't know what was going to happen. But he knew that Ben Holt had come down here to organize the miners—or to try—"

"Then it seems to me that he knew him better than you do, and you've seen him and spoken to him."

"I don't follow you."

"At least he knew that this would be news," she said testily. "He knew that Ben Holt would inject something here —something we needed desperately and which he could give us?"

"May I ask what?"

"A chance to live—instead of slow death. And a man who can bring that to you, Mr. Cutter, is a man you should be able to form some opinion about."

Stupidly and bluntly, I said, "Are you in love with Ben Holt, Miss McGrady?" and her answer was no more or less than I deserved. She informed me that it was none of my damned business whether she was or was not. When I tried to apologize, she snapped,

"Don't, Mr. Cutter. I asked to drive you back to Clinton because I am interested in writing and newspaper work, and I thought it would be pleasant to have an opportunity to talk to you. I see that I was mistaken. If you wish to include it in your story, I am not in love with Ben Holt. He has a wife and a child. He is also the kind of man you might do well to think about, and perhaps in time you will form an opinion of him. He's a miner's son. His father was killed in a mine explosion when Ben was twelve years old. He educated himself, worked in the mines from the age of twelve, got through college, helped build this union, and became its president. And his first action as president—his first—was to come down here to West Virginia and to tell the whole world that he was going to build a union here. Do you know what kind of a man it takes to do that?"

I remained silent, and after a moment, she continued, "I

was only trying to help you form an opinion, Mr. Cutter. I am sorry to have ruffled your feelings. If you don't take the first train out tomorrow but stay with us for a while, perhaps you'll make some sense of what I said."

It was just beginning to get dark when she dropped me at the drugstore across the street from the hotel. I had confirmed my suspicion that she was an unusual woman, but I did not find her less attractive.

10

From the appearance of the lobby of the Traveler's Mountainside Hotel, you would have concluded that a convention was in progress. The forsaken hostelry in a forsaken town had come to life with a vengeance, and it swarmed with newspapermen, uniformed state police, and hard-eyed men in plain clothes who carried their left arms awkwardly over a bulge. Every seat in the dining room was taken, and the hotel's small store of cigars and cigarettes had already been exhausted. I met one or two reporters who knew me, and they wanted to squeeze me for what I had seen in the morning, but I was out of cigarettes and I used that as an excuse to put them off until later, pushed through the crowd in the lobby, and crossed the street to the drugstore.

Laura McGrady was just leaving as I entered, and when I removed my straw hat and bowed slightly to her, as politely as I knew how, she shook her head, smiled and said,

"You *are* a strange man, Mr. Cutter."

"Strange? No, I don't think I am."

"I'm sorry I was so provoked before. You have every right to be angry with me."

"I could never be angry with you, Miss McGrady."

The dialogue sounds strange and stilted and out of another world—which perhaps it was—as I read it now; but it seemed right then, and as she stood there, in front of the store window, she was very beautiful to me, very competent too, very sure of herself. She went on to say that she was glad we had run into each other again, since she had something for me that she had forgotten to give me. I begged her to wait until I bought my cigarettes, and she agreed. When I came out of the store, she gave me a mimeographed booklet containing a biographical sketch of Holt, which I folded and put into my pocket. After all, I had come out to do an interview with Holt, yet I felt let down and irritated. As she moved toward her car, we heard the whistle of an approaching train, and a moment later the light of the night train from Washington appeared in the distance. We paused at the car to watch it come into the station, and then Laura took my arm and whispered,

"Take me over there."

I walked to the station with her. As she told me, it was rare for the evening train into Clinton to debark one passenger—and more than one almost unheard of; but tonight, an army of men poured out of the train—at least fifty or sixty, I would say, hard men with tight mouths. Seeing men like that in New York, where I had seen plenty of the same, I would have said that they were cheap hoodlums, two-bit punks and gangsters on the make and the climb; but they looked different here in this small mountain village, ominous and different and frightening. We neither of us spoke as we watched them, and when they were all off the train, standing on the platform in clusters and waiting for whoever had ordered them and would pay for them and meet them, Laura touched my arm and nodded, and we walked back to the car. The night, suddenly, was thick with fear, and I said that if she was afraid, I would ride back with her and spend the night at the camp.

"Afraid?"

"People are afraid."

"I'm not afraid, Mr. Cutter. Not at all. Good night." She had taken the crank handle and was moving to crank the car herself. I convinced her that I could perform at least

30

that kind of service, and then I watched her drive off into the night.

On the porch of the hotel, I ran into Mayor Macintosh arguing with two men, one of them in the uniform of the state police. The other was a tall, vital-looking man with iron-gray hair. This one was saying to the mayor,

"No, sir, I will not lay it all on Sheriff Flecker. That's too easy, sir. I say that the man behind these killings is Ben Holt, and that he's the man we want. He has come into a peaceful, prosperous community, and he has brought us disruption, agony, and death. That's plain enough, Mayor."

"Not when we have as many witnesses as we do to what actually happened," the mayor protested. "This man"—pointing to me—"is a reporter from a New York newspaper. He witnessed the fight. Am I right, Mr. Cutter?"

I admitted that he was right, and he introduced me to Captain Sedge of the state police and to the tall man with the iron-gray hair, Fulton Oswick, a coal operator, the largest in the valley.

"The hell with what he saw," Oswick said quietly and without anger, divesting his words of any offense they might have held for me. "He only saw the man who pulled the trigger. Don't tell me about hiring a gun, Mayor. I can give you lessons, as you know. We're talking about the man who hired the gun, and I think we both know who he is. He owes me something. Twelve lives. I got to collect. I want a warrant for Ben Holt's arrest."

"I just can't put my signature to such a warrant," Macintosh said stubbornly. "If you want a warrant for Flecker, that's something else. I'd have to think about that too, but that's something else."

"Where is Flecker?" Captain Sedge demanded. "He's your responsibility, Macintosh. You should have put him under arrest."

"How?" I began to revise my first opinion of Macintosh. He stood up to them. "How would I put Flecker under arrest? Would I arm myself? Shoot it out in a gun battle? I'm only asking you gentlemen to be reasonable."

"Isn't that after the fact?" Oswick demanded. "I can't remember a killing like this in the whole damn country, not ever. Twelve men shot dead. And you ask us to be reasonable."

"I hate to say this, Mr. Oswick," Macintosh said, forcing up the words, his face reddening, "but there was killing on the books once you sent those Fairlawn detectives in here. Now you're bringing in a whole army. There's got to be killing."

"And I got to protect my property!" Oswick snapped.

"I agree to that," Macintosh nodded. "But I'm mayor of Clinton. No coal operators live here, only miners. It's a mining town. I'm hung onto that, Mr. Oswick. How long do you think I'll last once I sign a warrant for Ben Holt's arrest?"

"I'll give you all the protection you need," Captain Sedge told him.

"Protection. We got the worst trouble this county ever saw, and you talk about protection."

I left them then, and pushed through the crowded lobby and went up to my room. It had been a long day, and I was tired.

11

After I got into bed, I smoked a cigarette and contemplated the situation in Clinton and tried to make sense out of it and to understand how it was moving and where. My own neutrality put me in an ambiguous position. I was twenty-two years old and wise to the ways of the world I lived in; but this was by no means that world. Until I met Laura McGrady, I was indifferent to the situation of the miners; my curiosity was limited; and I resented being stuck on an assignment in an out-of-the-way mountain village.

Meeting the girl had changed this only slightly. I was impressed with Ben Holt, but if I had gone back to New York the following morning, I would have forgotten him soon enough. I was conscious of forces building up, of conflict preparing itself, but the crux of the situation was confusing and annoying. I admitted to myself that a miner's life in West Virginia was not pleasant, but I felt at the same time that the miners were stupid and doltish—and to some extent deserved exactly what they got. I told myself that no one forced them to be miners and that no one prevented them from picking up and clearing out; and the more I learned about the unbearable poverty and tension of their lives, the less I respected them for enduring those conditions. If they lived in company houses, it was because they had taken the easy way out in the first place, and if they were body and soul in debt to company stores, it was because they did not have enough foresight and thrift to prevent such a situation from arising.

On the other hand, if men like Fulton Oswick used their own power to get what they desired, it was no more than right. Oswick owned the miners' homes; he had the right to say who should or should not live there. He hated the union and he was fighting it in the way he could fight best. If one objected to his action on humane grounds, then one interjected the question of humanity on most unlikely territory. I had not seen humanity or mercy as a profound or effective operational force, and I was not prepared to use it in my arguments with myself.

So my thoughts went. I finished the cigarette and decided that I would write the interview the following morning. But before turning off my light, I read the mimeographed biography of Ben Holt that his union had issued. I kept it and it follows verbatim:

BENJAMIN RENWELL HOLT
For release on April 1, 1920
Biographical notes

In keeping with its tradition, the International Miners Union has elected a coal miner as its new president.

Born on January 14, 1892, in the coal mining town of Ringman, Pa., Benjamin R. Holt is the youngest man ever to hold the presidency of his union. Of a coal-mining family, both his mother and father were of pioneer stock, Scotch-Irish on his maternal side and British and Welsh on his paternal side. His father and grandfather—paternally—were both miners and worked at the same Ringman Pits that Benjamin R. Holt entered at the age of twelve.

Until his twelfth year, Ben Holt was a student at the Ringman elementary school. That he was an extraordinary student is attested to by the fact that he had finished eight grades of primary school when his father's death forced him to enter the mines as the sole support of his widowed mother. There had been two older brothers—both killed in the Harkness cave-in of 1899.

His father was killed in 1904 in the tragic coal-gas explosion which is remembered as the Ringman Massacre. Along with Denby Holt, Ben Holt's father, 181 miners perished in a frightful accident that could have been avoided, had the mine operators only followed a few simple safety precautions that the miners had pleaded for.

Ben Holt has stated that the Ringman Massacre was one of the decisive events of his life. Together with his mother, he stood the deathwatch at the pit head until the last of the bodies was brought to the surface, a matter of over thirty hours. An indelible impression of the conditions under which coal miners worked and died was then left with young Benjamin Holt, who had seen the three men closest to him die in the mines.

During the following four years, Benjamin Holt worked in the pits at Ringman. He has never forgotten those years, for they forged a bond between him and the plain coal miner that can never be broken.

During those years, Ben Holt continued his studies, and at the age of sixteen, he passed the entrance examination for the State University, qualifying for a scholarship. This scholarship, together with the compensation paid by the Ringman Coal Company for his father's death and a part-time job, enabled Ben Holt to get an education and graduate with a college degree and with honors.

Shortly before his graduation, Benjamin Holt was singled out by a distinguished Pittsburgh law firm, with an offer of their support for his legal training and an opening to read law with their house. This, Mr. Holt declined, already determined to devote his life and energy to the betterment of his fellow miners.

A few weeks after his graduation, a second severe blow fell on Benjamin Holt. His mother, who had been his teacher and guide through the years, passed away. Thus, his closest family ties broken, Benjamin Holt decided to leave Ringman. For over a year, he traveled and worked in several western states. But always, his direction led him to share the fortunes of miners, to share and understand their problems. He worked in the gold and silver mines of Arizona. He also worked as a copper miner in Montana. While working as a coal miner in Colorado, he was trapped underground in the great Serpo mine disaster. Thereby, his early experience at Ringman was duplicated with himself as one of the victims.

As he was in the group nearest to the cage, he was one of the seven men rescued alive, and during the next twenty-four hours, he worked to exhaustion with the crew that attempted unsuccessfully to save the miners who perished. Once again, the tragedy that flows from bad working conditions and insufficient safety measures put its stamp upon Benjamin R. Holt.

In the winter of 1915, Benjamin R. Holt returned to Ringman, where he once again entered the mines. A few months later, he married Dorothy Aimesley.

In 1916, Benjamin R. Holt was elected president of the Ringman local of the International Miners Union. The following year, he was elected as the International Union's representative with the National Confederation of Labor, and during the two years he held that post, he worked incessantly to promote legislation, both state and federal, in defense of the coal miners.

His election to the presidency of the International Miners Union was with the largest majority gained by any candidate during the past decade.

12

I was up early the following morning, and at work in my room by seven-thirty. The *Mail,* which was among the several good New York City newspapers that did not survive the twenties, was an afternoon paper, and in those days the first edition of an afternoon paper was about an hour later than today. If I could put my story through on the wire at nine o'clock, I would be in time for the presses. I worked in my room, sitting by the window, and I had a clear view across the street to the station. The morning train had brought in another contingent of armed guards, almost a hundred of them by quick count; and they were being served breakfast from a truck converted into a short-order lunch counter of sorts.

My interview story was finished well before nine, and without stopping for breakfast, I filed it at the Western Union office. On my way back to the hotel, I stopped to speak to some of the new batch of detectives, as they termed themselves. But before I could get more than a few words in, a foreman type shouldered me away and demanded to know what in hell I thought I was doing. When I explained who I was, his apology took the form of an assurance that there was no news to be found here.

I objected to that. "When you bring hundreds of armed men into a town like Clinton, it's bound to make news."

"Who said they're armed?"

I shrugged and shook my head, but he was firm on refusing to allow me to talk to them. "Twelve damn good detectives were murdered here yesterday, mister," he said to me. "Do you want us to subject ourselves to the same thing? Not on your life. You want to talk—talk to these sonovabitch miners!"

Only there were no miners. The day before, the day I arrived, the streets of Clinton had been full of miners and their wives and their kids, but today not one of them was in sight, not a soul on the streets anywhere except the hard-eyed operatives who had been pouring into town. They were everywhere. They sat on the curbstones, swarmed over the hotel veranda, and pressed into the lunchroom and the drug-store; but there were no miners to be seen anywhere.

There was a garage in Clinton, and I walked over to it now. It was at the end of the business street, a ramshackle shed where a single mechanic was working under a car. He crawled out when I said "Good morning" to him, and eyed me without pleasure. He was a boy of eighteen or nineteen or so.

"I want to rent a car," I said to him.

No comment, no reaction.

"You have a car for hire? Or a taxi service? Suppose I want to go somewhere. Could you drive me?"

"I got my work," he muttered, turning away.

I told him that I was a reporter, and that made him pause. Then I got out my press card for him to look at. I pointed out to him that regardless of what he thought, Clinton, West Virginia, was at this moment the focal point of interest for the entire country, and was likely to remain so for some time to come. He might not give one damn for a reporter, but at least a part of the ultimate fate of the coal miners in Hogan County would depend on what reporters told of their fight.

Finally, he asked me, "Where do you want to go, mister?"

"Fenwick Crag—the McGrady place."

He thought this over for a while, and then he nodded. "Cost you five dollars."

I took out my wallet and paid him, and he said that he would be ready for me in half an hour. Then I went back to the hotel, paid my bill, packed my suitcase, and put in a call to New York. When I told Oscar Smith that I was checking out of the hotel and leaving Clinton, I thought he would explode. "Of all the damnfool, idiot notions!" he screamed at me. "There you are, by pure accident at the heart of the biggest story in the country, and you talk about pulling out! Either stay there or you're out of a job!"

"You sent me down here to cover a war, didn't you?"

"Forget that nonsense and stay where you are!"

"No, sir," I replied, politely but firmly. "I think there is going to be a war after all. Everyone else will be here on the home front. I intend to be with the enemy forces."

I explained all that I dared to explain. As far as I knew, someone might be listening in downstairs, and I didn't want any trouble. At least he began to see my way of thinking, and if I got no blessing, at least I got a warning to file material and not to think that I could turn into a bum on his money.

I went downstairs to the lobby then. It was crowded, as it had been since the evening before, and at one side of it, on a couch and a few chairs, half a dozen women were sitting. A few were women; the rest were just kids, and they were all dressed badly and cheaply, their faces covered with heavy, raw make-up. The operatives in the lobby were around them, loud and clever and making a big thing out of them. Bill Goodman of the *Times,* who had checked in early in the morning, spotted me and my suitcase and wanted to know where I was going.

"Out," I said. "I had enough of Clinton."

He didn't believe me, and kept pushing for some information. In turn, he described the extent of the operation here. According to him, there were some five hundred hired detectives, for want of a better name, in town already, and more coming. The batch of girls had just come in from Charleston, and they were the first of a large order necessary to keep the men satisfied. "They're doing it the French way," he said. "My word, I never seen anything like this before. They got an army occupying this town. What for? What are they up to? I heard of strikes and labor trouble, but so help me God, I never heard of anything like this before!"

"They just don't want a union here," I replied.

"That's an understatement if I ever heard one. Where are you going?"

"Just around. I want to look at the pits and see what's happening."

"With your suitcase?"

"You never know where you'll end up."

"It's damn funny," he said, "that you got here yesterday before anyone ever knew that there was a place called Clinton on the map."

"It's one of those things," I shrugged, and pushed my way through and outside. The car was in front of the hotel, the motor running, a battered specimen of a Maxwell, I think, and some of the operatives were examining it and trying to rile the boy in the driver's seat. He was nervous, for which I hardly blamed him. He was a lone native in a town whose population had melted away, and a good many of these operatives or detectives appeared to have only remote kinship with the human race. From what alleys and gutters of New York and Chicago they had been recruited, I did not know, but they were not specimens to meet on a dark night.

I climbed into the car, threw my bag onto the back seat, and we started off down the street. We drove in silence until we were out of the town, and then the boy turned to me and said,

"Mister, if you ain't a proper person to bring there, they're going to kill you. I guess you know that."

I didn't know, but I said that I would take my chances.

"Me, too," the boy nodded. "If they have to kill you, they are going to be mighty provoked at me."

13

A different armed guard stopped us this time, and he wasn't polite. His face was dark as thunder, and he cussed out the garage mechanic and demanded to know whether he didn't have more sense than to bring a stranger, and a city man at that, up to Fenwick Crag. I talked quickly and firmly about Ben Holt being a friend of sorts, but the two barrels of the miner's shotgun listened poorly. There was more discussion before he let us through, but finally he did.

Armed miners stood aside as we labored up the road, and the area around the farmhouse looked like an army camp. There must have been over a thousand men there, and it seemed like five thousand, and there were more tents, lean-tos, cooking fires, and some twenty-five or thirty old cars parked near the barn. Many of these miners must have been overseas during the war, for almost every one of them had some scrap of uniform, an army shirt, a tin hat, a cartridge sling—or khaki tape around the bottom of blue jeans, and most of them wore an arm band with the letters IMU stitched on it or marked on it.

As we rolled to a stop near the farmhouse, a miner who wore an officer's cap came over to the car, which was already surrounded by curious and unsmiling men, and asked who I was and what I wanted there. I told him, and left just the implication that Ben Holt had invited me back. I got out of the car, assuring myself that I was not nervous and that there was nothing for me to be nervous about. Meanwhile, the man in the officer's cap talked in whispers to the garage mechanic. I was relieved when I saw Ben Holt pushing through the crowd, but there was no welcome on his face, no pleasure, no mask of conviviality for a bright young newspaperman.

"I see you're back, Cutter," he said to me.

"Yes, sir."

"Why?"

I decided to tell him the truth. It was a sensible beginning, and through the years that followed, I kept it that way. "There's at least a hundred newspapermen back there in Clinton now. There's none with you. Am I right?"

"You're right."

"So that's my job. You're going to make news, and I want to write about it."

"Suppose I threw you out of here?" Holt said flatly.

I shrugged. "That's up to you. I think you'd be making a mistake."

"Why?" That was characteristic of Holt. If there was a chance for an explanation, he asked. "Are you on our side?"

"No. Not on your side, not on their side."

"Then, God damn you, mister, go peddle your lies somewhere else!"

"I don't write lies, Mr. Holt. I put down what I see."

He pursed his lips and stared at me for a long moment, and then he said softly, "What are you after, Cutter?"

"News. That's all."

"Crap and horseshit!" he cried. "News! What in hell is news! This is a country down here where men work like slaves and are treated like slaves! They pawn their souls to the company store, and there's a mortgage on their kids when the kids are born. We came down here to organize a union—just that—just to organize a union, which is supposed to be a right that some Americans have. And from the day we arrived, the terror never stopped, five thousand miners locked out of their jobs and their homes, kicked into the fields and the woods, men beaten, men tortured, women whipped and raped—all that because we tried to organize a union. Have you written about that?"

"A little. I suggested some of it in the interview I wrote about you."

He stared at me again, as if he were trying to see through me and into me, and then he told me to follow him, leading the way around the house to the barn in back. I looked for Laura but did not see her. There were men around the barn, most of them armed, and they stood apart, not for us but to let a group of women and children come out, gaunt, prematurely aged women whose last shreds of attractiveness had been washed away in grief. They had been weeping, but

41

it was not an act that came easily to them. We went past them and into the barn, and there on the floor, fifteen bodies were laid out. Some men at the back of the barn were sawing and nailing wooden planks for coffins. I looked at the bodies. Ten were men, miners wearing their badge of trade in the black lines etched on their hands and faces, two were boys, one was a woman, and two were little children, girls. There were more women in the barn, and they sat huddled in silent woe.

"It happened this morning," Holt told me. "An eye for an eye, a tooth for a tooth. Only Jim Flecker wasn't a miner. Jim Flecker was a murderer. This is the way they tried him and sentenced him."

I remained silent. There was nothing for me to say.

"Is this the way death should come, Cutter?" Holt asked me. "Should it come the way it does in the mines? Do you know how many miners have died in the past ten years? Do you have any idea how many tens of thousands? What are we! Jesus God, what are we? They slaughter cattle with more compunction. Are you still neutral, Cutter?"

"You showed me this. I'll write about it."

"That's all?"

"I'm not Lazarus. I can't raise the dead, Mr. Holt."

"No, you're not Lazarus."

"How did they pick them?"

"Pick them? They didn't pick them, Cutter. They drove out of Clinton this morning, a carload of them armed to the teeth, and they killed the first miners they found—or men. Those kids weren't miners, those two boys. The woman was Sadie Stewart, those are her kids, and that's her husband lying next to her. Her husband ran into their shack, and those hired heroes kept firing into the shack until a roach couldn't have remained alive in there."

"I will want their names, if it's not too much trouble."

Holt glanced at me sharply, then nodded. "All right, their names and anything else you want."

42

14

They let me work in one of the tents. I had no typewriter with me, so I sat on a stool and put down the story in long-hand in my notebook. One of the miners brought me lunch, a tin cup of poor stew that was a thin mixture of meat and potatoes and a slice of bread. It was nothing to grow fat on, but no less than what the others got. By three o'clock, I had finished my story; and I was standing by the tent, trying to think of some way to file it without returning to Clinton, when Laura came over and said hello to me. Her tone was not unfriendly. She wore a white IMU band on her arm, and a white cross was stitched on her dress at the breast. She told me that they were organizing a corps of nurses.

"Then it will be war?"

"This is our home, Mr. Cutter. This is our land."

"I know that."

"But you don't believe in fighting for it?"

"This is the twentieth century in the United States of America. I don't believe in private wars—no."

"Then what should we do?" There was no mockery in her question.

"Use the law."

"What law? This is West Virginia, Mr. Cutter. Their law is different here, what there is of it, and in Hogan County it belongs to the mine operators. We are used to starvation, Mr. Cutter, but not to being murdered in our beds."

I nodded, and then for a little while we stood in silence, and then she asked me what I had written and whether she could see it. I said it was not secret, and would she like me to read it to her? She nodded, and I read as follows:

"*May 27, 1920.* Somewhere in West Virginia. I am the only reporter present at the secret base of the International Miners Union. Here, at the headquarters of Benjamin R. Holt, as strange a situation is developing as American labor ever knew. Mr. Holt, twenty-eight-year-old strong man and newly elected president of the Miners Union, came down here recently to organize a union of the West Virginia coal miners. He brought with him a corps of organizers, and their arrival in the coal fields was the signal for an outbreak of violence unique even for this part of the country—an area that well remembers the notorious Hatfield-McCoy feud as well as many others.

"So far as this reporter can determine, the first violence was triggered, not by the miners, but by private detectives brought in by the coal operators. The first response of the miners to the union was enthusiastic, and several thousand of them signed union cards during the first few days of organization. Then the operators began the eviction of such miners as lived in company houses and had co-operated with the union. Since none of these miners had valid leases, the operators were entirely within their rights, both in the evictions and in the subsequent closing of the pits. About 85 per cent of the local miners were affected.

"These evictions were carried out by hired detectives, the local authorities being unwilling to take the measures requested of them. An argument between these hired operatives and the local sheriff, James D. Flecker, resulted in the death of twelve operatives. Here, in this mountain hide-out, I have just been shown the bodies of fifteen persons, ten miners, a woman, and four children. It is alleged by Mr. Holt that these fifteen persons were killed in reprisal for the deaths of the operatives, and he bluntly accuses the mine operators of a planned campaign of murder and terror against the miners.

"Whatever the truth of this assertion, neither Mr. Holt nor the miners are taking the situation lying down. Well over a thousand armed miners are gathered at this hide-out, and they have sworn that they will defend themselves and their families to the death.

"'We did not ask for this,' Benjamin Holt said. 'It was thrust on us. Rest assured, we will defend ourselves.'

"Events have proved that Mr. Holt is not someone to be taken lightly. He has a vital, magnetic personality, and appears to command the total devotion of the coal miners. When I pressed for his motivations, he insisted that he had none apart from the welfare of the miners. Nevertheless, it should be noted that in the brief time during which he has been head of the union, he has managed to raise his yearly salary from three thousand to five thousand dollars. He is a well-educated and articulate man, but it remains to be seen whether he will accept conditions of warfare as a solution to his problems. If he does, then it may be that we are on the verge of actual armed conflict here in this state, for on both sides armies are gathering. When you have thousands of angry men under arms only a few miles from each other, then an incident is inevitable. This is something that only time will tell."

Laura did not interrupt me while I was reading, and when I had finished, she stared at me in bewilderment. "You don't believe those things you wrote there, do you, Mr. Cutter?"

"I wrote it."

"With your tongue in your cheek, Mr. Cutter?"

"Now that was uncalled for," I protested. "You keep regarding me as a member of your faction. I told Mr. Holt otherwise. I am not here under any false pretenses."

"You certainly are not!"

"Yet I wrote what I saw."

"Did you? Is it only alleged that our people were murdered by the detectives? Who else murdered them? Did we, Mr. Cutter? And do you really think that the operators have the right to evict us from our homes when the mood takes them, simply because we have no leases?"

"The legal right, yes."

"And who gave them this legal right, Mr. Cutter? Aren't there any moral rights?"

"You're putting me in a position that's unfair. I can't judge this thing. I can't judge its background. I'm not equipped to."

"No. Not even to approve of starvation—or to disapprove."

"That's not fair, Miss McGrady."

"I am not trying to be fair, Mr. Cutter, any more than you tried to be fair."

She would have it that way, and there was no moving her. If she did not convince me that it was necessary to change

45

my story, I did at least decide to put off filing it until the following day. During the rest of the afternoon, I wandered around the farm, observing the preparations being made as the small army came into existence.

I spoke with Ben Holt once more, after the supper meal, which was as thin and unsatisfying as lunch had been. He acknowledged that Laura had told him about my story.

"Do you want to read it?" I asked him.

"No—no, Cutter. I don't want to read it. Write what you see, if that's the way you feel about it. I hear you feel that raising my wages from three to five thousand dollars is ambitious."

"I remarked on it. It's a news item. Am I wrong in thinking that no coal miner ever makes five thousand a year?"

"I'm not a coal miner now, Cutter. I'm president of the union. If I live like a coal miner and act like a coal miner, I'm no damn good to them, am I?"

"I don't know, Mr. Holt. From what I've seen of their lives, I'd break my back not to be a miner."

"Oh? Then maybe we should both thank God they don't feel that way. This country lives on coal or dies without it, Cutter—don't ever forget that. It eats coal the way we eat this stew, but it's nourished better. Someday, you'll understand that. Someday, I am going to take you into a coal mine. You'll open your eyes."

"I didn't tell you, Mr. Holt," I said slowly, "but there was some talk back in Clinton about arresting you and charging you with the deaths of those Fairlawn operatives. A man called Fulton Oswick was pushing for it. Do you know him?"

"I know him," Holt smiled.

"And here in West Virginia—ultimately, I mean—will you win, Mr. Holt?"

"We'll win," he said.

15

So I have set down, relying on yellowed clippings, old notebooks, and a memory far less dependable, the beginnings of my friendship with Benjamin R. Holt—a friendship that was to continue for the next eighteen years, when it was at least in part dissolved by certain events. I call it a friendship; others might call it something else. There were times when we needed each other, which makes for friendship of a sort, but there were more times when he needed me. Yet if I left him, I returned to him, so it may be that my need was the larger one.

I look at him through my memory somewhat differently than I regarded him then, thirty-nine years ago. His tolerance was calculated, which I did not know. He despised me, but he wanted a newsman to see things from his side, and I was the only reporter available. Yet to this day, I know no more about his real feeling for the miners than I knew then; and it is possible that he never knew much more than I did about that particular subject. What he felt about them then, at that moment, up on Fenwick Crag, was something he could hardly have stated more clearly than I could. Certainly he knew and comprehended entirely the sheer madness of the war that was shaping up between the armed miners and the growing army of private operatives, but he also knew exactly how far he would proceed with that war, and I did not. Years later, discussing it at a moment when his guards were down and when he was as relaxed as he ever became, I asked him what his purpose was. "You knew," I said to him, "that you were moving toward the edge of madness— toward a tragedy so enormous that nothing exists for comparison."

"I knew that," he agreed. "When it finished, Al, we had six thousand men under arms. They had almost two thousand opposing us. That makes for a pretty large war. I took a calculated risk there—a large one, but calculated."

"Why?" I asked him. "To what end? You knew it would be called."

"You don't understand, do you, Al?"

I told him I didn't—not then, not when it first happened.

"Because you don't understand coal, Al—and coal is the key to all of it. When you mine silver or gold, you are mining something which man values for its scarcity and which possesses all the fake values of scarcity. When you mine coal, you mine power, power—every kind of power, steam and gas and electricity. That black filth is the soul of our civilization, or of the farce that we like to call civilization, and without it civilization curls up and dies. Power. Coal is power and the key to coal is power. I learned that, and I never forgot it, and down there in West Virginia, it was stripped naked. I pushed the scenery out of the way and let them see the stage as it really was. They never talk to miners except in terms of life and death. I let them see that we could talk back in the same terms."

"And if it had been war, Ben?"

He shrugged. "I play it by ear," he smiled. "There's no use going back and trying to play it any other way."

16

I said before that Laura became my wife, and while this is Ben Holt's story, there's still the end to what happened in West Virginia. My own involvement in that situation played out on the following day. Early in the morning, I was awakened by rifle fire, after no more than an hour of sleep; for I had slept in the open, shivering in one threadbare blanket. I learned that the first or outer guards, stationed about a mile down the road, had been attacked by a car of operatives out of Clinton. The detectives had then retreated two miles, where they made a stand, sending back to Clinton for reinforcements. By the time I began to move in the direction of the firing, a small but very real battle was in progress. A first-aid station had been set up about a mile from the farm. When I reached it, it contained four wounded men and a woman who had been shot in the right lung. The woman was Laura McGrady, and the bullet had caught her when she went down to the fighting to try to help those in need of first aid. She was badly hurt, and the other women at the first-aid station were of the opinion that she would die unless she was taken to a hospital. The nearest hospital was at Charleston, almost fifty miles away, and the road was blocked by the operatives.

It was my idea that if we put her in a car and I drove, the operatives would let us through. I argued that they would not kill a newspaperman, and that since they did not know what my influence with the *Mail* was—very little, in all truth—they would not make themselves responsible for a woman's death in my presence. Ben Holt had come on the scene then, and he disagreed. Laura's mother tipped the balance, and Laura's father agreed with her. Holt could hardly persist in his objections. He had too much of a debt to the McGradys. He gave in, and I got the car. Laura's mother came with us, and firing on our side was suspended to give us a better chance.

I approached the roadblock slowly in an old Ford draped with white rags, and then for fifteen minutes I talked as I never had talked before. I told them that Laura was dying, something I believed at the time, and that I would hold them responsible for her death. I pleaded, cajoled, and threatened, and finally they let us through.

There is little to tell after that. I drove to Charleston, put Laura in the hospital, found a room for her mother, filed two stories I wrote while waiting at the hospital for some news of Laura's condition, and then slept the clock around when I heard that she was out of danger and would recover.

I remained in Charleston for the next three weeks, the time Laura was in the hospital. During those three weeks,

Ben Holt's forces swelled to six thousand men, an army that was ready to break the siege on Fenwick Crag and move in to occupy Clinton.

But the United States Army moved in first, occupying the town and the surrounding area. The miners were disarmed. Ben Holt and his IMU organizers got over the mountains to where a car was waiting for them, and then out of the state. The charges against them were eventually dropped. Jim Flecker and his deputies met violent deaths during the next twelve months, but who their killers were was never established.

Almost fifteen years were to pass before the West Virginia miners had a coal union.

PART II

1

October 14, 1958

MY DEAR ALVIN:

Back here in Ringman, in Father's house, it is hard to believe
that time has had its way with all of us. These are the good
autumn days, the trees gold and red and brown, and from
Father's study window, the great hump at Mt. Babcock is
such a pile of beauty that it quite takes one's breath away.
At first, the big old house was rather somber and musty, but
Norah and her three children spent the summer here, and
there is nothing like three high-spirited grandchildren to
drive the smell of death and decay out of a place. Ben, Jr.,
was with us for two weeks, and I think his children were
quite happy during that time, but his Susan and I are not as
compatible as we might be. I always said that I would never
be a typical mother-in-law, but that, I am afraid, is a pit no
one truly avoids.

Now I am alone, but not lonely, if you understand, and I think you do. In any other place, it would be different, but I feel that I belong here in Ringman and certainly I am quite content.

Father's death was not such a blow, even coming as it did only a few weeks after Ben passed away. Father was a very old man—I am myself going to have a sixty-first birthday, in case you have forgotten—and the years were better to him than to most. I felt the pangs of his passing, but not real grief; and perhaps after watching me, dry-eyed at Ben's funeral, you will think me coldhearted. I wish it had been otherwise, Alvin; love and closeness are worth all the pain of the ultimate sorrow, and nothing death brings to those who survive is as bitter as to stand by the grave and know that the man who lies there is almost a stranger. No, not a stranger. You will know what I mean—I think you remember it all only too well—and the three weeks I then spent in the house in Washington were my own punishment. Father's death rescued me, not from grief, but from the loneliness and and the hopelessness that I remained with there in Washington. I had to go to Ringman; there were things to be taken care of, not the least of them, the house. I decided not to sell it, but to live here—and I think you will understand when I tell you that during the months since then, living here, I have been closer to Ben than during most of the twenty-five years before his death.

How strange, now, that you should want me to tell you about myself and Ben in the beginning! That was so long ago—another time and another world, and I wonder who will care now or be interested?

Not that you shouldn't be writing the book. Books were written about Ben while he lived, and I suppose other books will be written about him now that he is dead, and there are two professors at the University of Pennsylvania who say they will spend the next five years on a scholarly and definitive work about him. I have a letter from them, asking for material and my co-operation, and I see no reason to refuse.

52

We both know what Ben's reaction would have been, but I see no harm in it. Nowhere in any of these books is there anything of Ben as he was, only what he did and the results of what he did, and there is no reason to think that this new scholarly book will be any different. But in your case, you want to write about Ben—and that makes it terribly hard, doesn't it? Because loving both Ben and me as you did— how much can you tell, truly?

But then, I am a woman, and I think that we differ from men in our acceptance of the plausibility of a good many truths, not one, unshakable and single answer to any question. So I can write a little about Benjamin Renwell Holt as I knew him; not that I claim to know him so much better than anyone else did, but I did know him in one way that no one else had the opportunity to know him.

And about the old days—they are surprisingly clear to me now. They say that when you grow old, those areas of the brain which deal with the memories of youth grow most perceptive. Forty years past is clear and bright, while last week becomes muggy. Do you find it so? Or perhaps it is being back here in Father's house, where I was born and where I hope to spend the rest of my days, that makes those old times so vivid.

2

I began the letter to you, dear Alvin, yesterday, and then I put it aside, and a day intervened before I could come back to it. I had all of Ben's personal letters and notes crated and shipped from Washington to Ringman, but it took a long time with two of those bright and eager young men on the research staff of the union going through the material and separating what, as they felt, properly belonged in the union's archives or in the Library of Congress. The results of their labor arrived yesterday, five large crates of material. I attempted to deal with it, but it defeats me, and I am of a mind to bestow all of it on the public library here. That would be a sensible place for it, a proper place. And I like the thought of interested people going to our library for information about Ben's life—not the same one-room cottage free library he went to as a boy, but still the same library in continuation.

So there is a problem solved, and isn't it true that at our age, most problems are relatively easy of solution? It's the problems of youth that are vast and terrible and overwhelming. You know, it was such a problem that brought Ben to our house here in Ringman for the first time—yes, the first time I saw him. Or at least I think so. Ringman, then—it was September of 1914, just forty-four years ago—was not a very large town, less than twenty thousand people, as I remember, so I may well have seen Ben Holt before he came to our house. Being an only and motherless child, I was at boarding school and finishing school for my education but my summers were spent here, and I certainly could have seen him many times. But not seen him to know him and look and remember; that happened when he came to our house.

Mrs. Privit was our housekeeper then, already aging and slow on her feet, and I ran past her to open the door. I was expecting my cousin, Jimmy Aimesley—he died in France in 1918, poor fellow—who was coming for a few days, and I wanted to greet him myself. But when I flung open the door, there, instead of my Cousin Jimmy, was Ben Holt.

"Is that Mr. Holt? And if it is, your father is expecting him, Dorothy, so ask him to come in!" Mrs. Privit called out to me, but I was speechless and neither asked him to come in nor to remain there on our doorstep, only staring at him. You see, it was a different time than this one, a different age, and I don't suppose there was a properly raised young woman like myself who didn't wait from day to day for the man she dreamed of to walk into her life. How she knew, I can't say; but I knew. I knew it would be a young giant, like this one, with eyes of sparkling blue and brown hair in a

54

great rumpled mass that he tried to comb, but so unsuccessfully, and a mass of arm and shoulder to fill the whole doorway, and his cap in his big hands, held nervously and turned round and round nervously; and afterwards he said that all he saw was my open mouth and my own wide eyes staring at him and making him feel what he already suspected, that he was a sort of a freak, badly dressed, badly groomed, at the front entrance of a rich, great house where he had no business being.

"Well, Dorothy, is it Mr. Holt or isn't it?" Mrs. Privit called.

"I'm Mr. Holt," he said, confirming my hope that his voice would be rich and deep. "I have an appointment with Mr. Aimesley."

"Yes. Yes, of course," I managed to say, and then, at once and together, I realized that he was a miner, his hands ingrained with coal dirt, his fingernails cracked and broken, his neck skin lined with the black net of his trade, his suit too small for him, and himself no fairy-tale prince but one of the men of the Ringman Pits; and I thought my heart would break with the dream shattered as quickly as it came into being. I let him into the house, closed the door behind him, and then ran upstairs to my bedroom, ashamed of myself for opening my heart to him—whether he knew or not—and giving my precious accolade to someone like himself. Mrs. Privit said afterwards that I had behaved strangely and badly, and discourteously too, and she was absolutely right. Although she knew as little as Ben Holt what had happened to me when I first opened the door.

In those old houses, privacy was always modified by an air vent, and my father's study was directly under my bedroom. I was mortified and dismissed Ben Holt from my life as expeditiously as I had taken him into it; but curiosity was ever my weak point, and I had to know what this great, oversized coal miner had to do with my father. I opened the vent and listened.

Ben had come out of the University of Pennsylvania the

previous spring. You know the story of what that meant to him, what he went through and what his mother went through for Ben to have that degree. Today, going to a college, even for a coal miner's son, is matter of fact, not a miracle; but my father knew a miracle then and accepted miracles with the grave and thoughtful wonder of a man who regards his species each new day as if it were a newly created miracle. So the spread of silence when I opened that vent must have been occupied by my father looking at Ben, studying him with interest and respect, and smiling that slow, warm smile of his, until he said,

"Sit down, Ben, won't you. You don't mind if I call you Ben?"

"No, sir, Mr. Aimesley."

"I do it as a matter of seniority, not as a point in class relations. I make that plain, because our conversation here will not be fruitful if I give any impression of patronizing you. Do you have any notion that I am patronizing you?"

"Not yet, sir." The reply came after a moment of hesitation, and there was the note of a smile in his voice. I wanted to see him smile and felt cheated.

"Tell me when it occurs," my father said flatly. "Do you smoke?"

"On occasion, sir."

"Then you don't mind if I do?"

"No, sir."

"All right, Ben." Silence as my father lit his cigar and took the two or three puffs that established his pleasure. "First, I want to thank you for coming here. A miner's Sunday is precious."

"I was glad to come, Mr. Aimesley."

"Good. Have you any idea why I sent for you?"

"No, sir."

"All right. We'll come to that. First of all, I know something about you. Ten years ago, I represented your father and the other miners who died in the Ringman Massacre, as

56

it's called. The settlement was small enough, shamefully small, but at least it was something."

"I know that. I've been grateful."

"For what? No, don't say things because they sound right, Ben. You were not grateful—you were as bitter as the others, and with reason. I'm not a labor lawyer. I should have done better; I should have known more, stood on firmer ground. Well, that's done. The point is, I've watched you. It's news when a miner's son fights his way into the university, and more news when he does it without a father's help. I don't have to tell you what you did. You know what you did, better than I can ever know. Your mother passed away recently, didn't she?"

"Two months ago."

"And that left you alone, didn't it?"

"I have no brothers or sisters, if that's what you mean. I have relatives here in Ringman—"

"That's what I meant," my father said. "You have aunts and uncles, but you prefer to board with Mrs. Tarragon."

"What did you do, sir? Have me investigated?"

"Simpler than that," my father laughed. "I asked a few questions. Tell me something, Ben—why did you go back to the mines?"

"I'm a miner."

"That's a statement of condition, not a reason."

"I have my reasons, Mr. Aimesley."

"But you prefer to keep them to yourself. You resent the rich lawyer who puts his nose into your affairs, and you think that none of it is any of his damn business."

There was a stretch of silence. Deliberately, my father had provoked Ben Holt, and now Ben was weighing the provocation, studying my father, and trying to gauge direction and meaning. I didn't have to see this to know it; I knew my father, and in some strange way, I seemed to know Ben Holt—just a little.

"No, sir," Ben said. "I guess your business is whatever you choose to make your business. But we live in Ringman. You are Joseph Aimesley, and this is the Aimesley house, and I'm a digger out at the pits."

"And never the twain shall meet?"

"Something of that sort, Mr. Aimesley."

"The hell with that!" my father snorted. "Don't talk to me about class or pride, Ben. I've lived my life in Ringman as well as you, and for a little longer, and I've bucked this damn miner pride until my head is sore. Don't tell me about pride. If they gave classes in it, there's no one but a coal miner fit to teach it. I'm not hiding anything. If I seem periphrastic, it's only because I am attempting to avoid offense to that pride of yours. Now to get down to facts. While you were still at the University of Pennsylvania, you received an offer to read law with the firm of Lee, Cadwallader and Seely in Pittsburgh. Am I right? No. I don't spy on you. It just happens that Arthur Lee is my brother-in-law. I wrote to the university for your record and sent it to him and suggested that he make the offer to you."

"Why?"

"Why? Because if you are avaricious for gold and you hear about a nugget buried somewhere, you will go and dig it up. Let us say that I am avaricious for human intelligence. Does that make sense to you?"

"Well, sir—yes. In a way."

"But you turned down Arthur Lee. Why?"

The silence stretched again, and my father let it stretch. He would be lighting his cigar again, I decided, and regarding Ben Holt moodily, as he so often regarded me. When Ben answered him, his voice was so soft that I had to strain to hear.

"I had two brothers, sir."

"Oh? I didn't know that, Ben."

"Daniel, fourteen years older than I. Franklin, fifteen years older."

"What happened to them, Ben?"

"The Harkness cave-in. Eighteen ninety-nine. It's forgotten by now. They worked together, as a team."

"I see."

"Well, that was a good offer from Pittsburgh. I'm very grateful to you for thinking of me, Mr. Aimesley."

"I wish it wouldn't end there, Ben. A lawyer is well armed. You can do a lot as a lawyer, Ben."

"Yes, sir. I know that. But first I have to figure out what I want to do."

3

So my letter to you, dear Alvin, goes on and on. I put it aside yesterday, and later that evening I rummaged through the drawers of my old bedroom chest. Father never changed my room, never got rid of anything, and there in a drawer I found the diary I had kept for three years, from the age of fourteen to the age of seventeen. So you see that I was a very usual young lady who kept a diary during just those years when a girl is expected to. It continues up to a point, and my point was the day I met Ben Holt. Late at night on that day, I made the following entry:

Today I met a divine, awful young man. His name is much more exalted than he is, since he is only a coal miner. His name is Benjamin Renwell Holt, and he has caused me nothing but trouble, so I hope I will never see him again and that Father forgets the whole thing. Cousin Jimmy also arrived.

That was the last entry I ever made in the diary. Can it be that when you first touch the manner and meaning of your existence, a teen-age diary is put aside? Anyway, during dinner, my Cousin Jimmy Aimesley said something about Ben Holt. He had arrived as Ben was leaving, and Father introduced them. I remember that Jimmy was terribly impressed with Ben's size, bearing, and a certain quality of magnetism so striking in Ben, and he mentioned this. Jimmy was small and underweight, and had always admired and envied big men.

"I don't think he's anything to admire," I said.

My father raised his brows. "Then you know him, Dorothy?"

"No, I only opened the door for him."

"But you know he's no one to admire," my father went on. I think I was forewarned; I knew that tone of my father's; but I had to go on and hit out somehow against Ben, I couldn't stop, and I said,

"He's just a miner, but even a miner's hands and neck could be clean when he comes calling on Sunday."

Father's face clouded, but he would never allow an argument during dinner. "That's enough, Dorothy," he said quietly. "We'll discuss this later."

After dinner, Father gave Jimmy a copy of Mr. Jerome's *Three Men in a Boat*, an old favorite of his which, he felt, would amuse Jimmy and improve his outlook on the world, and motioned me to follow him into his study. Poor Jimmy was no great prize, but to be marched off like this on his first night with us was almost more than I could bear, and in the study, I stared at Father morosely.

Bluntly, with no moral precepts to introduce the matter, Father said, "We'll stick to the facts, Dorothy. They are more enlightening than speculations on egalitarianism. You feel a personal affront in the fact that Mr. Holt did not remove the signs of his trade before he came calling here."

"It is Sunday. He could have washed."

"I've raised you poorly," Father sighed, "but we'll let that go by the board for the moment. How the hell do you know that he didn't wash?"

I was taken utterly aback, and I simply stared at him. He had never used that word to me before, or the tone—or looked at me in such a cold and melancholy manner. I was speechless, but he went on remorselessly,

"I can say at least that I am more to blame than you. Here you are, a fine young woman, very good to look at and not unintelligent, born and grown to maturity in a coal town, and without a smidgen of common sense in your head as to what it's all about. Oh yes, you may think that this is a very small point, Dorothy, but I assure you it is not. It is directly to the core of the matter. That young man who was here this afternoon is Benjamin Renwell Holt. He is twenty-two years old, the son and grandson of coal miners. If you went to the public library here and looked at your history books, you would discover that Renwells and Holts have lived in this county since Isaac Holt led the first group of settlers here in 1771—a good half century before an Aimesley bought property here and sold it at a sound profit. That's beside the point. But much to the point is that fact that Ben Holt is a brilliant and ambitious young man—sensitive, strong, and able. Ten years ago, his father was killed in the great disaster here. He put himself through college—and took care of his mother, and came out of it an honor student. I assure you that before he came here today, he bathed and scrubbed, but you don't scrub away the mark of the mines in one day—or in ten days. So from here on, you will think twice before you remark on how clean or dirty a miner is. That is all. You may go."

This was my own father, who adored me and granted my slightest whim and had never spoken harshly to me before in all the seventeen years of my existence. I would have burst into tears, except that I was too furious to weep and too affronted to give him the satisfaction of seeing me weep. I ran upstairs to my own room, locked the door behind me, threw myself on my bed, and wept. There I waited all evening for my father to appear and beg my pardon, but evidently the matter weighed less heavily on his mind than on mine. He let me have that evening to myself, while he played Jack of Diamonds for toothpicks with my Cousin Jimmy.

4

There were three precious weeks left before I would have to leave to complete my final year at finishing school, and one of those weeks was wasted with my Cousin Jimmy, rest his soul. How I grudged him every minute of my time!—for my mind was full of fantasies of how I would use those hours spent with Jimmy to meet Ben Holt, and in my mind I held a hundred conversations with him. But when Jimmy finally left on Friday afternoon, my dreams dissolved. Between my fantasy of meeting Ben Holt again and the reality of the problems it presented, there was an almost uncrossable gulf. I don't know, Alvin, whether you remember anything of the social structure of a Pennsylvania coal town in those years before the First World War. The class cleavage was absolute and unbridgeable. Father was not a millionaire by any means, but in comparison with a coal miner, he was a person of unthinkable wealth. My whole world was sharply separated from the world of the miners. Ringman was not one town, but two towns. You will recall that time when you spent a weekend with us here at Ringman and we picnicked on the top of Belfast Ridge, and I pointed out to you the pits and the miners' homes to the south and the fine and well-kept homes to the north. Belfast Ridge is only seven hundred feet high, but it separates two worlds. When you were there, the mines were already working out, and today that part of Ringman is only a ghostly reminder of the past, but then in 1914, you breasted Belfast Ridge and looked down into the devil's own estate, great black heaps of wasted earth and culm, dust and dirt, the gloomy tipples and scaffolds, the tracks and cars and the piles of coal, and beyond it, through the haze, the flat, red brick company buildings where the miners lived. It was peopled with dark men who clawed inside the earth's belly, like trolls. In town, I had seen them so often and close, but the Main Street contacts brought me no nearer to them and their sad-faced, faded women and their grave, reticent children. From across the ridge, they were alien and unapproachable.

So nothing of the hoped-for happened. Saturday, I was in town, drifting along Main Street, ostensibly to complete my shopping, but Saturday was a working day for the miners. Saturday night, it would be different, the stores along Main Street lit up and crowded, the street packed with miners and their families, but I could find no reason or excuse to be alone in the business section on Saturday night, and I remained at home, restless and miserable, until my father said to me,

"I hope, Dorothy, that you can be reasonably pleasant and hospitable tomorrow. We're having that young miner, Ben Holt, to Sunday dinner. You are part of the reason for the invitation. You live in a mining town, and I want you to be able to talk intelligently to a miner in your own house."

So much for that. You see, Alvin, it was not fate but my father's interest in Ben Holt that brought us together in the first place. Yet I do not have to defend myself to you as prepossessing; it has always appeared to me to be somewhat comical when a woman in her sixties or seventies parades the admirers of her youth; still I am old enough to state and accept the fact that I was a very attractive young woman, comely if not beautiful, with a good figure and good health. Even at seventeen, I had all the suitors I desired, and at seventeen, in those days, a young lady was accepted as mature more readily than today. My picture had been in the paper in Scranton as the debutante of the year, and in Wilkes-Barre, I had been chosen as the queen of the May Festival—all pathetic boasting and flying of ribbons, my dear Alvin, but to the point, I think, in this little story I am trying to write for you of Ben and myself and how we met and what our courtship was. I did not turn to Ben because there was no one else, but because there was no one else like him.

You know, in those days, we were all of us reading Jack

London with great eagerness; it was a time, for us in the middle class, at least, of life wrapped in flimsy romantic paper, the end of a strange age in the best of all possible worlds—a time to be shattered forever by the great war. Jack London gave us the romance we required but punctured it here and there with flashes of reality—and his romantic and implausible labor heroes were very much in the order of our dreams.

So it is no wonder that it seemed to me that Ben Holt had stepped directly from his pages. You never knew Ben as he was then. Many things changed him—nothing so much as power and the sweet, terrible taste of it—but many other things as well; but at that time, when he was twenty-two years old, there was a certain rocklike, indomitable purity about him, a youthful wisdom, a torrent of energy and words—words, words, words, like a great vessel filled to the bursting point with knowledge and certainty.

Not at once was this apparent, by no means at once, for he came into the Aimesley house as before, clumsily, his Sunday cap clenched in his massive, broken-nailed hands, wearing his cloak of resentment and suspicion. How nervous he was at first! I remember that I wore my pink organdy, which was the very best and most beautiful dress I owned for daytime wear, and how I worked for two full hours on my hair and applying rouge so subtly that it would not be noticed, since I was not supposed to possess it at all! But the effect on him was to make him even more nervous; every time he looked at me, he would turn his eyes away. I tried to put him at ease, and perhaps I succeeded just a little, but the whole conversation between us then before dinner was on the subject of the weather, and what a fine, cool September it was, and how early the mosquitoes had vanished. Yet it had its effect, and if he didn't talk to me, by dinnertime, he and my father were hard at it. To tell the truth, most of the talk in my life had been small talk, social, polite, and restricted in subject. If politics or business were to be discussed, the men waited until the women left the table. But Ben didn't wait, and on this Sunday, neither did my father.

They began with the local mayoralty race, and agreed that there was little to choose between the two candidates. My father was a graduate of Princeton, and for a while they discussed that school relative to the University of Pennsylvania. Then they launched into national politics, foreign policy, and the war.

Had it not been Ben Holt, I suppose that I would have been bored; it was the manner of the young lady of that time to be bored with such talk; but since it involved a young man I had every intention of conquering—even though my intentions were riddled with doubts, fears, and confusions—I listened intently. In spite of myself, I found myself interested.

"I have no favorites in this war," Ben Holt was saying. "It's as naked and dirty a struggle for money and power as any war ever was."

"The German atrocities," Father said. "You don't believe them?"

"Do you, Mr. Aimesley?"

"I'm afraid not. Not that men aren't capable of indulging in atrocities—but they're more capable of inventing them." My father glanced at me. With two of my friends, I had labored at a booth all through August, collecting money for Belgian Relief. "I've shocked Dorothy. The women treasure the horrors. It provides a rare opportunity for a public display of rage and pity."

"That's not fair!" I burst out, and with a slight smile, Ben said gently, "Of course it is not, Miss Aimesley. And I don't think for a moment that Mr. Aimesley means it seriously."

"But I do. I do," Father chuckled.

Ben's face hardened just a little, but in the same soft voice, he said, "Then begging your pardon, Mr. Aimesley, if you think that the opportunity for a public display of rage and pity on the part of women is a rare thing, then you have only to make your way over Belfast Ridge. There you will find rage and pity enough on public display, but if you wish to make doubly certain, then wait until you hear the disaster whistles screaming from the shaft head to tell the women of Ringman that two or three hundred of their men are trapped down there in the hell of gas and darkness—"

His voice was low and soft and thoughtful, the words like music in their cadence. It was the first time I really listened to a miner speak; if they were a race apart, I had put them into the class of brutish dirt and ignorance—and now I sat openmouthed listening to one of them come to my defense against my father. Had I ever heard Father contradicted in such a manner before? I don't know, and neither did I have any idea of what his reaction would be. But he only looked at Ben thoughtfully for a long moment, and then said,

"You are right, Ben. And by God I have no business talking flippantly of any aspect of this monstrous war in Europe."

"But you have, I think, for only when enough of us poor boobs are beaten or shot for king or kaiser will we appreciate the senselessness of this bloodletting. Still, that comes badly from a miner."

"Why, Mr. Holt?" I asked him. "Why does it come badly from a miner? I won't say that I equate the Kings of England and Belgium with the German Kaiser, but I think you have every right to feel as you do."

Father, watching me narrowly, whispered, "Hear, hear!" but I don't think Ben heard him. He was looking at me as if he had just now observed me for the first time. He nodded slowly and said,

"Thank you, Miss Aimesley, but, you see, we miners wear the badge of Cain, because the war that means misery for others means bread and meat on our tables. I have tried to be most careful of what I say here in your house, for you people have been very kind to me, and believe me, Miss Aimesley, I have no liking for the poor man who hates the rich out of his envy. You're not expected to know our problems."

66

"That's only kindness on your part," I replied. "If I am ignorant of what lies across Belfast Ridge, in our own back yard, I can't think that I'll ever learn anything of importance."

"No more ignorant than most of the operators who own the mines. Many of them don't know the difference between bug dust or the gob pile—"

"Nor do I."

"You're not expected to, and it doesn't add up in dollars and cents to you as it does to them. Bug dust is the powdered coal left on the floor when the cutting machine rips into the face, and it must be loaded into cars and tracked back to the heading before we can handle the rock coal that pays off. The gob pile consists of dirt and pieces of slate and other rock that we separate from the coal—"

I shook my head. "I can hardly follow you, Mr. Holt. All this is underground?"

"Sometimes—miles underground."

"The thought of it makes me shiver. I don't think I could ever bring myself to go underground, not if my life depended on it."

"Well, if your life depended on it, Miss Aimesley—well, a woman will do a lot for her kids or just to stay alive. You know, only a hundred and thirty years ago in England, the women and children worked in the mines with their men. They went down the shafts on rickety wooden ladders, and then they crawled, sometimes for a mile or two, along black tunnels never high enough for them to stand up in, and never dry either. When they laid track, the women and kids pulled the cars, crawling with the leather harness on their shoulders, while the men lay on their bellies and backs to pick at the face. A miner lasted five years, and the kids who grew up in the workings were half blind and never able to stand straight, but the women outlived the men. They had more stamina. They worked stripped to the waist, and they were bought and sold since they were indentured—"

He saw the look on my face and stopped suddenly, and

stammered his apology, feeling perhaps that his reference to half-naked women had bruised my Victorian sensitivity. I explained quickly that it was the horror of it—how could one believe that such things had ever happened? And in England, a civilized and cultured nation.

"The Boers didn't think so," my father remarked, watching me with curiosity and interest. "What Ben spoke of is true —and much worse. Dickens wrote about it, and I am sure you read what he wrote, Dorothy. It's hearing Ben talk about it that brings it home. But exactly what did you mean about war, Ben? Is that the only time a miner has steady work?"

"Year-round work? Yes, sir, just about the only time."

"But I thought last year was a good year."

"In a way of speaking, because war was in the air. In a normal year, it's work when the market wants coal and lay-off when it doesn't. As a kid, even when my father was alive, I can't remember a time when I wasn't hungry, and when my father died and I went into the mines—why, my stomach became a bottomless pit. I heard an operator once say that miners eat too much."

"How callous!"

"Yes and no, Miss Aimesley. He had watched miners eat. What he didn't understand is that the kind of work a miner does burns up food like a fire. Miners do eat more than anyone else I ever heard of—but if they don't eat, they can't work. Have you ever seen a fat miner?"

I shook my head and said, "But, Mr. Holt, I've heard so much of the horrors and suffering of a miner's life. I don't remember the great disaster of 1904, but just this past summer, I heard the disaster whistles screeching twice, and every other summer too. Perhaps I'm not as sensitive as I should be, but I do live in a mining town, and I know something about how hard it is for the miners. I remember one winter, before Mother died, when she said to me, 'I won't have to take the curtains down for cleaning, Dorothy.' But her face was so sad that I asked her why, and then she said,

'When the curtains stay white, the miners are starving.' I mean—some of it I can understand. Only, one thing I never understood—"

"Yes, Miss Aimesley?"

"Why miners remain miners. They're not slaves. Those people you told us about in England, well, they were indentured servants, weren't they? But today in the United States, no one is forced to stay with one job. When there's no work, why don't the miners go somewhere else where the work isn't so cruel, perhaps? Why do they stay in the mines until they are hurt or killed or worn out?"

"We need coal and someone has to mine it," Father said.

"But that's not the answer. Not to my question."

"I guess it isn't," Ben said. "And I think that if I heard your question once, I heard it a hundred times. Last week, your father told me that miners were too proud—"

"Not too proud. Just damn proud to a point of irritation!" Father interrupted.

"But you're right, sir. They are proud and headstrong and independent, and they're that way because they're miners. It's hard to explain a miner to anyone who hasn't lived with them, and the hardest thing to get across is that most miners love their work and they take pride in it and—well, it's just what they want to do. As dangerous and dirty and back-breaking as it, it's what a miner wants and what he loves. I work in the mines because I want to and because I'd rather work in the mines than do anything else."

"But how can you say that?" I burst out. "You're a college man, Mr. Holt. Surely you want something more from life than to be a miner?"

"Do I? Should I, Miss Aimesley? I'm not being impertinent —I'm perfectly serious. I love the mines and I love the men who work in the mines, and I hate them too. I love them and hate them, and there have been nights I couldn't sleep, trying to understand what it all means to me. I remember the first time I went down a shaft. I was only fourteen then, and when the elevator car sank into that pit of black—blacker than any black in the whole world—I wanted to scream with terror. And down in the pits and tunnels, the terror became worse and worse. All I wanted was to get out of there before the whole weight of the world fell on me and choked the life out of me, and all I could say to myself was that I'd die of hunger before I'd ever be a miner. And other miners have told me that it's always that way the first time. But the second time, the fear is less. And a time comes when it goes—and the tunnel is your home and your life, and you live with danger and death and it nourishes you and it makes you proud. Because no one else in the whole world is as skilled as you and as brave as you. Every time you put up a timber, your life depends on your skill and judgment, and every time you set off a blast, it's the same thing. You hate it and curse it, but you want it—and a time comes when you're its prisoner just as surely as if you were indentured."

He finished, and Father and I sat there in silence. Remember that I was not yet eighteen, and I had never seen a young man like Ben Holt before or sat across the table from him. The young men I knew talked about tennis or the shows they had seen on their visits to New York or how much money they hoped to make and how successful they hoped to be. They did not talk, vibrantly and poetically, of Stygian pits of darkness, where men drove dynamite into a black rock face and lived and worked in clouds of coal dust and deadly gas. Nor must you feel that this was a pose or a charade on the part of Ben. Ben knew as well as anyone else what a deadly, hopeless hell the life of a miner was; but, as he told me afterwards, confronting me, he had to paint a picture that was brave and romantic. And to a very large extent, he believed it. You see, in the beginning, then, I did not fall in love with the Ben Holt you knew—no, not even with the headstrong, desperate man you met in West Virginia, leading an army of armed miners, and certainly not with the white-haired, somber giant who taught a whole world the meaning of power. I look back through time as an old woman, my dear Alvin, and there was not one man but many men. In some ways, we don't change at all; but in other ways, we do change so much.

Shall I finish my story of that evening? I am not putting down the actual words that were said—you must realize that—it was so very long ago; but not so different, either, for while there are things that have become vague and fuzzy, those first days with Ben are clear and unclouded. We talked some more at the table, or rather he talked while Father and I listened. Once the barrier of place and class was broken, the words poured out of him in an endless torrent, and nothing he said was dull or familiar. From his point of view, he found there in our home a sweetness and warmth that he had never encountered before. He had no illusions about the virtues of the rich, but neither did he promote the legend of the virtuous poor. He had lived with poverty all his life, and he had sufficient knowledge of the degradation and suspicion and ignorance and hatred it breeds. In later years, I have seen Ben stalking like a raging lion in the homes of millionaire coal operators, filled with and voicing anger and contempt; but there was another Ben, and we were not millionaire coal operators, only a small-town lawyer who lived alone with his daughter.

After dinner, we went into the parlor, and Father asked me to play something for them, while he and Ben smoked cigars. Father's one extravagance was cigars, and he always kept a large humidor of panatelas, fragrant and mild, that he had sent to him from Cuba. Ben, on the other hand, smoked a brand of cigars which I remember seeing only in the coal towns of Pennsylvania, and which has today suffered a well-deserved demise. They were referred to as "the digger's" or "miner's consolation," and in those days sold two for five cents, and no one who ever smelled their fragrance will forget it. Ben had a pocketful of them and longed for a cigar, but did not dare light one in our house. I remember his face as he lit the panatela Father pressed on him, and in after years, whenever he speculated on the psychology of a union leader who sold out, I would twit him about that cigar. Anyway, there he sat, with a cigar in one hand and a glass of brandy in the other, trying his best not to look self-conscious, scrunching his long arms and legs, so that he would show less shirt cuff and less skin between pants and socks, and listening to my rendition of the "Moonlight Sonata," an important part of the repertoire of every serious young lady pianist of the time.

He had been wonderfully possessed and at ease all evening, but now he began to withdraw into himself and become surly. It was not that he didn't enjoy the music; I have almost never known a miner who didn't have a feeling for good music—perhaps because there is so much of the Welsh blood and influence in them; but rather because he suddenly saw himself in his position and resented it, the fact that he did not dare to smoke his own cigars and had to sit there in silence and listen to my less than noble performance. He felt that he was being patronized. When I had finished playing, he made some polite remarks, and a little while after that, he took his leave.

Then, as always, I was sensitive to his every mood and action. Father was not. After he had seen Ben to the door, he turned to me, rubbing his hands with delight and grinning, and asked me,

"Well, what do you think of your unwashed digger now?" —for all the world as if Ben was something he had created specially for that evening.

"I think that's a dreadful way to characterize him!"

"Honey," he cried, exploding with laughter, "that was your characterization, not mine."

"At least I want to forget it."

"Then he got through to you."

"I found him quite interesting," I said demurely. "I just wonder what happened when I was playing. He became very surly and unhappy, I think."

"Did he? Well, a young man's to be forgiven his moods. The point is, he's quite a man with quite a mind. You'll agree to that, won't you?"

72

"He's certainly the most opinionated young man I ever met."

"You mean that he has opinions and voices them. That's not exactly the same thing as being opinionated."

"He's very sure of himself."

"And with reason," Father said. "He's had no one to depend on but himself."

Should I have told Father that I was in love? It was something I hardly dared to admit to myself—that for the first time in my life, I wanted a person so desperately that I could not think of anything but Ben Holt. I don't believe that these things are accidents. If I had left it alone, perhaps I would never have seen him again, although Ben insisted that he was already in love with me. But that was after the fact, and people love differently, and to be in love—if indeed he was—meant something else to Ben than it meant to me.

So here is a whole day, another day, gone with my writing, dear Alvin, and now for the first time, this journey so far back into the past is beginning to trouble me just a little. But I will finish it as truthfully as I know how, which is little less than truthful. I mean that the Dorothy Aimesley and the Ben Holt I write about are like two people I have read about or been told about. Have you ever remarked on the fact that in a dream you will see yourself in the third person, so to speak? This remembering is somewhat like a dream.

5

Two days, and I have written nothing, but I have gone back into a past I never thought I would revisit. What sort of people are we, Alvin, that we look upon growing old with such skepticism and fear—yet avoid the past as the plague and revisit it with even greater fear? But I have been prowling over the old house, going through drawers and rummaging in the attic, and I have even wept a little over this and that.

In my old bedroom, just where I had placed it more than forty years ago, I found a long, long letter from Ben, and I am sending it to you but in its proper place. You may peruse its intimacies without embarrassment and use it just as your own judgment dictates.

I thought that I had the letter I wrote to Ben after the Sunday evening I spoke of above; I had some notion that he kept it and gave it back to me some time later. Well, perhaps he did—or perhaps he threw it away. Ben did not suffer from sentimentalism—and I mean that more as praise than criticism. In any case, I could not find it, but I remember the general tenor of it. The evening after, Monday evening, I wrote to him:

Dear Mr. Holt:
I enjoyed our evening with you, and would like to see you again, if you can find time. Since I am leaving for school soon, I have only this coming Sunday free. If your day is also free, I think it might be nice to pack a picnic basket and spend the day out of doors. Providing the weather is suitable. If you can let me know before the weekend, I will be happy to fix the picnic basket.

Or in much the same sense, if perhaps even more restrained. Still, then, in 1914, it was a piece of impropriety, and shattering in that I addressed myself to a coal miner, a person of no family, figuratively and literally. It explains my state of mind better than anything else might, and when I had mailed it to Mrs. Tarragon's boardinghouse, I felt that I had indulged in an action little short of criminal. Don't smile at the desperateness of my situation, for that would only be evidence of the poverty of your own later years. A girl of seventeen, truly in love for the first time, experiences something as rash and wonderful as anything that will ever happen to her again—and more so, believe me. So if I could not eat and could not sleep and breathed air as sweet as honey and walked in a world of music wherever I went, this was not unmixed with guilt and remorse. My advances were improper and reckless, and whatever Ben Holt had thought of me before, surely he would think only less of me now.

I had planned not to tell my father of my action until I received some reply from Ben, but on Wednesday, at dinner, he said to me,

"Dorothy, even if you have fallen in love with that young miner, you'll prove nothing by a death of starvation."

I stared at him in amazement and mumbled denials, but he had lived with me too long not to recognize the first substantial break in an appetite that had been healthy, to put it mildly. So I blurted out what I had done, indulged a few tears, and surprisingly was able to eat a proper dinner. Father was responsible for that. He shrugged and pointed out that at worst, Ben Holt could only say no.

"Then you're not angry at me?"

"When you decide to marry Ben Holt or John Doe or anyone else, we'll get down to basic things. Meanwhile, you've only invited a boy to a picnic. If your mother were alive, she might sensibly insist on a chaperon—"

"But you won't—please, Daddy?"

"He hasn't accepted yet, has he?"

"But I'm going off to school. What harm—"

"I am not worried about your safety or your honor, Dorothy. We'll talk about it when you hear from him."

I received my reply from Ben the following morning. "Dear Miss Aimesley," he wrote, "Thank you for your kind invitation. I will be at your home at eleven o'clock in the forenoon on Sunday." And he signed it "Benjamin R. Holt." How I scrutinized it and analyzed it! In time, Ben told me that he had rewritten it three times, but I never knew whether to believe that; although it may have been. I never fully understood why Ben wanted so desperately to make a proper impression upon us. Certainly, he wanted nothing from my father. Was he in love with me? Not then, I don't think; yet all of his actions were formal and thoughtful, unlike himself. Or am I being unfair to him? It is so easy to worship Ben, as so many did, that perhaps I am bending over backwards to form a fair picture. I do know that we, myself, my father, and our whole way of life were of a special significance to Ben. I do believe that during the whole course of Ben's life, Father was the only man of close relationship with whom he never quarreled and never broke. In later years, when Ben would rant about the iniquity and hypocrisy of the rich, all the rich, I would remind him of Father. "That's another category," he would bark at me. "Joe Aimesley's a civilized man!"

Anyway, I showed Father the note. "Do you want to go?" he asked me.

"Of course I do. I wouldn't have written him otherwise, and I'm so ashamed of it."

"Of letting him know that you like him?"

"Yes."

"If he couldn't see it for himself, he has no sense."

"And you won't make me have Aunt Alice or someone like that for a chaperon?"

Father just looked at me and shook his head in despair, and so it had worked, and I had my day with Ben Holt. And it was that day that made all the difference in the world, and I don't regret it. I don't suppose I could have loved anyone who wasn't like Ben, and I'm glad it was Ben.

Those were the days of long dresses. I wore a pink cotton with a red silk sash, but before that I was up at six o'clock to see to the picnic lunch. At seven-thirty, when Mrs. Privit entered her kitchen, I had turned her work table into an utter confusion of boiled eggs, sliced olives, mashed anchovies, ham paste, liver paste, and pickles. She drove me out of there and said she would finish it herself. Not only did she disapprove of my plans for the day, but she saw it as an alternative to church.

We were only intermittent churchgoers, for my father was an unprejudiced agnostic, but when I was home, his sister, my Aunt Alice Aimesley, who was one of the leaders of the woman's suffrage movement in eastern Pennsylvania, would turn up each Sunday morning to see that I attended church.

Her attitude mystified my father, for most of the year Aunt Alice was lecturing here and there and all over the country on the suffrage movement with never even a nod to religion. It was only in Ringman that she took an interest in the godless upbringing of her poor motherless niece. This Sunday I had finished dressing, at about half past ten, and came downstairs to hear her arguing with my father.

I paused on the stairs to listen to her contention that my wickedness was threefold: not only was I missing church service to picnic, but my companion in iniquity was a miner, and I was proceeding unchaperoned. To which my father replied,

"That comes poorly from anyone, but badly from you, Alice."

"Just what do you mean?"

"Do you wear one face for the suffrage movement and another for Ringman?"

"Of all the insufferable accusations—"

"I am not accusing you of anything, Alice. I am simply pointing out that this is Dorothy's last Sunday at home before she returns to school, and I intend for her to spend it as she desires. I will not have you questioning her morality or her intentions. If you are going to fight for the freedom and liberation of your sex, you might as well apply your credo here in Ringman as anywhere else."

I had never heard Father talk to his sister like that before, and the result was that she stormed out of the house without waiting to speak to me. When I came downstairs, Father had gone into his study. He never mentioned the incident, and promptly at eleven, Ben appeared, scrubbed and cleaned and wearing the same black suit. He brought me a bouquet of roses, beautiful, long-stemmed red roses that even then were quite expensive. It was a lovely gift, and after I had put them into a vase, I called Father out of his study to admire them. Then Mrs. Privit, her mouth drawn into a thin and disapproving line, appeared with the picnic basket, which Ben took and hooked on his arm, just as though a Sunday picnic were a weekly matter with him. Father told us to enjoy ourselves, and we walked out of the house and down the road with never a word between us until Ben thought to ask me where I would like to go.

"We might climb Belfast Ridge and picnic on one of the flat rocks there."

He agreed, and then remembered to tell me how pretty I looked.

"Thank you," I smiled.

"I mean, I thought of it when I first saw you, but I didn't have all my wits about me."

"Oh?"

He didn't speak for a while after that, and we strolled down the road, each of us immersed in meditation. Away from our house, toward the wagon track that went up Belfast Ridge in those days, were only farmhouses. Today, a part of that area has been developed for small homes and the rest of it is a golf course. There is a shopping center where the new highway cuts into Belfast Ridge, and it is all very busy and garish; but at the time I write of, there were only the rolling fields and the clumps and windbreaks of maple and oak and birch, the colors changing already in the early autumn and glints of yellow and gold all over the landscape. One of the ironies of coal and the men who mine it is that so often the veins lie in the most beautiful country imaginable —a good description for the hills that surround Ringman. And that was such a cool and clear morning that my whole memory of the day is crisp and glistening.

It was the first time we had ever been alone with each other, and I was still smarting with shame at my boldness for having written to him. Ben must have sensed this, because he mentioned that he was grateful to me for having taken the initiative and written to him. He thanked me.

"Don't thank me," I said. "I can't pretend that I am pleased with myself."

"Why not?"

78

"Because young ladies don't make advances toward young men they barely know."

"Well, surely it's not an advance to write me a note and say that you would like to see me again."

"It certainly is!" I snapped.

He looked at me with amazement and pointed out that if I hadn't written the note, we probably would not have seen each other again for a long time—if ever.

"That doesn't matter."

"Well, please tell me, Miss Aimesley," he said, stopping short and facing me, "do you or don't you want to spend the day with me?"

"Of course I do," I blurted out, almost in tears at this point.

"Then what's this all about?"

"*You* should have written to *me*."

We walked on again and for a while in silence. Ben was shaking his head. "Oh no," he finally said. "I guess you never open your eyes and take a good look at the world, do you, Miss Aimesley?"

"Of course I do."

"You keep saying that."

"What?"

"Of course I do."

"Well, what do you want me to say, Mr. Holt? I'm afraid I'm a very ordinary person. I'm afraid pearls of wisdom can't drop from my lips every time I open my mouth."

"You're not a very ordinary person at all, and I'm not much good at polite small talk, Miss Aimesley. How could I write you a letter? Or call on you? Or anything like that? I'm a miner. My name is Ben Holt, and I live in Mrs. Tarragon's boardinghouse, and if I had a brain in my head, I would have torn your letter to pieces and forgotten all about it."

"Why didn't you?"

"Because I'm a damned fool enough to think that you're the most desirable and loveliest woman I ever saw in all my life, and because you and your father made me feel like a human being."

That quieted me. We walked on for ten or fifteen minutes without a word being said, and then I saw three young men coming down the road on bicycles. They were miners in Levis and blue shirts, and they rode girls on their handlebars, skinny, giggling, screeching girls, and they all set up a shout of welcome when they saw Ben, "Benny!" "Benny, buddy!" "Oh, what a nifty, what a peach that is, Benny!" They braked to a stop, two of the girls tumbling off, and gathered around us. Flustered and mumbling for the first time since I knew him, Ben introduced me. The boys were shaggy-haired, pale, their skin tattooed with coal dust. Their speech was the strange nasal dialect of the miners in that part of Pennsylvania. They looked at me closely; they recognized my name; they nodded, muttered a few words, and then rode off. The girls said nothing at all. They departed in a mixture of restraint, irritation, and deference; and all I could think of was that here on Sunday, when the poorest workman put on his best, three young miners were out in Levis. It was a small, unworthy thought, but they became the image of Ben and Ben became them, and my heart sank, and I think I would have given everything I owned in the world to be back safely at home, never knowing that a Ben Holt existed in this world.

As for Ben, he seemed to know what was going on in my mind. His wide face was thoughtful and grave, and as we walked on, he appeared to be a thousand miles away; so much so that I was shocked when he said to me, very gently,

"Would you like me to take you home, Miss Aimesley?"

"Oh? Oh no—no. Why should you think that I want to go home?"

"Well—well, it's kind of hard for someone like you to be out with a roughneck for the first time and enjoy it and feel secure."

"You're not a roughneck," I replied indignantly. "If you

80

were, I certainly would not be out walking with you on a Sunday!"

"Or any other day?" he smiled.

"Or any other day, Mr. Holt. And as for *someone like me* —I hardly think you have a right to talk in terms of *someone like me,* Mr. Holt, since you know nothing about me."

"I'm sorry."

"And as for feeling secure, I feel perfectly secure. Or are you suggesting that I ought to feel afraid of you, Mr. Holt?"

"You know that I'm suggesting nothing of the kind, Miss Aimesley. And the last thing in the world I desired was to make you angry."

"But I am not angry, Mr. Holt—not at all."

And now, suddenly, we were both of us smiling and relaxed for the first time, and feeling young and splendid in the fine noonday sun, and climbing bravely up the wagon track to Belfast Ridge. Once or twice, where the road was very rough, Ben gave me his hand. I remember the size of it. It closed over my hand and devoured it, and the hard, calloused surface of his palm gripped my fingers like iron. We didn't say much going up the hill; it's a hard climb, and we saved our breath, and then presently, we stood on the top, the world unfolding beneath us, woods and fields and hills on one side to the west of us, and on the other side, eastward, the collieries, the scarred earth, the piles of culm, the spur tracks and trestles and clefts of erosion, and the dull, dirty brick company houses of the miners, lying in the haze across the valley, terrace upon terrace, swinging around and folding down finally into the streets of Ringman.

Ben found a broad, flat rock, and I said that it would do splendidly as a table. I refused to let Ben help me unpack the basket, but insisted that he sit down and rest himself. He hardly took his eyes off me now, and he was relaxed enough to ask me whether I would mind his smoking a cigar.

"Not at all," I said. "I like cigar smoke."

"Well, the miner's consolation is not exactly a cigar, but

81

up here the wind will blow away the smoke, Miss Aimesley — Miss Aimesley?"

"Yes?"

"May I call you Dorothy?"

I nodded, going on with the lunch and not daring to look up at him right then. I knew that his eyes were on me. He went on,

"You see, Dorothy—those kids—well, a miner's kids—it's hard to talk about mining. It's just so hard."

"I don't understand why."

"Well, how can I explain it? Where do you start? It's like we're a people apart—a race apart. I once read a book by a man called Kingsley, a book called *The Water Babies,* supposedly a kid's book in England. I was just a kid when I picked it up and read it—a book about a chimney sweep who was dirty because he didn't care about being clean. I remember how enraged I was when I read it, not because it was a snobbish, silly book, but because this damn fool who wrote it didn't understand that you can't clean chimneys without getting dirty—and that soot is not just dirt." Ben held out one of his big hands. "I scrubbed for fifteen minutes this morning, and the tattoo of the mines is still there."

Now I faced him, and our eyes met. He grinned suddenly, spread his arms, and leaned back where he sat there on the ground. I offered him a sandwich. It was tiny. He swallowed it in two bites, and I gave him another one and a hard-boiled egg. He was hungry, and I was pleased to see that he liked the food. "Tell me about yourself, Mr. Holt," I said to him. He said, "Ben Holt." "Ben Holt, then. Tell me about yourself, Ben." But he wanted to know where to begin, how to begin. He looked at me in my pink dress, and I sensed what he was thinking. "There was a man called Ollie Bricker, whom I tried to kill once by dropping a lump of coal off a tipple onto his head. But I missed him. I was just a kid. Is that the kind of thing you want to know about me? Does it tell you anything about me?"

"I'm glad you missed him and that you don't have anyone's life on your conscience."

"When you say something like that," he asked curiously, "you mean it, don't you? Everything you say?"

"Yes. Why did you want to kill him?"

"He was a cracker boss."

"Oh? What's a cracker boss?"

"He runs the screen room," he grinned derisively. "Now you want to know what a screen room is."

"Yes." I gave him more sandwiches and another egg and some pickles.

"I suppose you know what kind of coal we mine here?"

"Anthracite. I know some things about coal."

"All right. You don't treat anthracite as you do bituminous. The bituminous falls to pieces as it burns, but the anthracite has to be broken into pieces of approximately the same size. It's what we call a fancy product, and some people think it's the best coal in the world. It is, for some purposes—but it's hard to fire. When it was first discovered here in Pennsylvania, back in colonial times, they couldn't market it in Philadelphia because people didn't know how to fire it. They called it 'black diamonds' in contempt, but that's just what it was, and when you do fire it, it burns with a hot, beautiful flame and gives off almost no smoke. After the anthracite is mined, it's broken down into small pieces by a machine we call a breaker. But at this point, the coal is mixed with slate and other undesirable rock, and this rock has to be picked out of it. That's a job done by kids—even today—they're called breaker boys. The broken coal passes through a long chute, and the breaker boys sit on benches over the chute, and all day long they crouch over picking the slate out of the coal. They can't stop because the coal doesn't stop, and by midday, the chute is so full of coal dust that you can't see, and your eyes are burning and your throat and lungs are full of the stuff, and the roar of the chute has taken your hearing away, and in the summer you sweat and roast and dream of a drink of water and in the winter you shiver and freeze, and the dirty swine who sees to it that you never stop and never take a rest is the cracker boss; so I just made up my mind to kill him, and that was it."

All this poured out of him casually, almost indifferently, between bites of sandwich and sips of hot coffee.

"How old were you, Ben?" I whispered.

"Thirteen, I guess—"

"How terrible!"

"It wasn't terrible, Dorothy. It was normal and ordinary."

"For you."

"Of course for me. I didn't resent working in the chute; it took away my summers—it took away the best part of being a kid, but I didn't resent it because I didn't know any other way, and you have to know another way to resent."

"And now you know another way, and you're full of resentment," I said.

"Yes and no. When I look at you, Dorothy, I see a girl like no other girl I ever knew. Maybe not. Maybe I don't know you well enough. But I tell myself that. And then I resent the way it's been for you, easy and clean and gentle all your life, and for your father, and that big house of yours—"

"Is it only hard your way? What do you suppose Father felt and I felt when my mother died?"

"What I felt when my mother died," he replied bluntly. "And maybe something of what my mother felt when two sons and a husband died in the pits."

"I'm sorry, Ben."

"Sure. You're tender and compassionate, but you're in another world. How do I cross over? If I want to. I don't know if I want to. I don't know if you want me to." He held up one of our tiny picnic sandwiches. "I've never eaten anything like this before. I'm twenty-two years old, and I've never eaten food like this before. Or been to a picnic before. I couldn't sleep last night for knowing I was going to see you today and be with you, but Jesus Christ, how I resent you!"

84

"I don't own a coal mine," I said slowly. "I didn't make any of your world, Ben Holt, and neither did my father. The first time I saw you, I resented the way your hands looked. That makes as much sense as for you to resent me because I've never been hungry and because my father has a nice house."

"I know that."

"I'm glad you do—sometimes. And as for myself, I'm not very unusual. There are thousands and thousands of girls like me. You went to college. You must have met girls like me."

"You think so?"

"I'm asking you, Ben."

"I held two jobs one year in college. I waited table in the dining room during the day and I worked off campus late at night. In an all-night counter place. The kids with money used to wind up their dates there. I remember a girl came in one night with a feller—she was pretty enough to take your breath away. I guess I stared at her, and she said to stop staring at her and annoying her. You can imagine what I felt like. She ordered eggs and left the bottom of her plate covered with the yellow. Then she tipped me. She borrowed ten pennies and pressed each one of them into the yellow muck on the bottom of her plate."

"You remember that," I nodded. "I guess you'll remember that until the day you die. You don't want to ever forget it, do you, Ben Holt?"

"No! Because I dug those pennies out and washed them! Because I needed that ten cents!"

"I suppose there might be cruel miners—bad miners. Even plain wicked miners. Even a miner's daughter who was just nasty through and through. Or couldn't that be?"

I think the most wonderful thing about Ben was his smile. His face would become like a storm, dark and brooding and full of impending wrath, and then he would smile the way he smiled that day; and when he did, my whole heart went out to him.

"It could be," he nodded.

And that was when our day began, really, a wonderful day with a Ben Holt so few people ever knew.

6

A whole week now, dear Alvin, since I broke off what is already a considerable manuscript. The truth is that during this time, I had to resist an impulse to destroy what I have written—and then talk you out of what you propose to do with all our memories of Ben's life. I read it through. What possible meaning or importance can such meanderings have? I have been quite depressed, which is unusual for me, and this searching back into our past makes life seem even shorter than it actually is—and if anything, more meaningless.

Well, I went down to Washington last week. The union had a large banquet—of course you know this—to celebrate the completion of their new building, and I had hoped to see you there. I was disappointed when you didn't come. You will recall the meeting we had with Frank Lloyd Wright—is it possible that twenty years have gone by since then?—when Ben first asked him to design the building. The excitement I felt watching them meet for the first time —what was it someone said? "Two giants of our time"— or something like that. They struck it off, didn't they, but really, neither of them knew or understood each other. I am so suspicious of the flashy "great men" meetings that are sprinkled through history. What excited Ben chiefly was the fact that he and the union were commissioning the greatest living architect to do a building for them. It was another step, another rung in the ladder; but I don't believe he ever cared about the building itself. Mr. Wright talked about the material and symbolic significance of a building to house the union that mined coal. Ben was a thousand miles away; he had a strike on his hands and he was being attacked from within the union again—

But all that is beside the point. They wanted me at the dedication of the building because, as they put it, "It marked the fulfillment of Ben's fondest dream." What nonsense! I know the good and bad of Ben, but the last thing in the world he gave two damns about was that building or any building.

Well, I came and I went, and at least it lifted me out of my doldrums. The public-relations man at the union—the new one, Smithson, a bright, alert young thing with *ivy* written all over him; they tell me he majored in trade union- ism at college—had made arrangements for me to lunch at the White House with the good mistress there; but at the last minute, it was called off, due to pressures of this and that. I suppose that one of the minor rewards for being a hostess in such a position is an exemption from explanations. If matters intervene they intervene, and that's all there is to it. Just as well.

I drove back from Washington to Ringman alone. I never used to enjoy driving, but lately I seem to have developed a taste for it. I drive slowly—I am sure every other driver on the road berates me and that I confirm all the clichés about women drivers—and driving gives me a chance to think, not thinking in any constructive sense, but to allow my thoughts to wander here and there and everywhere.

I lived through, once again, that golden September Sunday with Ben—much as I wrote of it and much different too; so I begin to mistrust all accounts of things that have hap- pened, and I shall never again read anyone's account of a real life with any real pleasure. I have a sort of theory that in a person's life, any moment is an eternity and utterly peculiar unto itself. I am no more able to recapture the moods and fancies and exultations of a girl of seventeen than you are, my dear Alvin, and I do respect you as a writer. In my mind, I watched Dorothy Aimesley and Ben Holt with considerable detachment and some obtuseness. I watched him kiss her for the first time. I watched them sit there on the rock on top of the ridge for their own eternity, in the wonderful silence of discovery. I watched them walking, hand in hand, his big bulk in black looking over her small pink self.

I tried to remember why I fell in love with Ben Holt. Is the answer as unnecessary as the question? In the manuscript you sent me about your own first involvement with Ben in West Virginia, you mention the first time you saw your Laura. You saw her not as she was, but as you wanted her to be. Do we actually operate that way, like children who see toys in store windows and desire them? Perhaps we do, and with no more sense or purpose; and at least it provides for me a memory of a day that was rich and golden.

But nothing was consummated or finished on that day. Ben brought me home at five in the afternoon and left me at the door to my house, and he left without even a small kiss for farewell.

That was his own shyness at our house, and it lessened my state of beatitude not an iota. Up the stairs to my room, my feet never touching the steps; and at my mirror, I conducted a thorough examination of what had so fascinated and captured Benjamin Renwell Holt. At dinner, my father looked at me long and curiously before he said,

"Dorothy, are you in love?"

"I don't know. I'm not sure."

He referred to it only once more. "Until now, Dorothy, you've known boys and dated boys. This is a man."

"I know that, Daddy."

"Then the only advice I have is to use common sense."

I told myself that it was good advice, and I determined to follow it. In any case, I would be leaving for school on Friday, and after that, my romance would mark time. As for seeing Ben again before Friday, I hardly thought that it would happen. But it did. Tuesday night, he telephoned and asked whether he could call on me the following evening. I invited him to dinner. He protested but I insisted, and finally he agreed. I didn't know that he would have to take the day off at the mines, pleading illness, to be at our house on time and clean and presentable.

When I told Father that I had invited Ben to dinner the following evening, his only reaction was to say that Ben was always welcome. Then I asked Father why Ben had turned down the job with the Pittsburgh law firm.

"Did Ben tell you that? Why didn't you ask him?"

"Ben didn't speak about it. I listened at the register the first time he was here."

"Did you? If you lack other virtues, Dorothy, I'm gratified that you're honest."

"I've always been too curious. Why did he turn down the job, Daddy?"

"I'm not sure I know," Father replied thoughtfully. "Perhaps he didn't want to be a lawyer. There are people who don't, you know."

"Did you have something else in mind when you asked him here?" I pursued it.

"Oh—possibly. My own law practice is nothing to write home about, but I could take a young man on."

I nodded. "It could never happen now."

"Why?"

"I think he likes me a great deal. He's too proud to work for the father of a girl he likes."

"I see."

But at dinner the next evening, Ben was as formal and reserved as he had ever been—more so, for he said next to nothing compared to the last time he was here. He and Father talked a little about the case of one Steve Padowski, a miner who was accused of theft and assault, and whom Father was defending. It happened that Ben knew the man, and was able to tell Father something about him. Then the war and local politics. After dinner, Father pleaded work and retired into his study. Ben and I sat in the parlor. I showed him an album of family pictures that evening, and I remember that I was a little disappointed at his lack of interest. He tried to appear interested, but made a poor show of it. Then we talked about one thing and another and then about my going away.

"You'll forget about me soon enough, Dorothy," Ben said flatly.

"I hardly see why in just two months. I'll be back for the Thanksgiving Day weekend."

"It's not a question of time."

"Then what is it a question of?"

"The two different worlds we exist in. You know that, Dorothy."

"You keep talking about two different worlds. I haven't mentioned it once, but you can't forget, can you?"

"Because you've never seen my world, Dorothy. You've never walked into it the way I walked into yours."

"I'm sure that if I spent an evening in a coal miner's house, I'd never want to see you again," I smiled.

"Perhaps so."

"Then you ought to try me, Ben Holt."

"It's not as simple as that, Dorothy. I'm a miner. That's the basic thing. You don't just walk into a miner's house. You walk into a miner's world and remain there, day after day, year after year. Could you ever see yourself doing that?"

"You are also a college man, and a person of will and intelligence. Do you intend to be a miner all your life, Ben?"

"Possibly."

"You can't be serious."

"I was never more serious. Doesn't it make any sense to you that a person should want to be a miner?"

"No," I said plainly. "No, not at all. It's a cruel and heartbreaking life, and it makes no sense to me that anyone should choose it when he has an alternative."

"I imagine there are a lot of things about me that make no sense to you," he said bitterly.

"Well, for heaven's sake—of course there are, and there must be any number of things about me that make no sense at all to you. But that doesn't make things impossible, does it? And that's no reason to have a quarrel, is it?"

"I'm not quarreling!" he snapped.

"You're angry."

"I'm not angry at you. I'm just angry. I'm angry at a world that makes you ashamed to think of yourself as a miner's wife."

"Ben—Ben, believe me, I'm too young to think of myself as anyone's wife."

"In your middle class, sure you are. In my class, it's different."

"Ben—" I shook my head. "It takes time to know people."

"There's only one thing I can do for you, Dorothy," he said dramatically, "and that's to walk out of here and never see you again."

"You'd be doing that for yourself, not for me. And I don't see that you're obligated to do anything for me—or that I am to do things for you. We're good friends, and I would like it to remain that way."

"So that you could turn the whole thing into a suitable middle-class fairy tale!" he snorted.

"What whole thing?"

"Whatever we feel for each other."

"Ben," I said gently, "I like you a great deal. You said you never knew anyone like me before. Well, I never knew anyone like you before. So we have to give it time—don't you understand?"

He nodded, and I must give him credit for trying to be polite and amiable about it; but Ben was never much good about being polite and amiable. About a half hour later, he said good night to me, and a year went by before I heard from Ben Holt again.

7

Why did I finally marry Ben? That's a poor question for sixty-one to ask seventeen, or twenty, for I was almost twenty before Ben and I were married. I think I loved him; I admired him; I made a hero out of him; and he was intelligent and positive and filled with a wild violence of energy. I felt proud and fulfilled when I was near him, and all those are reasons, aren't they? But after I said good-by to him, there was no letter, no word from him all winter long. When I came home for the Thanksgiving holiday, I telephoned the boardinghouse where he had been living, without giving them my name. They said that Ben had left during the first week in October and that they had no forwarding address. I asked Father whether he couldn't find out what had happened to him, and meanwhile all sorts of dread possibilities crossed my mind. I was not without imagination, as you may have gathered. Father tried, and came up with the information that Ben had left Ringman, apparently for good. A few of his friends supplied the information that he had intended to go out west, naming places as far apart as Texas and California, but no one knew for sure and no one Father spoke to had heard of Ben.

"Why would he go away like that?" I asked Father. "Why would he cut himself off like that?"

"That's hard to say. Maybe he's having a turn at running away from something. Or looking for something. I don't know."

"Why wouldn't he write to me?"

"Perhaps that's part of the point. To forget you. But I can't say, honey. We'll wait and see, but believe me, we'll hear from Ben Holt again one of these days."

I was less optimistic than Father, and as the winter wore away and turned into spring, and spring into summer, I came to the conclusion that Ben Holt had passed out of my life for good. A healthy young woman of eighteen does not pine away over a lost love. I had eligible boys clustering around, dances and parties to attend, and my responsibility as president of the Junior League for Belgian Relief. Time passed. I visited with my Aunt Martha in Massachusetts during the latter part of August, and when I returned to Ringman a letter from Ben was waiting for me.

That was the letter I spoke of before, a long letter, which I am enclosing with this apparently endless letter of my own. It will interest you, I believe, and you may use any part of it or all of it, just as you wish. I don't feel that I am violating any confidence by allowing you to read it—or the whole world, for that matter. So far as I know, it is the only writing of Ben's that is uninhibited, emotional, and unguarded, the last being particularly important. In all truth, I don't know whether Ben would want it published or not, but I can never know that, can I?

You must make the decision yourself, Alvin. Here is the letter, a little yellow with time and somewhat faded—but as alive, to me at least, as the first time I read it.

Denver General Hospital
Denver, Colorado
October 3, 1915

Miss Dorothy Aimesley
Ringman, Pa.

Dear Dorothy:

Or should I call you Miss Aimesley? It is so long now since I received your permission to call you by your first name that I wonder whether it is still in effect?—that is, if you remember me? In case you have forgotten, I am the oversize miner with the dirty hands who once ate three quarters of a picnic lunch on the top of Belfast Ridge. In case you feel that my own memory is at fault, I can remind you that it was the first time I ever ate a sandwich composed of a mixture of stuffed olives, anchovies and cream cheese. It was very good, too, much better than the hospital food here.

The fact that I am in this hospital is nothing to worry you, if you are disposed to worry about me. That is a presumption on my part, but then I guess that even daring to write this letter after a year of silence is just as presumptuous. I could say that I am writing to you because I have no one else to write to, but you would know that to be untrue. I have three aunts, two uncles and better than twelve cousins back in Ringman, so I could write to any one of them. I am trying to be light and make small of things, but it doesn't become me too well, does it? I keep telling myself that you may be married by now and that I have no right at all to express any sentiments to you, but I cannot keep from saying that there was never a day since I left Ringman that you weren't in my thoughts. There also was no day when I didn't consider writing to you, but that always slammed up against my purpose of getting out of your life completely and leaving you alone. If you prefer it that way, just tear up this letter and leave it unread. If you read on, I will take it for granted that you are interested in what I have to say and in the things that happened to me.

About the hospital, I am here with an infected leg that was badly cut up. They operated, and now it is healing successfully, and they tell me that I won't even limp. I will be here another week if all goes well—longer if it doesn't. But everything seems to be going well.

A few days after I saw you the last time, Dorothy, I made my final payment to the university. I had been on scholarship and on jobs there, but I had to take a loan to round it out. I sent them a money order for two hundred dollars, and that completed payment on the loan. I had thirty-seven dollars left, and a miner I know, Tom Llewellyn, was caught under a beam and brought home with a broken back. I put the thirty-seven dollars in the kitty for him. He'll never walk again, and we all tried to salve ourselves off with a little money. That night, I walked out to the yards and climbed into an empty boxcar. I had no money, no destination and no love for anything that lived. Not even for you, Dorothy, at that moment; I wanted only to put distance between us and forget that I ever knew you or Ringman or Tommy. I rode that string of empties out to St. Louis.

I spent a month in St. Louis working as a freight checker in the barge terminal on the river . . . It was easy work, just checking manifests and keeping a simple set of books, and the first day I learned all there was to know about it. I lived in a furnished room, ate in cheap restaurants, and spent most of my time after the job reading in my room. Sundays, I took long walks and poked around old bookstores. My boss at the terminal was a Swede, Jack Thorsen, and he took a liking to me, and had me over to dinner once, and wanted me to stay there and learn the business. He paid me fourteen dollars a week, fair enough pay when you consider how light the work was and how I came to it with no experience at all. But it wasn't for me.

I never looked at a girl there either. I feel foolish saying that, but I want you to know.

I had no reason to remain in St. Louis and no reason to leave. My existence was rootless and meaningless—and if there is anything in the world more meaningless than to live in a furnished room and go to work each morning and come back each evening, then I don't know about it. It wasn't the loneliness. I'm used to being alone, to doing for myself and fending for myself. But I used to tell myself that I had a direction. Even if I was never sure just what that direction was, I had a direction to cling to. Now I had none. I left St. Louis because it was no better and no worse than remaining there.

In turn, I tried Kansas City, Topeka and Wichita. In Kansas City, I found a job in a cotton warehouse. It was heavy work and I hated it, which is strange, because I always enjoyed heavy work. After a week, I moved on. In Topeka, the only work was as a laborer on a big city sewer project, and if there's one thing that's an anathema to a miner, it's to work as a laborer. There's another puzzle to add to your book of miners. In Wichita, no work at all, and I was running out of money. But there in Wichita, at the Royal Hotel, a miserable hostelry where I put up for one night, I ran into a kid called Larry Hurst. He was nineteen and broke and he reminded me of my brothers, and for some reason or other, I took a liking to him and bought him supper. He had been working as a cowhand at a big ranch west of Dodge City—for eighteen dollars a month. That's the gospel truth, eighteen dollars a month. I had thought that mining was a rotten deal in dollars and cents, but after I listened to his story of work and hours and treatment on a big ranch, I had new respect for the whole mining industry.

Anyway, he had sworn an oath to himself never to take ranch work again, and he was in Wichita trying to make some kind of a stake to get up north to Montana, where, as the story went, there was work at good wages in the copper mines. His father had mined copper in Montana twenty years before, when hell was a gentle word for the conditions in the mines there; but he had heard that things were different now and that working conditions and wages were good.

The next morning, after I had paid my hotel bill and the price of breakfast, I had about two and a half dollars left. Larry was broke. It wasn't much of a stake for two men, but we decided to take off and see how far we could get, one place being about as good as the next.

There's no way directly out of Wichita to the north, but the Atcheson runs west, and at a little place called La Junta, there's a spur line to Pueblo and the main line through Wyoming to Montana. But when you ride the railroads without tickets, you can't plan it as well as you might like to. We found an empty car on a slow freight, supposedly for Dodge City, fell asleep and found ourselves in Kansas City. It took three days more to make Pueblo, and we were close to starving then. We hired out for a week on a sheep ranch, three dollars each as wages and as much boiled mutton as we could eat. I can make myself sick now just by thinking about boiled mutton, but it was preferable to starvation. When we left there, the rancher dropped us off at a coal mining town called Serpo, and I talked Larry into trying the mines for a stake.

It was to be for no more than a week or two. With the war in Europe, no mine could produce enough of anything, and wherever there were mines, they were taking on men. Larry had never mined coal before, but we hired on as a team, and I took him as my day man or helper. He was a goodhearted kid and learned quickly—not that it isn't more back than learning that a man wants; but what there was to learn, he learned, and he had the back too. He was strong and willing and cheerful, a good man to work with.

The mine itself was a rotten mine, a deep shaft and two and a half miles underground to the cutting face. It was bituminous, not anthracite, and the operators were greedy. Colorado never was a first class coal region, and until this year, the going was rough for the owners. Now the world has a lust for coal that nothing seems to satisfy.

So instead of going on to Montana, we remained at Serpo and worked in the mine. I don't know what we had in mind. We talked about a lot of things—in particular about saving our money for a good stake and then going prospecting on our own for silver and gold. Every miner, no matter what he digs, has at one time or another made a little daydream out of prospecting. We read books on metallurgy and mineralogy, and we only got drunk once, and Sundays we'd go out to mule farms and talk prices and mule lore, and other Sundays, we'd sit around at the Muskat Saloon, where the old men gathered to talk about the days when there was a gold strike over every hill. Weeks passed. Twice, we decided to quit, and each time, they raised the tonnage price.

It wasn't a good life and it wasn't a bad life, Dorothy. I wanted you, to be with you—well, more than I can say, and I had some crazy dream of returning to you rich and mighty.

But, you see, the mine was worked out, and now they were robbing the pillars. That calls for some explanation, and without a treatise on coal mining, you can think of it this way. The seam of coal runs more or less horizontally with the surface of the earth, although it can pitch sharply in one direction or another. In what we call *pillar mining*—the way most coal is mined in the United States—a shaft is sunk to the depth of the coal seam. Then a main entry, or corridor, is driven into the seam and along it. On either side of this main entry, rooms, as we call them, are dug, that is, the coal is mined out of sections and these sections are separated by walls of coal. These walls support the roof and keep the mine from falling down around our heads—that is, the coal pillars and the timbering that we put up as we work into the mine. After a mine is pretty well worked out, they sometimes go through a process called "robbing the pillars," that is, taking out the sections of coal seam that were left to support the roof and collapsing the mine from the finish of the entry back to the shaft. This can be very dangerous—or no more dangerous than first mining, depending on the conditions in the mine and the skill with which the pillars are removed.

In this case, we had too many new hands for real skill, a mine that was badly ventilated, and a bad case of operators' greed. The thing happened one day when we dynamited the face of a section. Afterwards, I learned that one of the blowers in the ventilating system had broken down. The other blowers continued to operate, but at best, it was a poor system, and now a dust mixture began to build up in the rooms. At the same time, there must have been a heavy firedamp, or methane, where we were working.

Briefly, Larry and I and four other men who were working in the room took cover in the entry while a charge was exploded. The room we had left blew and then the entry blew, and then the blast skipped from room to room, where the dust-air mixture had built up. I have very little heart to try to tell you exactly what happened, and I remember it poorly at best. Think of yourself suspended in darkness, explosions on every side of you, smashed and thrown by the concussion, your lighting gone, mules and men screaming with pain and horror, dust thick enough to feel, your sense of direction gone, and a certainty that the whole world is collapsing on you. Or somewhat like that. Or any other nightmare you care to put in its place.

In such a situation, the plain fact of your existence is unbelievable. Human sound, beyond the fact of terror and pain, is meaningless. It took me a while to understand that Larry was calling for me, and it took more time to find him, crawling around in that obscene blackness—not darkness the way you know it on the earth's surface, but a darkness beyond all darkness. I found him. There was a beam across his staved-in chest and half a ton of coal on the beam and on his body, and he died there under my fingers without me ever seeing his face again. I had matches, but to strike one there might have started the dust explosions all over again and more violent and lethal this time.

I got out. You look back, and it's impossible to understand why one person gets out and another doesn't. But I got out with no more damage than some bad cuts on my leg, which in time became infected and landed me here in the hospital at Denver. Larry died there, and with him one hundred and sixty-seven miners. I brought one man out to the shaft with me, but that didn't save his life. He died before they could bring him up. I got up the shaft and I went down again, not because I was brave, Dorothy, but because I was filled with guilt. I wanted to bring Larry's body out, but there were more explosions. Why, we'll never know. We worked there the rest of that day, and all night long I was at the shaft, while they brought up the bodies, while the wives and the mothers kept the deathwatch there. It's hard to remember too much of that night, but I remember hearing someone say,

"Anyway, at least half the dead are Mexicans, so what the hell!"

I felt an impulse to kill the man who said that, but there had been enough killing and enough pain and suffering—and all of it added up to nothing, no sense or rhyme or reason except the fact that a blower went out and the dust-air combination piled up in the rooms.

I feel that you are asking yourself whether he hasn't had enough—whether Ben Holt isn't content now to turn his back on mining forever. I don't know what the answer to that is, Dorothy, so help me, I don't. I am filled with all kinds of unreasonable fury and anger, and sick to death of a society that builds itself on a foundation of the dead bodies of miners, and the other day, as a sort of macabre game, I added up the statistics of miners killed on the job since the Civil War, as much as I could remember them, and I got a figure of over a hundred thousand, but maybe my statistics are wrong, and I left out those who are maimed and broken, and I got the feeling that it was like a war. A war that doesn't end. And when I fall asleep, the explosions start, the booming from room after room as the chain reaction ignites the dust—

So there is my story, and since you have read this far, I presume that you are interested. Here in the hospital I have thought of nothing else but you, and if nothing else makes sense, then I can fix my mind on you, and in some way, that makes sense and logic out of my existence.

But I make no claims. I have no right to, and I never had. If you are in love with anyone else, or engaged to be married, or married, I will not intrude on your life again. But if none of these are the case and you should see fit to write to me here, I would be both grateful and happy. If I was uncertain about my feelings for you once, I have absolutely no uncertainty now. I hope that this finds you in the best of health, and I look forward to seeing you soon and to hearing from you.

Very sincerely,
BEN HOLT.

8

I think that after you have finished reading the letter, Alvin, you will say that there is much of Ben in it, and also nothing at all of Ben. The terrible tragedy at Serpo, which, with our national passion for alliteration, we have put into history as the Serpo Slaughter, left a mark on Ben that was never eradicated; he was unable to forget the simple fact that the miner lives with death. You've heard him lose his temper at wage negotiations and roar out, "What's the price of death! Name it!" I heard that for the first time—but I'm going ahead of myself, and by now this document, which you so artlessly asked for as a letter concerning Ben's courtship, has become a needle in my side, and I'll know no peace until I have finished it and sent it off to you.

I showed the letter to Father. Did I tell you that one of Ben's suspicions was true, or almost true? I wasn't formally engaged, but I had an understanding with George Cummings, an eligible and very nice boy from Scranton, and I wore his fraternity pin. His people owned the Cummings Mills, and I suppose they were very rich—real rich, I mean, and not the genteel state we were in, which in those days was defined as "comfortable." But I can truthfully say that George's financial prospects played no part in the matter. He was a nice and good-natured boy, and my Aunt Alice approved of him because, as she put it, he was "my kind."

Well, after Father read the letter, he looked at me thoughtfully and said, "An interesting letter, Dorothy. Don't you think?"

"Interesting?"

100

"To me, I mean. He says he's in love with you. I wonder what that means in Ben Holt's terms?"

"I don't know. But it's going to be hard to give George's pin back to him and tell him I can't be his wife."

"Oh? You feel you must tell him that?"

I nodded.

"Suppose Ben doesn't come back?"

"He'll come back," I said.

He did. He returned in December, and he brought me, as a Christmas present, a gold bracelet. You've seen it, a striking piece, two serpents intertwined, a strange design and a strange choice. He had spent all that remained of his compensation money on it. Father debated the wisdom of my accepting it, but I pleaded that Ben would be hurt if I refused; and after remarking on the wide range of variation my solicitude included, Father agreed with me.

I passed my nineteenth birthday, and Ben was working in the mines. Father never brought up the subject of law again, not with Ben and not with me. My friends were getting engaged and married, but Ben did not ask me to marry him. We saw each other on Sundays, and often enough, Ben had dinner with us. My aunt suggested that I go to Massachusetts for a long visit, and when I put my foot down about that, she began to work for a long cruise, one of those five-week affairs through the islands and the Panama Canal to California; but the U-boats were already skirting our coast, and Father wouldn't hear of any sort of boat ride.

Father usually knew pretty well what went on among the miners, and one day he remarked that Ben was making something of a name for himself.

"In what way?" I asked him.

"A number of ways. He called a stoppage at one of the collieries and the men followed him out. He held that the ventilation was no good and the mine was a deathtrap."

"He never mentioned that to me."

"No? Well, perhaps he thought you'd worry."

"You said a number of ways."

101

"I meant he's been getting around among the miners. They like him and respect him."

"Why shouldn't they?" I demanded.

"There's every reason why they should. The operator who owns the pit where Ben works is a damn fool by the name of Nate Stisson. I've had some dealings with him. He's a bullhead who takes every man's measure by his own image, and he sent his cracker boss over to buy Ben off with five hundred dollars and a foreman's job. He probably figured that it was an irresistible offer and that he could use a man like Ben as a straw boss, and with the price of coal what it is today, half the operators have gone out of their heads completely."

"To buy Ben off?"

"That's right. It was an idiot scheme, and only an idiot would send a cracker boss to do business with Ben. Ben beat the man. He broke his jaw and four ribs and put him in the hospital."

"Oh no. No, I don't believe that," I cried. "Not Ben. He wouldn't do that."

"He did it," Father said. "Stisson had Ben arrested, and old Stanley Kusik, the president of the union local here, talked me into taking the case."

"You had to be talked into defending Ben?"

"In this case, I'm afraid I did, honey. Oh, I could see Ben's side of it. He was being bribed. His whole basic sense of integrity was being impugned, and worst of all, he was being asked to forget the conditions in the mine—conditions that threatened the lives of the men who worked there. So he had every right to be angry and indignant. But he had no right to beat a man so savagely that he had to be hospitalized."

"But you asked Ben why and how it happened, didn't you?"

"Of course I did. And Ben said he lost his head—that he was still too close to what he had been through out in Colorado."

"You believe him, don't you?"

"Yes," Father said after a long moment, "I believe him." But there was no defense, as such, nor did Ben have to appear in court. Father went to see Jack Brady, the largest of all the operators in Ringman, and convinced him that if Stisson pressed his charges, the whole area would face the very real possibility of a strike. That was a year when operators had nightmares at the thought of a strike. Brady and some of the other operators talked to Stisson, and the charges were dropped. I happened to be in Father's office in town when Stanley Kusik, the president of the local union, came in to thank Father and to hand to him, personally, the union's check in payment for the case.

I learned later that Kusik was only fifty-five, but he had the appearance of a man ten or fifteen years older. He was a small, bent man, white hair, white mustache, tiny blue eyes and a seamed, leathery face. He had spent his whole life in the mines, and his election to the union post two years before was in the way of a tribute to his knowledge of the conditions in Ringman, as well as to the affection the miners felt for him. He greeted me warmly when I was introduced to him, a shy but charming smile of approval underlining his words as he said to Father,

"She is a very beautiful woman, your daughter, Mr. Aimesley."

"At times," Father nodded. He held the check for one hundred dollars that Kusik had given him. Most of Father's work was with estates and bequests, and he had served two terms in the past as county surrogate. Cases like this one were taken because he could not bring himself to reject them, and now he said to Kusik, "I am going to accept this check, Stanley, because I like you. I don't have much respect for a man who gives away his skill for nothing. However, my daughter here is one of the pillars of the local league for Belgian Relief. I am sure the union will not object to my endorsing this check over to her."

103

"The union won't object, Mr. Aimesley. In fact, our finance committee will feel good about it both ways."

After Kusik had left, Father turned to me and said, "I've been thinking about this whole business, Dorothy, and I've come to the conclusion that I've been unjust to Ben."

"Whether you were or not, you managed to have the charges dropped. That's what counts, isn't it?"

"I'm not sure. I'm not only thinking about what Ben means to you, but about him in a sort of basic way. Ben Holt is not just any man. Do you know what I'm getting at?"

"I'm not sure," I said slowly.

"Well, he's important—and it's all of him that makes for that importance, his violence, his anger, his brain—perhaps his ruthlessness as well."

"Ben's not ruthless—"

"You don't think so? Well, we won't argue the point. Let's have him over to prove I'm saying all this in good faith."

At dinner, neither Father nor Ben referred to the incident of the bribe. Instead, they talked about the West in general, Colorado in particular, about Mexicans and Indians and the treatment of both. I had come to expect and accept from my father a fund of knowledge about out-of-the-way subjects, but Ben continued to amaze me. It was not his knowledge of things, but the depth of his knowledge; if he went into a thing, he went into it thoroughly. They started with the treatment of Mexicans and Indians in general. Then Ben chose the Osages and the Cherokees in specific, detailed their history, and made his point flatly,

"They put their trust in others. That doomed them."

"They had to," Father insisted. "They were Indian tribes facing a powerful federal government. What else could they do?"

"Put their trust in themselves. In their own power and unity. That's the only thing anyone respects."

"Ben, they faced an army."

"What is an army? It's a part of the whole power idea—and the question was not one of army or government—the question was, where does power lie and how can it be used?"

"And where did this power lie, Ben?"

"In the land they occupied, in where they were and what they were, in what they stood for, a people of their own land. But most of all, their power lay in their unity. In knowing how to use it, and that's something they never knew and they never learned!"

The argument went on, but I heard only snatches of it. I was watching Ben. When an idea took hold of him, his face lit up; his reserve vanished, and there was something thrilling in his excitement and fervor—and when that excitement finished, it was as if he retreated deep, deep into himself. As if he removed himself utterly, and this was the case when we went into the parlor after dinner. I played the piano. Ben sat in a chair in the corner and listened without hearing. Father left. I finished playing and looked at Ben. He rose and walked over to the piano.

"I guess you heard about it," he said.

"The fight?"

He nodded.

I shrugged and shook my head. "I don't want to talk about it, Ben."

"Why not?"

"Because it's over. You did whatever you had to do. You always said that we lived in different worlds, and that I didn't understand your world."

"Even if that's true, I want you to understand my world. You have to."

"Why do I have to, Ben?"

"Because I love you."

So there it was, finally, plainly and straightforwardly, and I stood up and asked him what it meant or what he thought it meant when he said that to me.

"I want to marry you, Dorothy. I want you to be my wife, if you love me."

"Don't you know whether I love you, Ben?"

"I'm afraid to know or not know."

Then, for the first time, he wholly took me in his arms and kissed me, and it was over and I had agreed to be Ben Holt's wife. There was the culmination of our courtship and the agreement, no stranger, I suppose, than anyone else's. We sat and talked and made plans and raised our defiance to life and fate and the future; and it seems to me that it was very ordinary and unusual only in the fact that I was a middle-class girl and Ben was a miner. In that way, it was not usual; that made no sense or reason to me; and even in the middle of all the excitement of being asked this question that is so meaningful and absolute to a young woman, I was asking myself what would be now, and would he expect me to move across Belfast Ridge and rent one of those tiny soot-grimed sections in the long tenements where the miners lived, and was this to be my life, raising a family in the squalor and poverty of a miner's home, rising at four o'clock in the morning, in the pre-dawn gloom to cook his breakfast and then watch him go off to the diggings, myself broken and middle-aged at thirty and an old woman at forty, and to live each day through waiting for the awful howl of the disaster siren—was this it, and was this what he was promising me and what I, in turn, was accepting?

My elation, you see, was not unmixed with a sense of being caught and trapped in something I never knew or bargained for, and my questions couldn't be asked or answered. Ben, on the other hand, was swept along by his own plans and victories, and he spelled it out for me.

"Do you know when we'll be married, Dorothy?"

I shook my head.

"I should let you decide that, shouldn't I? I was going to say two months, but whatever you wish."

"Why two months?"

"Because in six weeks, the union elections come up. I'm going to run for president of the local union here."

Oh, he was like a little boy at that moment, and he

couldn't have been more excited or alive if he had announced his candidacy for President of the United States. For my part, I didn't know, I didn't have the vaguest idea of what it meant or where it would take him. Nor did I know whether the presidency of a local union was a full-time job or a part-time job, whether he would continue to be a miner or not; and in all truth, my own simple and direct wish was for him to be anything but a miner. When I asked him, he said,

"Oh, it's a full-time job, all right, Dorothy, and the pay is no better than a miner's pay, but that's not the point. You were always outspoken about how much you wanted me to stop working in the mines—"

"I only mentioned it twice, Ben."

"Perhaps. Perhaps it's been on my mind more than on yours. Don't misunderstand me; it's all mixed up, and I'm trying to make you see it the way I do. To be a miner's wife is not the most attractive life in the world, but there it is, and if you love a man, you go where he goes, don't you?"

He flung this at me, but I couldn't answer him.

"You see, I'm not doing this for you. I'd do anything for you, Dorothy, but I always have to go where my own blood leads me. I can't tear myself away from the mines. No matter what happened, I'd always go back. I'm a miner. But I think I have enough sense to know what it is to be a miner. There's no one in this world gives two damns about the miner except himself. For five thousand years, he's been crawling under the earth and leaving his trail of blood wherever he goes. Now it's changed; now the whole world needs him! That world out there—by God, it can't exist a week without the mines. And now's the time for the miner to have his due—but only if he understands his own power. Few enough of them do. They can think as far as the next side of bacon and the next bag of flour, and no further. I can. I understand power—and I understand the power of the miners, and someday I'm going to be at the top of a union of every miner in the United States—at the top, Dorothy!"

He knew where he was going. Perhaps he had always

known, perhaps from the first day I met him and before then. But he was the first one like that I had ever known. He talked about power, and his sense of his own power infused him and communicated itself to others. Think of the boys I had known and gone with, college boys who were polite, gentlemanly, well mannered. They would go into their fathers' firms, they would read law, and a few of them would study medicine and some would find proper jobs for their place in life. But none of them knew or cared very much what their ultimate destiny would be. Should I have been perturbed or frightened by Ben's declaration? But the plain truth is that I was thrilled and delighted.

9

I told Father about Ben's decision to run for the president of the local union, and I thought he would be as thrilled as I was. Instead, he seemed disturbed, and I found myself asking him whether he wanted Ben to go on being a miner for the rest of his life.

"No. But you see, Dorothy," he said, "I never shared your fear that Ben would go on being a miner. Being a miner was in the way of marking time for Ben. I just didn't know what his direction would be when he began to move. But that he would move—well, I had no doubts about that."

"Then don't you think he'll be elected?"

"He'll be elected, all right. Ben is in the way of being a local hero among the miners here. They know what it takes for a miner to fight his way through college. They know his worth, and they knew his people; and the fact that he went back into the pits after the university doesn't hurt either. He's one of them, and still they feel that he's a little more than any of them. It's just that I wish he didn't have to run against old Kusik."

"But it's not like taking someone's job," I protested. "Believe me, Ben doesn't care two pins about the job. The pay is no better than a miner's pay, about thirty dollars a week, I think, and Ben's not doing it for the job or the pay. He's doing it because this way he can serve his own people. He can make life a little better for them. He can see to it that they have something better to look forward to than a life of privation and danger."

"All by himself, Dorothy?"

"Not by himself. Of course not. That's what the union means. Father, I want you to understand Ben and to understand his motives—because he asked me to marry him."

Father stared at me in silence for a while. Then he nodded and said softly, "What was your answer, Dorothy?"

"I love him, Daddy. What could my answer be?"

"You're sure of that?"

"Since the first time."

"If you're sure, then that's all that matters to me. But you know what you're getting into, honey."

"I think so."

"It won't be easy. Whatever one might think of Ben Holt, there's one thing about him that's evident—he is what our society calls 'a man of destiny.' That's a stiff piece of elocution, but in plain English it adds up to a man who will place himself and his own needs above everything else. It goes deeper than selfishness. Nothing is going to stand in his way, and nothing is going to interfere with what he wants."

"How can you say that? What has Ben ever wanted?" I was indignant and hurt. "He could have had a career and money too! He put both aside to remain a miner and to remain with his own people!"

"Baby," Father said gently, "I'm not tearing Ben down. I'm simply stating a fact of his character. Ben is a wonderful man—an unusual and brilliant and purposeful man. I told you that the first time I brought him here to our house. In a way, I share the responsibility of your decision to marry him, for I made it possible for you to see him and to know him. But I want you to know what you're doing."

"I do know. You feel that Ben is ruthless because he's

running against Stanley Kusik? Well, what has Kusik ever done for the miners?"

"A great deal, but that's not to the point. Kusik is experienced and honest and he does the best he can. Maybe his day is over. Maybe the miners need a young, bold man. I don't know. I know little enough about mining or the local here, too little to pass any judgments. And I'm sure there are sides of Ben you know far better than I do. I only want you to know all of him before you make up your mind."

"I have made up my mind, Daddy."

"Then God bless you. There it is. I'll be the first to kiss you and congratulate you."

And in all the years that followed, I can hardly remember a time when Father didn't defend Ben—except once, as you know, Alvin. He put his own thoughts aside, and accepted what was inevitable.

What else to tell? I think a part of this was the annual meeting where the election took place; we were married after that. Father and I went to that meeting. Ben invited us and sent us passes. Father was eager to go, and I—well, I had never been to a miners' meeting, and it was high time that I began.

The miners had a hall in Ringman, but it was limited in size, and for large, important meetings they used the Shrine Temple at Lanton, twelve miles away. The night when we drove over there was bitterly cold, and though Father and I arrived early, almost every seat was already taken. The auditorium at the Shrine Temple had seats for twenty-five hundred people, but before the proceedings began, well over three thousand men were jammed into the place. I noticed a handful of women who were helping with the paper work, at most a dozen; I was the only one actually seated among the men, and thereby the target of numerous eyes and whispers. I wondered how many of the miners knew that Ben and I were to be married, and who I was and what I was doing there. At least enough of them knew Father to keep us from feeling entirely out of place, and as we entered, half a dozen men went out of their way to shake hands with

Father and say a few words to him. Like many sheltered young women of that time, I had a far from complete knowledge of my father's work or world, and it gave me a warm, good feeling to know that through him Ben's world and mine touched.

It was a Saturday night, and the miners were scrubbed and dressed in their good black suits, each of them armed with a pocketful of those indescribable cigars. The air was rapidly becoming unbreathable, when one of the men on the platform stood up and shouted, through the roar of conversation and greetings,

"Brothers, since we're here without masks or lamps and there's no hope of any compensation if this here hall blows up, the committee asks me to announce that there'll be no more smoking tonight. So when your stogies burn down, just don't light up again."

That may have helped a little, but miners are not easily told what to do and when to do it. Another thing that amazed me was the reading of the administration reports against the roar of conversation on the floor of the hall. I asked Father about this, and he explained that no one really listened to the reports, and that the miners had long ago learned that it was better to read them against the noises than to spend a fruitless half hour trying to impose silence.

"When they want to hear something, you'll be amazed at how quiet they'll be, Dorothy. There's nothing else in the world just like a miners' meeting, just as there's nothing else just like miners. Their union is the main rationale of their existence. They don't respect leadership and administration—they suffer it and mistrust it, and they won't give an inch to show it respect or obedience, unless they're moving toward a strike or a demonstration. It's not only that they're the most independent people on earth; they're men who spend their lives working with death at one hand and darkness at the other. It does something to them. It makes them different."

While the reports were given and the business of the night attended to, I watched the miners and tried to see this difference my father spoke about. There was a certain physical similarity among them. Their faces were lined and hard, and ingrained with coal dust. Ready-to-wear suits were not cut for people like them; the miners bulked too wide, and they were too heavily muscled across the arms and shoulders. Many of the younger men were strikingly handsome, blond, large. The older men were invariably bent. As the temperature of the hall went up, they took off their jackets, rolled up their sleeves and relaxed. A good many of them chewed tobacco and took snuff. I can't say that I was at my ease. I had never been in a hallful of men like these before; the smoke and the noise and the smells affected me badly, and I had to argue with myself to remain calm and self-possessed and in my seat. On the other hand, the men around me went out of their way to make me feel comfortable. They stopped smoking, and they said nothing that could be calculated to offend me. I had thought, as so many people like myself do, that because I had an intermittent relationship with repair men and delivery people, an occasional carpenter, the men around the stables, and the mechanics who serviced our car, that I knew what there was to know about working people. All my life, I had seen miners on the street, and always in the distance were the tipples and the man-made mountains of culm; but strangely enough I had spent the best part of almost twenty years of living in Ringman, and yet I had never been among miners before, not this way where there could be no separateness and I was an integral part of three thousand talking, shouting, snorting, smoking men.

Gradually, my fear and discomfort disappeared, and I was able to relax. When at last Ben walked up to the platform to speak, I was intent on him and what he had to say, and not even disturbed by the miners who rose to their feet and shouted,

"What do you say, Benny boy!" "How are your knuckles, laddie!" "Reach out, Benny—I want to hear what you got to say!" And more of the same. Oh, he was liked, all right, and he liked it, standing up there, a great bear of a man, with his shaggy head of hair and his disconcertingly pale blue eyes. He was of this group of men, but not like them, and they saw in him what they would want to be themselves, something young and strong and very powerful and very fearless.

There was no transcript of what Ben said that evening, and I don't pretend to remember his words or even all of the ideas he advanced; but I do remember the theme he put forward and that very clearly. It was the first time I heard Ben speak in public, and even then he had the basis for the manner and delivery that became so famous in later years. Between sentences, he paused and studied the men in front of him. He never hurried and he never spoke thoughtlessly. He despised the clichés of labor oratory, and he always tried to say what he meant in plain, simple English. But that didn't make it less studied. I have seen him stand in front of a mirror for an hour, practicing a manner of delivery; but when he used it, he managed to give the feeling of impromptu words and feelings.

Now, as he spoke, the hall quieted. He had them listening almost immediately. He was making small of things like the walkout he had led. "It's holding the line," he said. "It's standing still. It's coddling the damn little we have—and make sure, what we have is very little indeed. We don't have any of the safety measures we asked for—measures we've been asking for for half a century. There isn't a mine in this county with adequate ventilation. There isn't a mine with adequate safety measures, and because there's a coal hunger, we're working harder and longer than we ever worked before. And when do accidents happen? When a man's tired, when his reactions are a little slower, his response a little duller, his muscles too weary to respond to the demands of a situation. No, I'm not satisfied by the fact that we're working. Nor should you be. Because you and me, we know why we're working. We're working because there's a hunger for coal— and the name of that hunger is war. W-A-R—war! We don't love war. Our whole lives are war, and we know what it means to live with death. So don't anybody ever tell me that the miner loves war or wants war! Ask my mother, may she rest in peace, what it means for a woman to lose two strong sons and a husband—ask her that, and she'll tell you what war means to a woman! But don't ever tell the miner's woman that miners want war! Because it would be a lie!"

A storm of applause here.

"Still, the war is there, and an appetite for coal such as the world never knew before, and profits such as the operators never dreamed of before. But we work for the same wages. Yes, I know—we make more money. We mine more coal. We break ourselves that much faster. And in the end, we pay the price, not the operators. That's what I call standing still. But if we don't move now and make our demands now and win them now, we never will!"

That was Ben's theme, and he drove it home as long as was necessary, and when he sat down, even I could see that he was as good as elected. Stanley Kusik couldn't say anything that would change the outcome. I don't even know whether the old man wanted to. He admitted Ben's arguments, and he admitted that it was possible that the union needed a younger and more energetic man. He stood on his record, honesty and concern for the miners, but it wasn't enough. Ben had thought the thing through, and because he listened and knew what the miners were thinking and saying, he was able to not only echo their thoughts but to go a step further. When Kusik's vice-president got up to speak for the administration, he was shouted down and howled down. The miners had made up their minds. Ben was elected president of the local—almost by acclamation.

Three months later, Ben and I were married. It was not as happy a wedding as it might have been. Some of my relatives washed their hands of the whole affair. The rest mixed poorly and gingerly with Ben's relatives and friends. For myself, I knew that I was marrying a wonderful, strong man, whom I loved and admired—and at the time it seemed to be enough.

PART III

1

Three and a half years went by after I first met Ben Holt in West Virginia in 1920, and during that time I didn't see him; and it is possible that I might never have seen him again if my wife, Laura, had lived. She died of pneumonia—and indirectly of the bullet that had ripped through her lung in West Virginia. Of the life we lived together, I have no intention of writing here. It is not pertinent to this story, nor is it anything that I desire to recall. We had no children. We were very close, and possibly we had as much from our three and a half years as most people get out of a lifetime together. Or, at least, so I told myself at the time.

Ben Holt said to me once that since Laura had died from a strikebreaker's bullet, intended for a miner, I was left with a miner's heart and a miner's suffering; but that was precisely the kind of romantic hogwash that Ben Holt sometimes gave out with. I don't have the kind of nature that hates or remembers or connects in that way; and when Laura died, all I felt was my own personal grief.

We had not heard from Laura's parents for about six months before she died. Her letters were not returned, but neither were they answered. When Laura became too weak to write, I wrote for her, and that letter was returned. The McGradys had gone, leaving no forwarding address—or so the post office informed us. Laura wanted me to go down to West Virginia, but I was unwilling to leave her, and she died without ever seeing her parents again.

After that, there was nothing to keep me in New York or anywhere else. The only purpose I remained with was the need to discharge a few obligations to Laura, and first among these was the task of informing her parents that she was dead.

Four years after I had left there, I returned to Clinton, West Virginia. That was 1924. I was twenty-six years old, but neither young nor brash nor boyish, and in the process of discovering that the world was not my oyster. I was a thin man—some would call me skinny—about six feet tall, with sandy hair that was going prematurely gray about the temples. I had changed enough in those four years to educe no sign of recognition from people I had met before. At the Traveler's Mountainside Hotel, there was a new clerk but not much else was different. Max Macintosh, who had been mayor during my last visit, was now out of office, clinging to the sustenance of a tiny law practice. I spoke to him, reminding him of our former introduction; but before that, I hired a car to take me out to Fenwick Crag, where the McGradys had their farm.

As I suspected, the McGradys were not there. The farmhouse was posted with a tax notice, abandoned and rotting. The barn had been burned, and the whole place gone to seed. Back in Clinton, I talked to one or two people about where I might find the McGradys, and they suggested that I see Max Macintosh. His office was in a loft over the coal company's grocery and supply store on Main Street.

Macintosh had not changed a great deal, but he had not been anywhere nor was he going anywhere. His suit was shiny and his eyes were tired, his office small, dusty, and unimpressive.

"Sure, I remember you," he nodded, after I had properly identified myself and jogged his memory. "You're the wise-guy reporter who married Laura McGrady."

"That's right."

"A nice kid. How is she?"

"She died two weeks ago," I told him.

"God, no! Well, what can you say? I'm terribly sorry to hear that, Cutter. I can't tell you how sorry I am."

I nodded, being tired of the inanities that go with an expression of sympathy and the small guilt of people who face what is called the bereaved.

"Was it the bullet—that time down here?"

"That and pneumonia."

"By golly, I'm sorry to hear all this."

"I'm trying to find her parents," I said to him. "They don't know. Our letters were returned, so there was no way of telling them."

He nodded and asked me if I had been out to Fenwick Crag.

"I was there."

"Then you know about them losing that place. They had nothing but hard luck, Cutter—nothing else. But that's a broad label you could put on the whole county down here. I think that when God was most irritated with the human race, he invented mining, I do, indeed. You can talk about hard times and not even scratch the subject. Down here, the miners who work have it bad enough and maybe they just manage to keep body and soul together, but the three, four thousand who were black-listed after that stupid war in 'twenty—well, their lot is indescribable, it sure enough is indescribable."

"So you know where the McGradys are?"

He nodded again. "But you'd never find it by yourself. I'll take you there." He heaved himself out of his chair as I began to protest about him leaving his office and his work. He said that all the work he had could be accomplished with his breakfast, between the bread and the mush. "I'm a miners' lawyer," he explained sourly. "There's no union here to pay their fees, and as far as cash is concerned, there ain't one of them has two-bits to his name—or seen the sight of two-bits these past few years. I tell you, Cutter, if I had a brain in my head, I'd be out of here and never set foot in West Virginia again."

His car was an old Model T, and after I had cranked half a dozen times, he had to explain shamefacedly that he was out of gas. He felt around in his pockets and came up with fifteen cents. It took me a while to talk him into allowing me to pay for a tankful of gas. "Pride," he muttered, as we drove out of Clinton. "Short on cash and long on pride. This lousy state is full of that kind of virtue, Cutter."

It was full of beauty, too; with the exception of southern Illinois, where you find coal you will find more beauty than almost anywhere else in the world, and this was the kind of a spring it had been four years ago, crisp and moist, with the new yellow-green all over the mountains, the spring flowers and the rushing freshets, and the sky as blue as a sky can be. The old car rocked and jolted over winter-ruined dirt roads, and then we came down into a valley where coal was mined, full of haze and dirt and man-made mountains of slag and culm, the ugly tipples spread out before us, the road paved with cinders. The spring sweetness of the air gave way to the smell of coal; the slag heaps smoked, and the sky turned gray and clouded.

There were people there, and they lived in what, for want of another name, one would have to call houses. Broken, crazy, dirty, ugly shacks. Paintless, the wood warped, the inside and outside joined with holes, spaces, cracks. Children played in the dirt outside, and other children crawled like insects over the smoking slag heaps. Women came to the

118

doorways to look at us as we rattled by, skinny, hollow-faced women in shapeless dresses. Movements were slow; the soot-laced air was pervaded with the very slow motion of apathy and hopelessness. We passed through that place into another that was like it, and then into another. The tipples were strung like beads; the smoky, coal-scented air lay in the hollows.

"Pretty country," Macintosh muttered.

We turned into a little hollow where two old and broken tipples stood. The tracks that led to them were rusted, and one broken coal car lay on its side. We pulled up in front of a cluster of shacks. Half-naked children scattered in a mixture of terror and shyness, while barefooted men and women came to the doors of their shacks, to stare at us bleakly, hostilely, and hopelessly.

"These are all black-listed," Macintosh whispered. "Unemployable, and they squat here and rot and die of starvation. This is a bad place, Cutter."

He got out of the car and led the way toward the shacks. No one moved. "We're looking for Frank McGrady," Macintosh said. "This here is his son-in-law."

Still no response.

"Well, by golly, half of you know me," Macintosh said in exasperation. "I'm Max Macintosh, so don't just stand there looking at me."

"We don't know him," a man said, nodding at me.

"Now didn't I just tell you who he is? His name's Alvin Cutter, and he married Frank's daughter Laura and they been living up north. All I'm asking you is where Frank is."

At this point, a woman came out of the last shack and walked slowly toward us. She was barefooted, wore a loose gingham shift that was torn and patched, and moved slowly and tiredly; and though she moved like an old and sick woman, I recognized her as Sarah McGrady. She came up to us, looked over Macintosh, looked me over, then smiled wanly and nodded and said,

"Hello, Alvin. It's good to see you. How's Laurie?"

When we remained silent, she added, "I been poorly. We all been poorly, I guess."

"Mother, why didn't you let us know how bad things were. My God, why didn't you let us know?"

"Frank and me never did like to lean on the young ones," she said slowly. "We been independent."

"Where's Frank?"

"Inside. He'd come out to greet you himself, but he made him a vow."

I shook my head. Men and women now left the doorways of the shacks and gathered around us. More warily, the children were returning.

"Made him a vow," she said listlessly. "He always been a proud and headstrong man, and when there wasn't no place left for him in this world, no work, no respect, no dignity whatsoever, why, he laid down on his bed and wouldn't let no morsels of food pass his lips."

"Why?" I whispered.

"It's his way," she shrugged. "He just holds that if a man's life ain't worth one cent or nod of attention, then he might as well be dead and try to make his death count for something. I suppose that's what Frank had in mind," she sighed. "But it don't seem that any more attention's being paid to his death than to his life—it just don't seem so. It just don't seem that anyone gives a snap of their fingers whether Frank eats or don't eat, or lives or dies. It's a mighty poor thing, Alvin."

"How long has this being going on?"

"Three days. But tell me now if Laurie come with you, because I ain't sure I want her to see her daddy like this."

"Laurie's dead, Mother. She passed away a few weeks ago."

At first, Mrs. McGrady bent toward me, as if she hadn't heard my words. She shook her head, and then she began to tremble. One of the women came over and put an arm around

120

her. Mrs. McGrady forced her mouth into a grimace and said,

"I mistook you, Alvin, didn't I?"

"I'm sorry, Mother. Laurie's dead."

"That old bullet wound?"

"That and pneumonia."

"Poor child. Poor little child." The tears ran down her face. The ragged, skinny men and women from the shacks stood around silently while the woman cried, and then Mrs. McGrady swallowed hard and said,

"We best go in and tell Frank. Laurie was the apple of his eye."

I helped her to the shack and into it. It was a miserable, broken little hovel, one room, the whole of it like a great packing case, and in one corner, on the floor, some bedding upon which a cadaver of a man lay. The windows were covered with paper, and the press of people around the door blocked the light. In the gloom, there was a smell of poverty and decay. Mrs. McGrady went over to the man and asked whether he could hear her. He didn't stir. Macintosh whispered to me, "He looks dead, Cutter." I knelt down beside him and found his wrist and a weak pulse. He wasn't dead but he wasn't terribly alive either. "This here's Alvin," Mrs. McGrady whimpered, "and he come down here to tell us about Laurie passing away. So you better listen to him, Frank."

Frank McGrady didn't move, until Macintosh and I, after a hurried and whispered consultation, attempted to lift him —to carry him out to the car. Then, with surprising strength, he flung us off and cried at me,

"I hear you and her plain enough, Alvin Cutter. If Laurie's dead, that just backs up my resolve. So don't you lay a hand on me. I know what I'm doing, and I intend to do it."

2

As we drove back to Clinton, Macintosh observed to me that he had seen a good deal in his time, and that now he had seen it all. "Just all of it, Cutter—my good heavens, yes!"

"Will he go through with it?" I wanted to know.

"Well, what do you think? If you're asking me whether he'll starve himself to death, why he most certainly will. Why, this county is just filled up with the worst, most stiff-necked stupid folk you ever met, Cutter. If they make up their minds to do a thing, they do it."

"What can he hope to gain? That's what I don't understand."

"You got to look at it the other way, Cutter," Macintosh sighed. "Ask yourself what he has to gain by staying alive. Did you see that place? Do you know how they live? By begging from those who haven't much more than they have, and since they're proud, they have to be half dead of starvation before they beg."

Back in Clinton, I went to the hotel and called Oscar Smith in New York. He had no idea where I was, nor had I spoken to him since Laura's funeral. Now he got on the phone and wanted to know what I was doing in West Virginia. I told him about it. I told him what I had seen and what Frank McGrady was attempting. "Well, for Christ's sake, stop him!" Smith said. "After all, he's your father-in-law."

"I know that."

"You can't let him starve himself to death."

"I know that too. I can't stop him either."

"Well, call the cops."

"Cops! God damn it, Oscar, I'm in West Virginia. Don't you understand? A coal miner who doesn't even understand the meaning of the expression 'hunger strike' has gone on one to protest the fact that he's been robbed of his livelihood and his dignity. Doesn't that make any impression on you?"

"Sure, Al, I'm impressed."

"You once sent me down here on a big story—a story I didn't recognize and you did. Well, as far as I'm concerned, here's a bigger story. One man against the system. Pitting his life for his dignity—a man whose line goes straight back to the first pioneers who opened this country—"

"Al, it's not a big story," Oscar Smith said patiently. "It's ten lines on page six, and that's pushing it the limit for you."

"Oscar, you're wrong!"

"I'm not wrong, I'm right. You're involved, I'm not."

"Oscar, a front-page story could save his life."

"Could it? Who reads a New York paper down there? I can't do it, Al. Don't ask me to. Call the cops."

"Go to hell!" I told him. Then I asked him where he thought Ben Holt might be, and he said that the last thing about him over the wire was that he was testifying at an injunction hearing in Pittsburgh. That was the day before. I gave them enough facts in New York for the ten-line story on page six, and then I called the headquarters of the International Miners Union in Pittsburgh. They told me that Ben Holt would be there at five o'clock.

Because, I suppose, I had nowhere else to go and because I couldn't sit with myself and let the hours go by, I went back across the street to Macintosh's office and told him what I had been trying to do.

"You don't know Ben Holt very well, do you?" he remarked.

"Not very well, no. I spent some time up there on Fenwick Crag back in 1920, but not too much with Ben Holt."

"And you expect him to come down here to stop Frank McGrady from starving to death?"

"That was the general idea."

"You're plumb out of your mind," Macintosh smiled. "From what I know of Ben Holt and hear about him, he

123

wouldn't cross the street to keep his own mother from starving."

"That's a hard reputation for a man to have."

"I suppose it is. But even if he came down here, what makes you think that McGrady would listen?"

"McGrady worshiped the ground Ben Holt walked on."

Macintosh shrugged, and we talked about some other things, and then I returned to the hotel and called Pittsburgh again. This time I reached Ben Holt and spoke to him. He remembered me, and he remembered Laura better. When I told him that Laura was dead, all he said was, "I'm sorry about that, Cutter, deeply sorry." But he said it in such a way that I couldn't be certain that he was moved at all. Then I told him exactly what I had seen at the McGradys' place.

After a long pause, he asked me, "What do you think I can do for them, Cutter?"

"I think Frank McGrady will listen to you. Otherwise, he'll die. I know how much I'm asking. It's just the life of one half-dead unemployed miner."

"There's lots of miners," Holt said coldly. "In many ways, Cutter, my original estimate of you stands. I think you're an insensitive son of a bitch who is still teething. But the hell with that. You stay there in Clinton, and I'll be down on the morning train." Then he hung up; not a word more than that, and no opportunity to thank him or discuss it with him.

I was left with the impression of a man who disliked me deeply and earnestly, and I was young enough to react to this impression; but in the light of what followed, I hardly think I was right, even for the moment. The truth of it—somewhat harder to swallow—was that Ben Holt had never looked at me long enough or intently enough to distill any more than a name out of my personality. On my part, I had measured him by the cumulative newspaper history of the young miner from Ringman, Pennsylvania, who had fought and clawed his way to the top of the Miners Union. Add to that the fact that Laura adored him, and that I was young enough to be fiercely jealous, and you have the basis for my reciprocal

124

opinion. So for all practical and realistic purposes, my relationship with Ben Holt began the following morning, not four years previously.

After I finished talking to Holt, I went back to Macintosh's office and told him that Holt was coming.

"That beats me," he said. "That sure beats the hell out of me. Why?"

"Suppose you ask him. He's coming, that's all. I was wondering if you could meet the train with me tomorrow. This is hard for me to say, but suppose I hire your services for tomorrow. I can't keep imposing on you."

"What are you hiring me as, a chauffeur?"

"You know what I mean, Macintosh. Your business is lousy. If I give you ten dollars for a day's work, what's wrong?"

"Get off my back and get out of here, Cutter," Macintosh sighed. "I guess fresh kids like you grow up, but it takes so goddamn long. I'll pick you up in front of the hotel, at six tomorrow morning. Take it or leave it. I'm a lawyer with an old, beat-up car, and sometimes I drive my friends around in it, but I don't hire out with it."

I nodded and left. The next morning, Macintosh was waiting for me, and we drove down to the depot and got there just as the train pulled in—the sweet, cool spring morning, the dark, shadowed sides of hill and mountain bringing me back to my first time in Clinton, four years ago.

Ben Holt was the only passenger to get off the train, and he swung down with that easy, almost feline grace that was a part of all his movements. He carried a small valise as if it were weightless, and he stood there, big and thoughtful, waiting for Macintosh and myself. In the time since I had last seen him, he had put on a few pounds, not much but enough to thicken him slightly; there was gray in his hair at the temples, and he looked more than his thirty-two years. He shook hands with Macintosh eagerly and warmly, and then gave me his crushing grip and told me that he was sorry for his bad temper of the night before.

"I was more to blame than you, Mr. Holt."

"Forget it, Al. Forget the Mr. Holt. I don't know you half as well as I might, but I knew that girl you married. Every time I looked at Laurie McGrady, I fought it out with myself and told myself that I was a married man. I don't know whether I was in love with her or not—but when you told me she was dead, well, I couldn't think of anything to say. What *do* you say?"

I shook my head. Macintosh said, "Do you want to go to the hotel first, Ben, or to my house and clean up? You can stay at my place. It might be better than registering at the hotel. Or shall we go straight out to McGrady's? He's bad, if he's not dead already."

"Go straight out there," Holt said.

None of us said very much as we rode out to the little valley where the McGradys were living. Holt asked a few questions about the situation that drove the old man to it, and Macintosh explained, as much as explanation was needed. Ben Holt knew about West Virginia; he had been there before.

Again, the miners and their women and their kids stood in front of the rotten, crumbling shacks and watched us walk down the strip of cinder path to where the McGradys lived. Mrs. McGrady came out to greet us. It was very early in the morning, but people with empty stomachs sleep lightly. Mrs. McGrady apologized for her appearance. "Just think," she said to Ben Holt, "that you come down here, all the way down here, God bless you, and all the hospitality we got is this poor place and not even a bit of breakfast to set out for you. That shames me, Ben, truly."

"It's all right," said Holt. "It's yourself and Frank that troubles me."

"Not myself, bless your heart. Oh, I got my misery, sure enough, with Laurie hardly cold in her grave, but that's done. I don't want Frank taken. I don't want him taken."

"He won't be taken," Holt said. "He'll be all right."

"He's poorly now. So help me, he's so poorly."

We went into the little shack. In the twenty hours since I had been there, Frank McGrady had literally withered away, as if the remaining and frail support for his flesh had simply collapsed. The picture of how he looked there and then was to remain with me for many years, returning when I saw the victims of Hitler's concentration camps. He lay there with his eyes closed, breathing very slowly. Ben Holt felt the old man's pulse. Then he shook his shoulder slightly trying to waken him, but McGrady did not respond. "Please now, wake up, Frank," his wife pleaded. "There's good friends here now who are going to help us." I put my arm around her and told her that Frank was unconscious and that we would have to take him to the hospital. "I won't leave him," she protested, and I told her that she wouldn't have to leave him, that she could come with us. I had thought, when Laura died, that nothing else could touch me and that I had been hurt as sharply and deeply as hurt reaches; but this broken old woman—who had been so strong and healthy and certain only a few years ago—opened every wound that Laura's death had made. I felt that I had brought nothing but death to her, the news of Laura's death, and now this; and if it was unreasonable, still I felt that way and I showed it. Ben Holt must have understood. If I implied that he lacked sensitivity, that must be qualified. It was a part of his own need, whether to be sensitive or not. He could build a wall around himself, or he could open himself and be receptive to the slightest quiver of pain or joy.

He noticed what I did and said. He whispered to me to take Mrs. McGrady out to the car, while he and Macintosh carried out the old man. They put him in the back of the car, with his head on his wife's lap, and Ben Holt covered him with my topcoat and his own. We three, Holt, Macintosh and myself, sat in front as we drove to the hospital.

It was a long drive, almost two hours, through wild mountain country of almost indescribable beauty. Once Holt mentioned it,

"Rich and beautiful and sweet as honey—and it's brought nothing but misery to my people."

I noticed his use of the phrase "my people," and remembered it long afterwards, for I never heard him use it again about coal miners. But his use of it at that moment was real and meaningful.

As for Frank McGrady, I think I knew already that he was dying. I had seen enough men die in France to know the look and quality of someone who no longer struggles for life, or wants it very much; and when that point comes, when you don't want it and don't fight for it, it's easy to die. Frank McGrady died three hours after we reached the hospital. They didn't like to have the word starvation on death certificates, so they put it down as malnutrition, which is, I suppose, a way of saying the same thing.

I found a room in the hotel at Charleston for Mrs. McGrady. Macintosh had to get back to Clinton, but he said that he would return the following day for the funeral. "You don't have to," I said to him. "We've taken enough of your time, and you're not really involved in this, Mac." "I'm beginning to change my mind about Ben Holt, Cutter, so don't make me change my mind about you. 'I am involved in mankind because it numbers me and troubles me.' You're an educated lad, so figure out who wrote that. I knew Frank McGrady longer than you did. God damn it to hell, I think I knew him longer than you been on this earth. So mind your business and I'll mind mine."

"There's no need to blow your top at me. I only meant to save you trouble."

"Sure. I'm sorry, kid. But trouble is legal currency in West Virginia. You don't save it, only spend it."

He left, and I managed to persuade Mrs. McGrady to have a little supper and then to lie down for a while. They had given me some sleeping pills for her at the hospital. She took them and slept through the night. She was about as exhausted and empty as a human being can ever be.

Meanwhile, Ben Holt had registered at the hotel, his decision to remain there for another day made without consulting me. I met him in the lobby, and he asked me whether he couldn't buy me a dinner.

"Let me buy it. I owe it to you, and a lot more."

"You owe me nothing, Al, and the sooner you realize that, the better off we'll both be. I didn't come down here because you asked me to. The McGradys did a lot for me—more than most human beings ever do for anyone else, as you may remember. Now I'll see the poor bastard into his grave, which is little enough to ask of anyone. As for the dinner, I can afford it. I remember that you were quite impressed with the fact that I had raised my wages to five thousand dollars a year. I've raised them again since then. Eight thousand a year right now, if you're going to file another story about me. So I can afford to buy you dinner."

At dinner, I said to him, "What is it you've got against me, Holt—you and Macintosh, both of you? Is it the way I dress, the way I talk, the way I look? Maybe right at this moment I feel less kind toward the world than either of you, but I don't spew it out in bile. If a man is hurt, he can keep the hurt inside, not use it as a sledge hammer."

Holt regarded me thoughtfully for a long moment, before he nodded and said gently, "Maybe he can, Al. Maybe he can."

He went on eating, but then suddenly paused with his fork in the air and said, as gently as before, "I'm sorry, Al. I owe you an apology."

"You don't owe me a thing."

He went on eating. He finished the food on his plate, eating quickly, as miners do, and then looked up at me and grinned. It was the first time he had ever smiled at me just that way—and Ben Holt's smile was a warm, ingratiating thing, rewarding and difficult to resist.

"Maybe it's because we're miners, Al—both of us, Macintosh and myself. You didn't know Mac was once a digger did you?"

I shook my head.

"He was. And a digger lives with bile, not for another digger, but for the whole outside world. Maybe with reason. The world doesn't know that we exist, and the world doesn't give a damn whether we do or not. It makes us sour and nasty when we got no business to be sour and nasty."

He offered me a cigar, which I accepted; but as I lit up, I pointed out to him that he himself was a little more than a miner.

"As one college man to another, Al?" he asked me, raising a brow.

"You had four years of college, Holt. I had a year in Princeton and then I enlisted. I never went back. So it's not exactly as one college man to another."

"Suppose you call me Ben, which will equalize things a little. And who's using the sledge hammer now?"

"All right, Ben."

"Did you ever taste a worse cigar?"

"Never," I admitted.

"Three for a dime. That's a miner's smoke. Start with an already exacerbated set of lungs and bleed them on that cigar, and you shorten a man's years of misery." He looked at me inquiringly. "That's a lousy joke, isn't it? The hell with mining for a while! Tell me about you, Al. You know all about me, and I know nothing about you except that you disapprove of a man raising his own wages and that you remind me of my father-in-law. You had a year of college, and you went overseas. Then what?"

I found myself talking. When he wanted to be, Ben Holt was an easy man to talk to and a good listener. It was not often that he wanted to listen, but now he did, and I found myself telling him the story of my life for what it was worth, the son of a country-weekly newspaper editor in upstate New York who had to see what war was like and had to beat the big city at its own game. There wasn't much to tell. A lot had happened to me and nothing had happened to me, depending on how you looked at it, and the important

130

things did not bear talking about. I had no desire to discuss Laura with anyone.

"Now she's dead," Ben said. "What do you intend to do, Al?"

"I have a job."

"What kind of a job?"

"A reporter on a New York paper is a pretty good kind of a job, I think. I'm not ambitious. I do my work. I'll probably never be as rich as you."

"What kind of work? They tell you, go down to West Virginia and kill Ben Holt, you do it. Right?"

"It's not as simple as that."

"No. But it's not so complicated either. Or maybe you never thought about it?"

"I thought about it," I said.

He didn't press the point, and we talked about other things; but running through my mind over and over again was one salient fact, that this was Ben Holt, the most discussed labor leader in the United States, the man who had already been designated as everything from a tool of the Kremlin to a paranoiac despot, and he had walked out of all his involvements and problems to be down here in West Virginia to do some kind of small homage to an old, stubborn mountain miner. Writing about it this way and looking back at it through all the years, it may not seem like a great deal; but to me at the time, it was the finest gesture a man could make, and I honored Ben Holt for it as I have honored few men. I never forgot it either.

3

Through their generations, the McGradys had been buried in the yard of a small Methodist church outside of Clinton. But the old, slow and traditional mountain ways of Hogan County had crumbled under the impact of coal, and some years back, Frank McGrady broke with the church and its pastor. Mrs. McGrady refused to allow Frank's body to be returned to Clinton. She held that as a strong and willful man—which he was—a hundred deaths would not have driven him to make his peace with the people at that church. Macintosh had a cousin with a pulpit in Charleston, and though they were Baptists, Mrs. McGrady insisted that she wanted Frank buried there. She said that the denominational difference did not matter, since most of her people had been Baptists and it had never bothered Frank any. I purchased two plots in the cemetery, so that eventually Mrs. McGrady could lie next to her husband. Ben Holt went with me, and when I was short some twenty dollars in cash, Ben put it up for me. Later I cashed a check, and though I insisted, he refused repayment. With no sentiment he said the thought of owning twenty dollars' worth of a miner's grave in a state that had run him out at gunpoint was comforting.

Mrs. McGrady's sister and her family drove in for the funeral, their car loaded with as many relatives as it could carry. It was the only car for rent in Clinton, so the funeral was limited to a handful of people. Mrs. McGrady drove back to Clinton with Max Macintosh and his wife. It had been decided that she would live with her sister, and I told her sister that I would do my best to send some kind of stipend every month, so as to ease the burden. At the time I left for West Virginia from New York, there had been between six and seven hundred dollars in my bank account. I left three hundred dollars with Mrs. McGrady. To her it was a fortune, more money than she had ever seen at one time in all her life; to me it represented some attempt to square myself with my former indifference to my wife's mother and father and the beginning of an attempt to work out my own responsibility for what had taken place. It was not easy to get Mrs. McGrady to accept the money; she was proud and independent; but Ben Holt added his arguments to mine and she gave in. I left Ben Holt in Charleston; I planned to return to Clinton with Mrs. McGrady; but before we parted, he said to me,

"There's an old saying, Al, that you seal a bond with birth and with death. I hate to think that we won't see each other again."

I nodded, and told him that I couldn't properly thank him, so I wouldn't try.

"Maybe you could."

"Tell me how, Ben."

"All right—and this isn't off the top of my hat. I've been thinking about it ever since I got down here and met you. You know that I'm president of the union. That's a title. The Miners Union is like the League of Nations, bound together with a title and nothing else. Every local in the union is suspicious of every other local. Every region has some grudge against every other region. The diggers spend more time fighting and hating each other than they do trying to win something for themselves as a group—and most of all they mistrust and fear the International organization. All right, this is complicated and parochial and I can't explain the situation in five minutes. But there's no hope for the miners or the union unless I can unite it, weld it together, and put it under the leadership of a single man. This is what I face over the coming years, and this is what I have to do. In the immediate future, I face a strike—a big one and a hard one."

"How does that affect me?"

"I'll tell you how. I can't do this alone. I need a staff—a group of able and dedicated people who will work with me—to an end I think is pretty worthwhile, the raising of hundreds of thousands of working men out of virtual slavery. Well, I've been finding such people. I have some. I need more. I need someone like yourself, someone who is literate and intelligent and understands what it means to be a digger and to live a digger's life. I need a man who can write and who can think and who can influence other people with his thinking—a man who can direct research and come up with the facts and figures, because the facts are going to be our tools, our weapons, our bullets. In other words, I need a combination of a writer, a public-relations man, and a research director. Someday, this man will have a staff and organization of his own. Today, he has to be everything himself." He paused and watched me reflectively. "I think you're that man, Al."

I shook my head. "It's flattering, and I have to thank you, Ben—but I'm not your man. I only know enough about mining to be aware of what I don't know. As for writing, I'm a reporter, as good as some and worse than most."

"Is it the pay? The pay isn't much, sixty-five a week, but it will be better in time."

"It's not the pay—"

"I don't expect you to decide right now, Al. Think it over. Our national headquarters are in Pomax, Illinois, and I'll be back there next week. Send me a wire if you decide to say yes."

4

I had a good many things to think about on the train back to New York, among them, Ben Holt's offer. That was a time, then, in the middle 1920s, when the labor movement was beginning to bulk large on the American horizon. In the Northwest, during the wartime years, the International Workers of the World, the "Wobblies," as they were better known, had provided lurid headlines and meat for the anti-Bolshevik grinder. Against the background of the Wobblies, the Syndicalists, the Left Wing Socialists, and now, lately, the Communists, the National Confederation of Labor had emerged as a strong and almost respectable force. Under the sure, conservative and careful guiding hand of its careful leaders, it had laid down a pattern of American trade unionism that seemed destined to endure and become the blueprint for all the foreseeable future. Ignoring the great masses of American workingmen, it organized, where it organized, only the highest skills among workers, carpenters and plumbers and steamfitters and cigar makers and so forth—a so-called "elite" of working people.

The only fault in their plan of organization, at the moment, was provided by Ben Holt and his International Miners Union, a thorn in their side and a challenge to everything they stood for; for the Miners Union, based on the diggers, took in every workingman who had anything to do with coal, from the breaker boys to the highly skilled explosives experts. And whereas the Confederation held itself to careful, systematic exploration of every legal possibility, the Miners Union was as fierce and unpredictable as the individual coal miners who comprised its membership.

Ben Holt and the men around him were the "young Turks" of the labor movement, and already, in the few years since he had clawed his way to national leadership of the union, his name had become the best known and most discussed of any man in the labor movement. Whether he was conducting a private war in West Virginia or raging from the gallery of the Illinois or Pennsylvania State Legislature, Ben Holt made news and was news. Everything about him was flamboyant and dramatic, his great physical size and strength, his unruly, usually uncombed head of hair, his piercing blue eyes, his voice, which he used like a musical instrument, soft and gentle and cozening at times, and at other times booming with all the force of a bass drum, his manner of charging into legislative bodies and challenging the elected representatives in their own sanctuaries, his roaring anger at the condition of mines and miners, and the unremitting violence and purpose with which he pursued and fought his enemies in the internecine warfare that was tearing his union apart and which, according to those who commented on labor, would eventually destroy it.

All this about Ben Holt I knew. I knew that even among the miners, for every man who loved him and honored him, there were two who hated him and mistrusted him. I had personally witnessed him running the full gamut of his moods and violences, and only during these past few days, I had

135

listened to Macintosh's estimation of him, and then watched Macintosh's grudging surrender to the man's charm and purpose.

All in all, this was the last man in the world I should desire to work for. How, I wondered, could anyone work for and with such a man, adjust daily and possibly hourly to his varying moods, his violences, his infantilisms, his hatreds, his ambitions? Sixty-five dollars a week was precious small reward for that kind of existence. There were men, I knew, well-educated men, men of good families and wealthy families, who gave up all that might have come to them in the way of physical comfort, to join the labor movement and be a part of it. These were men of high ideals and unshakable purpose; but I was not one of them. When I was sent down to West Virginia in 1920, I had no more sympathy for the working class and its struggles than any other reporter on the *Daily Mail*. Perhaps less. I knew little about miners and I cared less. But that was in 1920, and in all truth, I had learned something, if not very much, about what it means to be a digger in a mine. I had married a miner's daughter, and I had watched her die from the final effects of a bullet originally meant for a miner.

As I turned over and over in my mind Ben Holt's offer, it made no sense—and still I could not put it aside. The man fascinated me. I was then and always have been suspicious of men who by some personal magic won the adoration of other men, and Ben Holt was such a man; but against my suspicions was his openness, his simplicity in the act of setting aside all that burdened him and coming down to West Virginia to watch a miner die. How much could Frank McGrady have meant to Ben Holt? True enough, when the miners were beleaguered and driven in 1920, Frank McGrady had turned his farm over to them; but he was a miner himself, and his scrubby, rock-strewn few acres were not much of a farm. Nor did he do it for Ben Holt. But when I asked Ben to come, he came—and I could not shake myself loose from that simple fact.

The truth of the matter is that the death of Frank McGrady, coming so soon upon Laura's death, had shaken me more than I cared to admit, even to myself. Laura's was a downhill road; she had never really recovered from the bullet wound; and I had seen the end months before it came. But never before had I known a man to do what Frank McGrady did; Gandhi and the whole history of non-violent non-resistance were still in the future; and there was no folklore or body of belief to assure a man that it was a noble thing to die silently for a principle. In fact, there was nothing visibly noble about Frank McGrady; to all apparent purposes, he was an ignorant mountaineer who picked his nose in public, spoke a grotesque, twisted version of English, and had spent most of his adult life scraping at a patch of poor soil or bent double in a coal mine. As a son-in-law, I had not been proud of him—and now I wondered whether there wasn't more strange and noble pride in his body and soul than in all the people I respected put together.

I had not wept for Laura's death, but that night, lying sleepless in my swaying berth in the train, I wept for her father and for all the mangled meaninglessness of man's toil and hopes and existence. Before morning, I had made up my mind about what I would do. I would work for Ben Holt.

5

We sat in Oscar Smith's small, partitioned office, able to look through the dirty glass at the whole length of the *Mail's* city room, the place that had been my life and school and training ground for better than five years, and he said to me,

"When I fire a man, Al, I feel guilty and rotten and a real solid member of the human race, but I don't doubt myself. When a young fellow like you quits, then I doubt myself."

"Why?" I shrugged. "It's no personal reflection on you. I just want to move on. I don't want to sit alone in any lousy room and remember Laura."

"You'll remember Laura. And wherever you go, you'll be sitting alone in some lousy room, because they haven't figured out any other way for respectable existence."

"I suppose so."

"If you want more money . . . ?"

"I don't, but it's nice to hear you offering more money to a punk you insisted was never worth the money you paid him."

"Even punks grow up. Sometimes. Only it makes no sense for you to go out there and work for Ben Holt. It's a quixotic impulse, and I think you have some notion of what would please Laura. I may sound like a person of no feeling, but let me tell you, Al, that you can't please the dead." I shrugged. "And for a man like Holt—you're not one of those starry-eyed worshipers at labor's shrine, Al, and you never will be. Not if I'm any judge. You can't work for Holt—you can only belong to him."

"You know him, Oscar?"

"I don't have to know him," Smith replied sourly. "I know his kind."

My father also knew his kind. I had wired Holt that I would be in Pomax in a few days. I sold everything I had, every stick of furniture that had been Laura's and mine, every possession, gave away her clothes, crated my books and sent them home to my father's house, and then packed my three alternate suits and sufficient linen into a suitcase. This and a portable typewriter comprised my worldly goods. I took the train to Rochester, New York, and there I hired a car to take me the remaining twelve miles to my home town. I had left behind me in New York a few friends and more than a few memories.

My mother had been cooking all day. She wept a little, and then she fed me as long as I would eat, and I ate to double my capacity to please her. After dinner, my father told me what kind of a man Ben Holt was. I listened and saw no purpose in arguing with him. "The point—the important point, I mean—is that I hate to see you fritter your years away. I know that Laura's death was a terrible blow, an awful blow. But you have to go on living. You had something important and worthwhile on the *Mail*. You were learning a profession we regard highly in our family. I had hoped someday you would come home here and take over the paper."

"Someday," I nodded. "You're still a young man."

"Not so young—not so young at all, Al. I just wish you'd think about this—"

I had thought about it. I always went home with high hopes and warm feelings, and it was never right. It wasn't right this time either. I spent the next day with my father in the little building where he published his weekly, and the day after that, I left for Illinois.

6

I have spoken of the bitter natural beauty of the places where men mine coal, and while it is true of the eastern regions and Colorado too, the part of southern Illinois they call Egypt is an exception. At the best of a shining spring day, Egypt is tolerable and no more; but it was pouring rain when I got off the train at Pomax, and under the black sky, I saw a sprawling, silent, soot-streaked town, a fairly large central square, at one side of which was the railroad station, a pavement of rough cobbles and sidewalks of ancient red brick, and around the other sides of the square, brick and frame buildings of two and three stories, each having in common with the others a drab, dirty, unlovely exterior. Two or three automobiles were parked at the curb, and a miserable horse hitched to a delivery cart stood in the beating rain. But of a human being, there was no sight or sound, only the wind-swept, rain-swept square.

There is a distinctive mark on any coal town, not simply

the stain of soot, but the singular and peculiar stain of poverty and frustration and unlike any other poverty and frustration; and by this a coal town signs its name, so that you know it when you come or when you pass by. But in Pomax, there was another factor—the unseen but felt aura of violence and bitterness that pervaded all of Egypt during the 1920s.

Why the southern counties of Illinois were called Egypt, no one really knew, but they had been called that for as long as anyone could remember. Some said it was because the conflux of the Ohio and the Mississippi rivers formed a delta; others held that it was due to the presence of the city of Cairo, on the Mississippi, in the area; and still others repeated a legend of frontier days, when the farmers of the region were said to have saved the rest of the state with their crops during a drought year—although this last is hardly plausible to anyone who has seen the wretched farms of the neighborhood. But the most likely explanation is that given by the miners themselves, that they live their lives not too differently than the way the Children of Israel lived theirs in bondage.

Whatever the reason for its name, Egypt contained what was probably the richest bed of bituminous coal in the United States, the poorest farms in Illinois, the bleakest towns, and the angriest men in the state. It was a flat, wind-driven piece of prairie, unenchanting at its best and never unlovelier than the day I arrived.

At the station, there was no cab, no carriage, not even an umbrella to be borrowed. When I asked the ticket agent whether I could telephone for a cab, he said that I could but a cab was not very likely to come. "If you're looking for a hotel," he added, "the Pomax House is right over there across the square." The wall of water that separated me from it appeared to give him pleasure; but the rain showed no sign of slackening and I decided to walk. When I finally entered the Pomax House, I was drenched and shivering, and the little love I might have entertained for Pomax had evaporated.

Abner Gross was the day clerk at the Pomax House then and for many years afterwards, a small, round man with pink cheeks, a pink mustache, spectacles, his face always ready with the saddest smile I ever observed on a human being. It had the effect of tears in another man, and he smiled now as I registered.

"What kind of a room do you want?" he asked me.

"The cheapest you've got."

"Staying long?"

"It could be."

"The cheap rooms got no baths. You want a room with a toilet and bath, I got to charge you two dollars a day or nine dollars a week. We only got five rooms like that in the hotel. You want it?"

The thought of a hot bath was irresistible, and I took it. Abner Gross whistled for the bellboy, a wizened, skinny man in his seventies. Aside from him, there was no one else in the lobby. He picked up my bag—I held the typewriter—and led me over the worn carpet, past threadbare overstuffed chairs that were upholstered in mohair and tasseled with a forlorn memory of elegance, to a broad mahogany staircase at the back of the lobby. There was a memory of wealth and opulence about the place, there and in the heavy dark furniture of my room and in the bathroom, which was more than adequate with its enormous tub and brass fittings. After he had opened a window and placed the key on the dresser, the old man turned to me and said,

"You a married man or single?"

"Single," I replied. I gave him twenty-five cents.

"I got a nice girl for two dollars, you want some company after dinner, sonny."

"No," I sighed. "I don't believe it."

He took a long, level look at me, and then spat a mouthful of tobacco into the brass spittoon that decorated one corner of the room. He departed with disgust.

7

Stretched out in a hot bath, I reflected on the existence of a town with so improbable a name as Pomax, situated in the heart of a bleak flatland that covered an inconceivable wealth of coal. I found it hard to face the fact that this might be my home and center of operations for years to come. Whatever lightness of heart I might have taken with me had disappeared by now, and as I put on dry clothes, I found myself reviewing and doubting the sequence of events that had brought me here.

However that was, I could reverse it at will. I was not yet bound by any of the invisible strings that attach a coal miner to his place and work, and if I found the situation here unbearable, I could leave it. But I wondered how I could face Ben Holt with an explanation of my leaving.

It was about five o'clock now, and the rain had stopped. I picked up the house phone and gave Gross Ben Holt's number at the union headquarters. "If you want Ben, he ain't there," the desk clerk said to me. I asked him how he knew, and he replied that he had seen him come past the hotel about fifteen minutes before, right after the rain had stopped. "He's home by now," Gross said. "You want me to get that number for you?" I said that I did, and a moment or two later, I spoke to Dorothy Holt for the first time. Strangely, whenever I think of her voice, I remember it best as it sounded that first time over the telephone in Pomax, gentle but strong, telling me,

"Of course—you're Alvin Cutter. He didn't expect you to go straight to the hotel, so we thought you had missed the train and would come on a later one. But now that you're here, you must come straight over and have dinner with us."

I made a few polite demurrals and then agreed and asked for directions.

"It's very simple, Mr. Cutter, and now that the rain has

stopped, you can walk. Your hotel is on the square facing the railroad station, on Lincoln Street. So when you leave the hotel, simply turn left along Lincoln, and when you come to the corner of the square, continue on Lincoln for three blocks. Then you're at Fairview Street, and if you turn left, we're halfway down the street, number 157, a white house with green trim and a porch in front. I will have a light on the porch."

Feeling much better, I set off for Ben Holt's house. The air had cleared, and a sharp, clean wind had torn the sky into a rummage bag of gray clouds. There was a sweet smell in this early evening, and here and there a human form was to be seen, dispelling the illusion that Pomax was a ghost of every drab and ugly town in middle America. Fairview Street was tree-lined and pleasant, graced with long shadows of the sun. It had never been a prosperous thoroughfare, but the reasonable size and pleasant aspect of the houses led me to feel that neither had it ever been the abode of diggers. Number 157 was a three-story frame house that might have been fairly elegant in the nineties. It was the kind of place a thrifty storekeeper might have lived in, but I was in no mood to moralize with myself concerning Ben Holt's residence there. After all, he was the head of a great international union of workingmen, and it would profit neither himself, the miners, nor the union for him to live in a shack.

As I mounted the steps of the porch, Ben came out to greet me, offering me a warm smile and his powerful hand, nodding eagerly and telling me,

"By God, I am glad to see you, Al. I was afraid you wouldn't take me up on it after all, and I just can't tell you how happy I am that you did."

But of course he had known that I would accept; he never had any doubts that I would accept, if the truth be told, and I think I knew it then as I said the appropriate things and moved through the door held open for me and into a lighted hallway to face the woman who stood there, three children crowding around her and behind her, the children giggling, hiding, peering out at me.

Dorothy Holt was twenty-seven then, when I first saw her in the house at Pomax, six months older than I, but so clear-eyed and youthful that I could not think of her in terms of age, not then or later. She was never a slim or delicate woman, but neither did her strength leave you with an impression of stockiness. She had a supple quality, an ease of motion that suggested repose and equanimity even when she moved. In defiance of or indifference to the style of bobbed hair—becoming so popular then in the middle twenties—she wore her honey-colored hair long and gathered at the base of her neck. Her brown eyes were wide-set and direct, her mouth full and sculptured, her manner easy and un-hurried. Seeing her, you thought not of a beautiful woman but of a singularly fortunate woman. You also thought of Ben Holt as a remarkably fortunate man—possessed of a home that appeared to radiate contentment, three healthy children, and a wife of grace and intelligence.

Such, at least, was my own feeling that evening, a mixture of pleasure and envy, pleasure at being among people who were free of bitterness and poverty, and envy for all that Ben Holt had and I had lost. I was introduced to Norah, age five, Sam, age three, and Ben, Jr., approaching his second birthday, good-looking and healthy children. Dorothy Holt shook hands with me and said a few words about how pleased she was to have me there for dinner. Then she went off to feed the children and bed them down, and I noticed that there was a maid to help with this and dinner. Ben led me down the hall, past a dining room where the table was already set for dinner, into a charmingly furnished living room. The decor here was early American, mixed with a few pieces of Pennsylvania countryside furniture, which today is called Pennsylvania Dutch. There were two wing chairs, covered with bright fabric and flanking a fireplace, bay windows, upholstered and inviting, a large old couch of the Federal period, some overstuffed chairs, and with it all, appointments

144

of taste and interest. Two large, handsomely framed Audubon bird prints dominated the walls, and to balance them some old prints and one delightful primitive country portrait. On the floor, a large hooked rug gave the room a casual unity; and the whole effect was rare and pleasant, such a room, while fairly commonplace today, being uncommon and unusual then. If the effect was not of wealth and luxury, it bespoke an undeniable elegance, but Ben Holt did not apologize for it. I think that pleased me, for I half expected some apology; but he gave credit to his wife, and said,

"I like it. It's a beautiful room."

"It is," I agreed.

He waved me to one of the chairs in front of the fire, and asked me what I would have to drink. Then he mixed the drinks—of good scotch whisky and not colored, bootleg sugar alcohol—and seated himself opposite me. The drink was good, and I was tired and relaxed and glad to be in front of a warm fire after the cold and rain.

"How was the trip?" he asked me.

"Fine—except for walking across your town square in the rain."

"You must have been soaked. Yet, you know, Al, I like that square. It's the only generous, broad, handsome thing about this town. Someday, we'll rebuild the whole place, but keep that square—build a fine, modern city of coal around it."

I nodded and smiled, hardly knowing what to say.

"I always start with the future, Al. You've got to believe in the future if you work for me. The present stinks. Right now, today, we're in a hole. That's why I like to talk about the future." I waited, and he went on, "We took the strike vote today—today."

Watching him, waiting, I was uncertain as to what reaction he expected on my part. I was still too new to the labor movement, and specifically to mining, to respond properly to all the implications, emotional threads, fears, hopes, and possibilities contained in the word "strike." And I doubt whether anyone who has not passed a great many years in labor in one way or another ever hears that word the way working people do. I waited, and he asked me whether I liked the whisky.

"It's good."

"Fine, fine— Hell, Al, I'm not going to beat about the bush. Do you think I tricked you into this because I never really explained about the strike down there in West Virginia?"

I shook my head and confessed that I didn't have the vaguest notion of what he meant. He stared at me peculiarly, and then the telephone rang—as it rang again and again through the dinner. His wife came in to tell him that it was for him, and then she remained with me for a moment, pleasant and smiling, and said,

"I do hope you'll stay with us, Mr. Cutter. From what Ben said, I know you'll be good company. Pomax is not New York, or Chicago or St. Louis—"

"I've been in coal towns before," I nodded.

"I know—" She paused uneasily, and then forced herself to say, "I do offer my condolences. I never knew your wife, Mr. Cutter, but I know she was a wonderful woman. I'm so sorry."

I thanked her, and then Ben returned and said that there would be a meeting that night and there was no way out of it. Dorothy's face fell, but she made an adjustment quickly. "Dinner in fifteen minutes, give or take a few," she said, and I made some remark about how much I was impressed with the room and its decor. She left. Ben Holt paced away from me and back. He said he kept forgetting that I was new to this whole thing.

"I'll learn," I shrugged. "I'm not a kid, Ben. I didn't come out here like a boy scout or a visiting congressman. I'm not a socialist or a communist, and I have no great desire to save the world or change it. I'd rather be here than working on a newspaper in New York, and that's it."

146

"Good!" He sat down facing me. "There's no time for you to learn your job—you'll be doing it, starting tonight, because we have half a dozen men to do the work of a hundred. Now I'm just going to fill in a background for you very sketchily, and you'll complete it yourself in good time. Do you know anything about my union?"

"What I've read, and I've read everything I can find."

"Then you know the general background and something of my own history here. The union, as it is today, actually came into being in 1882—it began here in Illinois. Tom Hennesy was the first president, and no finer man ever lived. That's not in the way of praise. I'm explaining something. Hennesy was a decent, honest, modest man who lived for no other purpose than the miners, and he gave them his life, and they crucified him. Why? Because a miner trusts no one, because they've been sold out too much, too long, because at heart they're anarchists. And the three presidents who followed Hennesy finished the same way. They weren't either as devoted or as honest as Hennesy, but in the end it was the same. When they set out to do something and fell short of what they had promised, their own miners destroyed them, threw them out and maligned them. Believe me, Al, it's no joy to be president of this union. My own father organized the first local in Ringman, and they voted him out of office after one term because some damn fool said he saw him talking to an operator in town.

"That's the disease this union and this industry suffers from—fear, suspicion, hatred, and mistrust. We've never had any unity. We break our own unions and we break our own strikes—and not this union and not one goddamn miner in this country will amount to a row of beans until someone is strong enough to unite the union and hold it together and lead it. I don't want anyone to work with me and hold any illusions about me. No one handed me the leadership of this union. It didn't come through virtue and talent, like the chairmanship of a debating society. I fought and clawed my

147

way to the top, and I hurt a lot of people and I made a lot of enemies. But I did what had to be done. I lead a union. It doesn't lead me—I lead it. That's the plain fact of the matter, which you have to take or leave. What about it?"

"I knew that," I nodded. "A lot of people know that."

"All right. That clears the air somewhat. Next, I'm building a machine. You don't do what I did without a machine. I know what I'm after, but I can't do it alone. I talk to communists and socialists, and I can see something of what they're after. That's not what I'm after. There's not going to be any workers' republic of social democracy here; there's only going to be more of the same as now, and it's the way the pie is cut that decides things. And it is power—power pure and simple —that will tell how the pie is cut. I have a very simple goal, higher wages and better working conditions, and that's it."

"It makes sense," I agreed.

"Hell, yes, sense without simplicity. The fact is, Al, that it makes no sense. Every local in this union still claims the right to make separate agreements with the operators. One local undercuts the next—in effect, the union scabbing against the union—and the whole thing becomes chaos. An operator who signs an agreement with the union for higher wages, finds the operator in the next county underselling him and underpaying too. And on top of it all, West Virginia— pouring seventy million tons of coal into the market every year—and paying slave-labor wages with no union at all. That's what we face, and either we face it or we're finished. Well, we decided to face it, and we called a strike—forty-eight hours from now, and once and for all, we're going to see this thing through and establish uniform and tolerable rates—here in the North, if nowhere else. That's what you've walked into, and it's going to be your job to sell this strike to the press and the people—and to make them understand that for us, it is survival, pure and simple."

148

8

Long afterwards, Dorothy Holt admitted that her heart went out to me that first evening at the dinner table, sitting across from me and waching me toy with the pot roast. She said that I appeared alone, bewildered and uncertain, and that she could appreciate the response of a man who came not only into Egypt as a newcomer, but into the drab ugliness of Pomax in a pouring rain, into the home of Ben Holt, into a strike, and into a job that he was a tyro at. In all truth, she had come to the conclusion that our acquaintance would be of short order, that after a day or two in Pomax, I would turn away for greener pastures. Since I reminded her of some of the young men she had known before she married Ben, she judged me by them, and not with too much respect or admiration. Perhaps, to a degree, she was right. Sitting there, I was frank enough with myself to tell myself that if I had known the circumstances that would greet me, I would have turned down the job. Or perhaps not. Hindsight is never very dependable.

To ease things, she made the conversation. She described the geological history of Illinois that had resulted in Egypt, the thoughtlessness of the glaciers, pushing their rich earth deposits in front of them, stopping short of the delta, the poverty of the land in terms of anything but coal mining, and the set of historical circumstances that had created here one of the great coal-producing areas of the world. She chatted comfortably and serenely while Ben Holt applied himself to the food. His was the case of a very large man who expended enormous energy—and who ate enormously and efficiently, not as a glutton, but as a machine that had to be fueled. It was a digger's habit, and I have seen many diggers eat just that way, with intense absorption. And while he ate, his wife completed her tale of Egypt and explained to me,

"That was my mistake, Mr. Cutter—an early attempt to

like Pomax. You come to a place to live, and your natural instinct is to like it, to feel for it, to identify yourself with it. But that's a mistake in Pomax. I don't think anyone likes Pomax. All you have here are differing degrees of distaste for it."

"But the people—"

"Ah, now that's something else, isn't it? I suppose you know something of the Pennsylvania miners, and certainly West Virginia, but Egypt is another matter, wouldn't you say, Ben?"

"They're miners," Ben Holt said.

"As Ben looks at it, if they pay dues, they're miners," she smiled. "But these people—yes, you can become fond of them, very fond of them, Mr. Cutter, and they're polite and they live decently. You should see the gardens some of them have. But they're not of our time, Mr. Cutter."

"I'm afraid I don't understand."

"These are the people who started the Civil War three years before it began, and who fought it for five years afterwards. Time stands still for them. Ben laughs at me, and according to Ben, they're no different from people anywhere else. But they are—they are something strange and wild and terrible, maybe admirable too, and they won't bow their heads for anything or anyone in the world. That's why the thought of a strike out here frightens me. They tell stories of strikes here in Egypt. At home, when the miners have no work, they pull in their belts and grit their teeth—"

"Is that good?" Ben Holt broke in.

"I didn't say it was good or bad, Ben. But the other night I went over to a neighbor of ours, Mrs. Landrey, and her husband was sitting in the kitchen, polishing this beautiful old rifle, utterly absorbed—"

"Dorothy's an incurable romantic," Ben broke in. "When miners strike they go hunting. Sure these are hard men. You can't live in Egypt and not be hard. The sun doesn't shine here—"

We talked about other things, about where I would live,

the possibilities among the boardinghouses in Pomax. The Pomax House was bad enough, but the thought of a boardinghouse was more than I could endure, and Ben felt that the cooking in the dining room at the Pomax House was better than anywhere else in town. They had a Chinese cook, whose name was Hop Sin. Dorothy agreed about his ability. "He can't find the ingredients here for the good Chinese dishes, but he has a sort of natural genius. Even when it's as simple as frying a pair of eggs, they're delicious. Ben and I go there sometimes to eat."

"It's up to you, Al," Ben nodded. "You can save a few dollars at a boardinghouse, but I know how you feel. I've lived in boardinghouses too much to ever think about it again."

Dorothy left to put the children to bed. The two older children, Norah and Sam, came to say good night to their father. They were round-cheeked, healthy children, good-natured and cheerful. My impression was of a happy home, but in my own state of mind, almost any family group would have added up to a happy home. I was too occupied with my own self-pity to examine them very closely.

Ben and I lit cigars over our coffee. Twice, he was interrupted by the phone while Dorothy was away, and twice before that during the meal. He was away from the table when Dorothy returned, and I had just a glimpse of an expression on her face that might have been sheer despair or perhaps it was nothing more than my imagination. Ben Holt returned pulling on a raincoat. "I hate to break this up," he said, "but we have to get over there. This is the first time, but not the last, Al. I want you to feel at home here." Dorothy was watching him. "I know," he said to her, and shook his head hopelessly. They didn't kiss as we left.

Clouds were gathering again in the growing dusk. As we walked, Ben Holt talked about the strike, about what faced him, and about what I could do. He admitted that no matter what the result of the strike was, they couldn't change the situation in the South. "Someday we'll go back to West

Virginia—but that will wait." The thing now, as he explained, was to separate the North from the South and get an agreement here. "And let the country know how miners live. That's your job, Al. Convince them that we're not a bunch of red Bolsheviks trying to overthrow everything."

He was taking another way than that which had led me to their house. After a few blocks, we were walking through unpaved streets, the mud sucking at our feet. The tiny houses on either side were grimy and unpainted, a shade less wretched than those in West Virginia, but bad enough. Here and there, a man standing in his yard or sitting on the front steps would come over and pass a few words with Ben. Ben knew them by name. He had an incredible memory for names, and he used this gift consistently and shrewdly. The miners themselves were physically no different from other miners I had seen, lean men, the mark of their trade tattooed into their skin; but the bitterness and the anger were evident—or was that my imagination in terms of what Dorothy Holt had said?

At one house, a strikingly good-looking woman in her twenties came over to us, and she said to Holt, "Who's your cute friend, Ben?"

He introduced me and asked how things were.

"Lousy. Living alone is lousy. Always was."

"Find yourself another husband, Sally."

"Another miner? The hell with that! The hell with the whole lot of you!"

We had started off, when she called after us, "I didn't mean that, Ben. Come over sometime. A girl gets lonely."

"She is poison," Ben said to me. "Husband killed in a mine, no kids—she lives there alone. I suppose it's all right for a night, but she'll claw your heart out." His comment was flat and indifferent; the indifference was like a seal on his attitude toward women. As I matched his long, rolling stride through the night, I began to sense some of the complexity that underlay the seeming simplicity of this big hulk of a man called Ben Holt.

152

9

The International Miners Union headquarters in Pomax, Illinois, has, in the course of years, become one of the famous buildings of America. In Hulter's painting, "The Miner's Family," he uses the Union Building on Lincoln Street as part of the background, a fact that mystified art critics who knew little or nothing of Egypt or Pomax. However, in the course of time, the three-story, red brick building, with its two stunted, pointed towers, its ten ugly windows, and its flat, dead exterior became a symbol of sorts. The union still owns this building, and over the years it has undergone a process of modernization and sentimentalization. In 1924, there was no money for modernization and no mood for sentiment; it was an old and dirty building and its only advantage lay in the fact that the union owned it and that it was situated in Pomax.

Pomax was more than the geographical heart of the bituminous coal country of Illinois; it was a mining town or small city in which almost the whole adult male population were miners, and you couldn't be mayor or chief of police or sit on the city council or the board of education unless you were a miner or had once been a miner. Before the war, half a dozen wealthy coal operators made their residence in Pomax, where they built large, handsome houses on Osborn Street. At the time, around the turn of the century, there was an anticipated future for Pomax; but when it failed to materialize except in coal, and when each successive year increased Pomax's coat of soot and grime, the operators moved north to more pleasant locations, and their residences were turned into boardinghouses. The Union Building had originally been built as headquarters for the Midwest Coal Company, which was owned and operated by the Mid-Illinois Railroad; but after some years of what was in effect enemy territory, they sold the building to the union and moved to Cairo.

The building itself was located on Lincoln Street, one block south of the Pomax House. As I approached it with Ben Holt this evening, the windows were lit, the sidewalk outside crowded with men—indeed the whole street alive and active and very different from the dead and deserted aspect it had presented in the pouring rain. On either side of the entrance to the building were large bulletin boards, men pressed around them, crowding up to read the notices— and other men clustered in small groups and others went in and out of the building. A very tall, thin man in a police-man's uniform, with a gold badge on his chest that read CHIEF, came out of the building as we approached. Ben, meanwhile, was surrounded by the miners in front of the building, greeting this one and that one, speaking a word here, a word there, trying to answer five questions at once, and exercising his uncanny ability to remember names. The tall man in uniform pushed through to him and said to the others,

"Look, boys, give me a minute with Ben, will you? I been waiting for him, and I still punch a time clock. I'm not going on strike."

The miners were good-natured about it. It was evident that the chief was liked. He drew Ben aside, and Ben pulled me along with him, and introduced me,

"This is Alvin Cutter, Andy. He's just joined our staff, and tonight's his first night at work. Isn't that a hell of a note? He's going to handle public relations and see whether we can't get through this one without every rag in America beating us over the head. So I want you to know him." And to me, "Al, this is Andy Lust, our chief of police in Pomax. Andy was a miner and his father was a miner, and he's a good friend of ours. I want you to know him and like him."

Lust shook hands with me. Unquestionably, if I remained with the job, I would know him, but whether I would like him was another question entirely. His pale blue eyes were cold as ice, his lips so thin that his wide mouth gave the appearance of a slit. His greeting was formal, efficient and short; evidently he was not impressed by whatever I would add to the local situation; he turned to Ben Holt and declared,

"I got to know, Ben, just when and how this strike is going to come off."

"I told you when and how, Andy. It's no secret. A day after tomorrow at the end of the workday."

"And suppose they lock you out at the beginning of the workday and jump the gun? That's what I'm afraid of. That could mean a lot of trouble."

"Hell, yes," Ben Holt sighed, "it could mean trouble. There's got to be lots of trouble all over. That's the nature of it. Andy, it's not just here, but Pennsylvania too, and out west, and Canada and the South—"

"The trouble's going to come first right here, and you know it, Ben!"

"Maybe, maybe," Ben nodded, smiling, pacifying. "You know Pomax better than I do, Andy. We'll try to think through some approach to a lockout. I'll talk to you about it."

"And give me time, Ben."

"Sure I'll give you time, Andy—sure."

We shook hands again, and Ben led me into the building. Just inside the door, he was stopped by a miner, desperate, almost in tears. The miner's daughter had acute appendicitis. It had been diagnosed. The case was urgent, and she had to be rushed to the hospital in Cairo, but they would not admit her without money, and the miner was penniless. When he began to go into the facts of how penniless he was, Ben stopped him, reached into his own pocket, peeled five tens from a roll of bills, and gave the money to the man. Ben cut short his thanks and pushed him toward the door of the building, avoided my eyes, and led the way upstairs.

The inside of the Union Building was as beaten and poorly

kept as the outside. The entranceway, the hallway, and the main stairs leading up to the second floor had been paved with what was once white marble—now almost black with grime. The walls, once buff, were brown, the paint peeling, the plaster cracked. On the main floor, two large rooms, left and right, opened off the entranceway. One was crowded with miners; the other was a duplicating room, mimeographs and stacks of mimeograph paper. I glimpsed them in passing then; we went upstairs to the union offices.

The main office, at the head of the stairs, was crowded, and there was a flow of men coming and going. Most of them were miners, but there were others, a few newspaper people, a coal operator, and various townspeople, storekeepers and others. Their attention centered around two men whom I saw here for the first time, but whom I was to see a good deal of during the coming years. The first of these two was Fulton Grove, a vice-president of the International Miners Union and Ben Holt's administrative assistant. He was a man of average height, pudgy in aspect, in his middle thirties, blond, with mild blue eyes blinking behind steel-rimmed spectacles. He was as unlikely a candidate for leadership of the most unbridled and militant group of workers in America as one might find—unlikely and improbable, with the manner of a bank clerk and the meticulous reactions of a bookkeeper. The second center of attention in the room was Jack Mullen, dark, muscular, black hair, deep, restless eyes, a handsome head on a thick, strong neck, and a calm, forceful manner. He was thirty years old, a miner since the age of twelve in the bituminous fields outside of Pittsburgh, and Ben Holt's chief field assistant. Curiously enough, Fulton Grove had also been a miner once, but only for a single year; then he had gone into clerical work at the mines, become a grade-school teacher, and served on the Pomax City Council.

As Ben Holt and I entered the room, the coal operator, a heavy, choleric man, strode over to him, thundering, "By

God, Ben, I am going to see you and talk to you if it's the last thing I do!"

"All right—all right," Ben replied, spreading his arms. "I talk to everyone, don't I? Give me a minute."

"I been here an hour."

"A man has to eat dinner," Ben grinned. "Am I allowed? Did you eat? Do I?" He pushed past and nodded for Grove and Mullen, who joined him, and then he introduced me. Fulton Grove slid through the formalities of greeting; he was glad to see me; glad to see anyone who might help. Mullen studied me coldly and thoughtfully, and said, "Stick around, Cutter. This is an interesting place."

"Can you talk to Al here now, Jack?" Ben Holt asked Mullen.

"Now? How the hell can I talk to anyone now, Ben? I got twenty people waiting to see me. Take him in to Mark. Mark will be able to tell him what to do better than any of us. Anyway, I don't know what his job is. All I know is that we got a strike here we're not one God damn bit prepared for."

"We'll be prepared," Ben said softly. "Take it easy— easy." He swung around and told the mine operator, "I'll be with you in two minutes, Mr. Klingman." Then he led me through the crowd and opened a door marked LEGAL DE-PARTMENT.

In a room that was furnished with a desk, a few chairs, some filing cabinets, and a case of books, a man was in the process of dictating to a strikingly attractive young woman. The woman, lean, long-limbed, glanced up as we entered, to reveal a strong-boned face, high, wide cheekbones, a wide, full mouth, and shrewd, appraising blue eyes. The man was in his late forties or early fifties, tired, sallow in complexion, his face fleshy and lined, his dark eyes deep-set under shaggy brows.

"This is Mark Golden, our attorney. Lena Kuscow, his secretary," Ben told me.

"Everyone's secretary," the woman remarked sourly.

"Alvin Cutter. I was telling you about Cutter, Mark."

Golden nodded. Lena Kuscow studied me deliberately and thoughtfully. "I want you to talk to him," Ben went on. "This place is a madhouse tonight. Klingman grabbed me as I came in. He wants to see me—"

"You know about what."

"Sure I know about what. He's got that damn steam shovel and the grading machines sitting in his open-strip mine, and he's going to claim that the machinery will bankrupt him unless he can use it."

"He's a liar," Golden said flatly.

"Why?"

"Because Arrowhead Pit isn't his mine. Eighty per cent of it is owned by the Great Lakes Company in Chicago, and he's just a cheap loudmouth they use as a front. They got the machinery on contract, but it won't bankrupt them. It could sit there all year and it wouldn't bankrupt them."

"You can't prove any of that, Mark," Ben said tiredly.

"All right, I can't. He's going to ask you whether they can't go on stripping the coal with the steam shovel and stock-piling it."

"That's right."

"The hell with it! Do what you want to do. You're asking for trouble."

"Thanks," Ben said angrily, and started for the door. I stood there, feeling like a complete fool, not knowing whether to remain or to leave with Ben Holt—feeling the effect of an accumulation of distaste and dislike directed toward me. At the door, Ben paused, turned back to Golden, and said,

"By the way, I gave fifty dollars to Gus Acuda."

"What for?" Golden demanded.

"What for? His kid's got a case of acute appendicitis, and he has to get her admitted to the hospital or she'll die."

"Why didn't you let him put in a plea and application to the emergency medical fund?"

"Because the kid would be dead by then."

Golden wrote out a voucher, handed it to Ben, and said,

"You can't go on doing this, Ben. You can't dispense charity whenever the mood takes you. You're not God and you're not Morgan."

"God damn it, what should I do?" Ben roared at him. "Let the kid die?"

"How many other kids die? How many die from pneumonia, from t.b., from pellagra, from scarlet fever and diphtheria —how many? You make me sick with this kind of sentimental paternalism! It's as unbecoming to you as to Andrew Carnegie. I've told you a hundred times that we need a medical program. We got ten thousand miners in this union spitting blood morning, noon, and night, and we don't have a doctor on our payroll or a hospital we can call our own—"

I had never heard anyone talk to Ben Holt like that before; I had never watched him listen to anyone begin to talk that way. Now he listened. His face became red with fury, but he listened, and when Golden had finished, he stormed out of the room, slamming the door so hard behind him that bits of plaster fell from around the frame. Golden said to me, quietly, almost in a whisper,

"Sit down, Cutter. We'll be through here in a few minutes, and then we'll talk."

10

During all this, Lena Kuscow had watched me, her face expressionless, her attitude seemingly indifferent, her interest almost clinical. She might have been bored by the whole thing. Golden finished his dictating, apparently an answer to injunction proceedings of some kind, and then asked me whether I would like some coffee. I nodded, and he said to Lena,

"Honey, would you?"

She rose slowly, her motion surprisingly graceful, and left the room. Golden then turned to me and smiled and asked me,

"You got in today, didn't you, Cutter?"

"At three o'clock."

"And now it's a quarter to ten—so you've had a bellyful already, and hardly enough time to change your clothes. Ben took you home for dinner?"

"That's right."

"And now you're asking yourself what ever brought you here in the first place and what kind of a lunatic asylum is this." He had an easy, ingratiating manner about him, and he was as prepared to like you as he was to judge you. For the first time since I had arrived at Pomax, I had the feeling that I might make a friend here and not spend my days talking to walls. Everything I felt was boiling up inside of me, and I had no desire to talk to anyone or confide in anyone; yet I found myself talking to Mark Golden. Then Lena Kuscow came back with three tin cups of black coffee. As she handed me my cup, she said,

"Poor kid. What in hell ever brought you to Egypt?"

Since I was certain that I was older than she, I resented the "poor kid." "I came here to do a job," I said. "I was hired."

Golden nodded and sipped his coffee. "And you walked into a strike. It's not always exactly like this—well, more or less—but not exactly like this. I guess trade-union people use their heads as much as any other kind. But a lot of them, when they hear the word 'strike,' they stop thinking. They're overcome by a need for action and they get excited. I'm as bad as the next one. I had no business talking to Ben like that, and he had no business acting as a one-man welfare agency. I hate it when he thinks like a slob—I don't like it when anyone does. Now about you, Cutter—I don't want you to pour out your guts to me, but I would like you to tell me what you see out here. All I know about you is that Ben likes you and trusts you and thinks highly of you. Ben is a pretty good judge of people—but he also has some axes of his own to grind. You come into this situation and, unless I miss my guess, people like Fulton Grove and Jack Mullen

160

treat you like poison. No one welcomes you with open arms. Am I right?"

"You're right," I agreed.

"So you feel rotten. Are you an idealist, Cutter? Are you one of these dedicated young men out to help labor fight the good fight, and to show labor the proper way to do it?"

"Why do you ask?"

"Because if you are, give it up. You'll hurt yourself and maybe the union too. This isn't the Carpenters Union or the Cigar Makers—and maybe it isn't even a union. It's an attempt, a crazy hope, a lost cause led by some people too thickheaded to know that it's lost. It's a pack of ignorant diggers who had the temerity to get tired of choking and dying in the belly of the earth for three or four dollars a day. This strike isn't the end of anything; it's the beginning. It's like the beginning of a war. Ben Holt has three hundred thousand members on the union books and six hundred thousand dollars in the treasury. It sounds good, doesn't it, but it doesn't mean a damn thing. Half of the membership is out of work, and the other half doesn't make enough wages to keep body and soul together. The whole country is booming, but you only have to look at those diggers outside and the rags that constitute their apology for clothing to know what the boom means here in Egypt. So we're going into a strike, and we've as much chance of winning as a snowball in hell, and we need someone like you desperately. But not someone with stars in his eyes. Someone with guts. Do you have guts, Cutter?"

"That's a hell of a question, Mr. Golden, and beside the point. I was a reporter on the *Daily Mail* in New York. I gave up the job to take a job out here. To take a job out here—that's all."

"Why? Why?"

"I don't know why," I shrugged. "I have some ideas, and when I put them all together, I'll bring them to you. If you're still interested."

He smiled at me then. He had a warm, pleasant smile. He

161

took out a pipe and stuffed it and lit it. I got my cigarettes and offered them to Lena Kuscow. She accepted one, and Golden held a match to our cigarettes. We smoked and sipped our coffee, and Golden said to me,

"What about it, Cutter? Are you staying?"

"I'm staying."

"For how long?"

"Until I'm fired. I got too much pride to go back to the *Mail* and ask for my job again."

Golden looked at Lena Kuscow, and she nodded and said, "I think he'll make it, Mark. He's fancy, but you can't tell about anyone these days. Can you?"

"Lena's a pretty good judge of people too," Golden nodded. "All right, Cutter. You have three jobs. We all have —three, five, ten—reach in the hat and pick a title. This is the kind of operation we are trying to run. I'm the union lawyer. I'm also comptroller. Also some other things. Eventually, you'll be in charge of research, when we have some time for research. You'll head up a legislative staff when we get around to creating one—and providing you're still with it. Right now, the pressing need is the kind of propaganda that reaches the public. We need press notices that make sense, that are simply and directly written, and that allow for the smallest margin of error. We need to win some friends. You say you were a reporter—well, this place will soon be swarming with reporters, and it's up to you to know them and blunt their fangs when you can—not only here, but in Pittsburgh and Scranton as well. As soon as the strike deadline is past, Ben will take off for Pittsburgh, and he'll want you with him. We have to state our cause and keep stating it—which means that you must live and breathe this industry's life. We'll help as much as we can, but most of it is up to you. No one's going to be kind to you here—and no one's going to give you a break."

"And what about information?" I demanded. "Do I just guess what this union and this strike is all about, or am I permitted to talk to people?"

162

"I know, I know. You should have had at least a few weeks to study this situation, but now there simply isn't time. You'll just have to bone up as best you can. Questions? Sure, ask questions. Some people will be snotty and others won't. Read the releases and information bulletins on file in the mimeograph room. Most of them were put together by Lena and myself and Ben and his wife, and they're not very professional. Ben said that you were with him in West Virginia in 1920, so you know something about miners."

"Very little."

"It's a beginning—"

At that moment, the door opened, and a young man said that Ben wanted us in his office. Golden led the way. We crossed the main office, still full of people and a babble of talk and excitement, and went through a door that opened from the rear of this large room.

Ben Holt's private office was as unadorned as the other rooms in the building. It was furnished with a desk, eight or nine chairs, a bookcase, a filing cabinet, and a clothes tree. As we entered, a bitter argument was in progress between Ben Holt and two men I had not seen before. Jack Mullen and Fulton Grove stood at one side of the room. The two strangers faced Ben. One of them, short, fat, a bullet head on a thick, red neck, was—as I learned later—Gus Empek, president of the Associated Miners Union, a small, independent union that numbered some ten thousand middle-western miners at its high point of membership. The other man, Joseph Brady, was vice-president of the Associated Miners. Supposedly a onetime miner, Brady looked more like a corporation executive, impeccably dressed in dark blue serge, white shirt, silk tie, his shoes shined to a mirrorlike glow.

Although I had some vague impression that there was a small union challenging the International Miners Union in the fields, I knew nothing very much about it at this time. The only factor that gave the Associated Miners importance was their strength in one part of Egypt and their

163

potential danger as strikebreakers. Altogether, they were a dubious lot, and eventually it turned out that Joseph Brady had been, for years, on the payroll of the Coal Institute, the organization of the operators.

But at this moment, I knew nothing of these two men or what they represented. I entered the room and saw Ben Holt standing behind his desk, one arm directed toward Empek, his hand flat and menacing as he shouted,

"No! God damn it, no! Your men will not work! What in hell do you think we're doing—playing a game of tiddly-winks?"

"Just take it easy, Ben," Brady said.

"Say that once more—once more, and I'll come around this desk and belt you the hell out of here, Brady! I don't want to talk to you, so keep your trap shut! I'm talking to Gus Empek. Gus came here to see me. I opened my door to him because it was Gus Empek. If it was you, Brady, I would have had you thrown out of here on your ass."

Brady's pale, good-looking face contorted and began to twitch, but he kept quiet and maintained his control. Empek said wearily, "I wish you wouldn't get so excited, Ben."

"Don't I have reason? We're all being starved to death by that rotten southern coal undercutting prices and rates. It keeps on and this will be West Virginia all over again. We'll be paying the operators for the privilege of digging coal. So we're trying to do something about it, and you tell me you're going to cut our hearts out?"

"It's not that simple, Ben," Empek protested. "I can't just tell my membership that they're on strike. We got to discuss it and take a vote."

"Don't make me laugh!" Ben snorted.

"All right—so you're laughing. Where does that leave me?"

"I'll tell you just where. We got three hundred thousand members in the International. Day after tomorrow, we go out on strike. Day after tomorrow, your ten thousand members go out on strike. You don't break our strike and you don't scab. I'm not arguing about it. I'm telling you."

"It's easy to tell me," Empek nodded. And turning to Brady, he said, "Come on, Joe. There's nothing to talk about here. They talk and we listen. They don't want to listen."

They left then. Fulton Grove sat down, his face creased with trouble and unhappiness. Jack Mullen whistled a bar or two, and then stopped abruptly and shook his head. "What I like about the trade-union movement," Golden said, "is the sense of brotherhood that pervades it." And Grove asked querulously, "What's in it for them? That's what I don't get."

"They got a little pie and they want a big pie," Mullen answered. And Ben Holt spread his hands and said,

"Forget it. Gus Empek's nothing and Brady's less than nothing. The time comes and they make trouble, why we'll take care of it. Meanwhile, it's late and I want to get out of here. The six of us are together now, and there's a lot of things coming up. This is Cutter's first day in Pomax, and it's been quite a day. I know that no one rates in this union, especially where Jack Mullen's concerned, unless he can show three generations of miners behind him. You know, that kind of an attitude makes me sick. Personally, I think Cutter's an idiot to take my offer of a job and come out here; but he's here. So let's shake hands all around and get down to work."

Mullen looked at me and nodded. "All right, Cutter." He smiled slowly and grudgingly.

"Unless you want to run the union all alone, Jack," Ben Holt said.

11

It was almost midnight when I left the Union Building to walk back to the hotel. I was just closing the door of the building, when a voice said, "Hold up a moment, Al. I'll go along with you." It was Lena Kuscow. She asked me whether I minded the first name, which struck me as rather peculiar. I would have said that she would call anyone anything she pleased and not think twice about it. She fell into step with me, and wondered if I was too tired to walk home with her. Four blocks there, four blocks back to the hotel. "Only for the pleasure of your company," she assured me. "Pomax is a dangerous place, but not for girls who walk home at night."

"For whom?"

"Anyone who values his sanity. There are places that don't have much to offer, but Pomax is unique. It has nothing to offer—nothing but dirt and grime and poverty. It's a country slum. Do you know, Al, we don't even have a public library here. We have one movie house. A week after the strike starts, they'll close it up. No money for admissions, no money to rent films. We have seven pool parlors and three churches. I've been to towns upstate half the size of Pomax where they have twenty churches. Nothing grows here, not corn or culture or religion."

"But you live here—your family."

"No. No, I'm from Chicago. I live in Mrs. Ellen's boardinghouse on Cooper Street. Four blocks, if you have nothing better to do."

"I have nothing better to do."

We walked along the dark, dimly lit street. The diggers had disappeared. The town was deserted, utterly deserted. The clouds had gone, and it was a clear, starry night.

"You'll be bringing your family out here?"

"I haven't any."

"Oh? I thought you were married."

"I was."

"Divorced? Ah, it's none of my business. Ignore me, Al."

"My wife died a month ago."

"Oh. Oh—I'm so sorry, Al."

I said nothing. I never felt any impulse to argue with people who offered sympathy, even when they couldn't possibly

166

feel any. It was at least a human gesture in a world not over-stocked with human gestures.

"Why did you come here?" she asked suddenly. "This is no place to forget anything."

"Why did you come here?"

"It's a job. I worked for the union in Chicago. They had to close the office there. So I came here. I didn't have much to forget or remember."

"Neither do I."

Then we walked along in silence. I left her at the board-inghouse and went back to the hotel. My first day at Pomax was over.

12

For the next ten days, with the exception of a single Sunday afternoon that I took for myself, I lived and worked at the Union Building, subsisted mainly on black coffee and sandwiches, and returned to my hotel at night for a few hours' sleep, a change of clothes, and a bath. I had witnessed strikes before this, but I had never been a part of one and I had never worked within the mechanism of a strike. It had always appeared to me that when a labor union called a strike, it was a comparatively simple procedure. The men stopped work; they organized picket lines; and they pro-claimed their demands to the world. I had never really con-sidered the fact that nothing in so vast and far-reaching an effort as a national strike just happened; it had to be watched, pushed, nursed, co-ordinated. The pay checks of thousands of men were blotted out. That was 1924, and most of the miners who went out on strike were poverty-stricken before the strike ever began. Their larders were empty, their clothes patched and worn. In Illinois, as in West Virginia, at least half of them wore no shoes. Far from having savings, many of them had not seen hard cash in years, being permanently in debt to company stores and company housing.

And these were conditions that hardly varied at all from state to state. The technical blueprint of the strike projected a situation where the local unions, who clung to their autonomy with fierce possessiveness and suspicion of the national organization, would cover their own needs for at least the first ten weeks of the strikes. But already on the third day of the strike, pleas for financial aid were pouring into Pomax. Mark Golden, sitting like a tortured demon over the union funds, would be torn to figurative shreds, as he attempted to guard and husband the union's shrinking bank account. Ben Holt, Jack Mullen, Fulton Grove, and the other union officials had already begun their own attacks on the precious store of money that spelled the difference between disaster and success. Faced with incipient revolts of various distant locals, locals claiming that they were unable to bring off the strike, endure it, stand the fury of operators and company police, and faced with the intransigeance of the Associated Miners, under Empek and Brady, they began a process of juggling strength and balancing forces. They played a vast chess game in which they were outnumbered, outmatched, and outclassed, and they played it with bluff, front, and arrogance.

In addition to this, they had the local situation in Egypt, the key strike of the thousands of miners in the incredibly rich bituminous fields of southern Illinois, the practical business of organizing relief stations, soup kitchens, and the whole complex table of command that supervised the closing of the various mines, the establishing of pickets, and the endless discussions with the operators, the state legislators, the local mayors, and the governor of the state.

For my part, I learned quickly. I had to. I had to learn not only to deal with my own material but to prevent myself from being pulled in five different directions, drafted as an assistant for anyone who needed an assistant—and sent off to do whatever errands had to be done. I learned the fine difference between truth and necessity. I learned how to deal with reporters who demanded,

"Just how many men are out on strike, Cutter?"

"Three hundred thousand."

"Now look, you know that's a lot of crap, just as we do. You never had three hundred thousand men working. And the story goes that half the mines are still working."

"That's not true. As far as the northern states are concerned, the mines are closed. No coal is being dug."

"How about New Mexico and Colorado and Wyoming and Montana?"

"It holds there too. The mines are closed."

"And how long do you think you can stay out?"

"As long as we have to."

"And what about the Arrowhead Pit? They're digging coal there."

The full truth was that they were digging coal in a great many places where we claimed none was being dug. The strike was far from total, even in the northern states; but the Arrowhead Pit was right under our noses, five miles outside of Pomax, a great excavation where the first local large-scale stripping operation was under way.

Today, a vast and increasing amount of coal is mined by stripping, as opposed to the older method of tunneling. In stripping, the overlay of earth and rock is stripped away by steam shovel and earth mover; rock is blasted and removed; and the black pay vein of coal is wholly exposed from above. As tons and tons of earth are removed, a wide craterlike opening in the earth is formed, and finally the steam shovel bites into the virgin coal, tearing it loose half a ton at a gulp. The method has all the advantages of a machine operation, but with the drawback of requiring an enormous capitalization in advance—and is based, of course, on modern earth-moving machinery. In 1924, the method was unusual and partly experimental—and looked upon sourly and suspiciously by both the miners and the union. The Arrowhead Pit, outside of Pomax, was an attempt at truly large-scale strip mining, based on what was considered then to be the largest steam shovel in the world.

Though no coal was being moved out of the Arrowhead Pit, the shovel had continued to work since the first hour of the strike, digging the coal and stock-piling it. At first, Ben Holt was of half a mind to allow Klingman, the operator in charge of Arrowhead, to continue to dig, so long as no coal was moved. On the second day of the strike, we learned that Gus Empek of Associated Miners had enrolled the shovel men, the truck drivers, and bulldozer operators into the Associated Miners—which union was still against the strike and claiming their right to work. Until now, the Associated Miners didn't have a member within twenty miles of Pomax. Arrowhead gave them their first opportunity and foothold.

The newspaper people kept pressing me with the question of whether we had worked out a separate arrangement for strip mining—and I dwell on this because of the subsequent sequence of events at Arrowhead Pit. It seems incredible today that the very name of Arrowhead is forgotten to all but labor historians; then, shortly, it was to become known to almost every person in the United States; but that was still in the future, and my own problem was to convince the newspapermen that we had made no separate deal with the strip mines. I was trying to sell the world a picture of a national strike called by the Miners Union and effectively carried out —the mines closed, the diggers firm in rocklike unity; and the picture simply was not true. Ben Holt and the others felt, however, that the projection of this picture was of prime importance. I, in turn, was carried along by my hasty immersion in the excitement of my first strike, the long days and sleepless nights, the thousands of miners crowding into the Union Building each day, their drawn, earnest faces, their determination, the picket lines I saw at the collieries I visited, the soup kitchens and relief stations. I accepted it because I wanted so desperately to become a part of it, and the more I worked with Ben Holt, the more my admiration for him increased. I accepted his views, his dreams, his decisions, and I tried, somehow, to convey them to the press.

And to tell the whole truth, I enjoyed the sense of immediacy, of urgency and struggle, the feeling of being an integral part of a great body of men fighting, in a sense, for their right to survival. I enjoyed the feeling of excitement and importance—and of belonging. I had been bitterly alone since Laura died, but in a way I had been alone since my discharge from the Army in 1919. I had walked in the city as a stranger and worked on the *Mail* as a stranger. I had made no friends that I regretted leaving behind me; and no strings were ever permitted to penetrate my veneer of the sharp, wisecracking young know-it-all of the twenties and tie me to anything. Now, I was able to let my defenses drop. I had people around me who valued me, and I was a part of something. When a committee of the state legislature came down from Springfield to investigate the strike, Ben appointed me their guide for one afternoon, leaving it up to me to say the right thing and do the right thing. And when I missed fire, as I often did, he seemed to understand.

13

During the first weeks after the strike was called, I took only one Sunday afternoon for myself. A combination of the need to get away from the Union Building for a few hours and a desire to see the Arrowhead Pit led me to borrow an old bicycle Abner Gross kept chained to the gutter pipe at one corner of the Pomax House. Gross and I had become good friends. I learned that he had been a drummer boy in the Civil War with the 5th Illinois Infantry—which put him into his early seventies. I had thought he was younger. He was a storyteller and I listened well and enjoyed the listening; also, the union was the best and only customer for the private dining room and the apology for a ballroom that graced the Pomax House. Gross worshiped the *Spoon River Anthology,* and when he discovered that I knew half the book by heart, our bonds were sealed.

He had told me that the bicycle was mine any time I wanted it. After lunch, I set out along the dirt road that led to Arrowhead. Once the dismal shacks of Pomax were behind me, the road led through a pleasant wood of second-growth birch.

It was a fine spring afternoon, cool but sunny, with the yellow-green of the budding birches giving this part of Egypt a strange and improbable beauty. For two miles, except for a muddy little stream, there was nothing but the birches; then there was a stretch of farms, poor farms with fields of new corn and pens of skinny brown pigs; then open country with the ragged edges of shelf rock showing. Here, where there was no overlay of glacial soil, the thick bituminous seams lay sometimes as little as fifty feet below the surface and never much more than three hundred. Now and again, one saw a dark hint of outcropping coal, and finally in the distance the piles of rock that marked the Arrowhead Pit. No one was working the mine today. It was deeply silent, and there was no one in sight except another bicyclist, who stood with her wheel at the lip of the crater, where the road bent for its first wide curve down to the bottom.

I dismounted and walked my own wheel toward her, and as I approached, she turned around and I saw that it was Dorothy Holt—but in appearance so young and fresh that I had to look twice; and she smiled at what must have been a foolish, gaping face.

"Hello, Mr. Cutter," she said. "How nice to meet you here!"

I nodded and muttered something in response. Her honey-colored hair was drawn back and tied with a yellow ribbon. She wore a white shirt, a suede vest and an old riding skirt, long woolen socks and moccasins. Somehow, by the miracle of the spring day, the sunshine, the bicycle, and a yellow ribbon, the grave mother of three children had become a young girl. It was a magic I did not try to analyze; it reminded me of Laura and of every other girl I had seen wonderfully in spring sunshine, and it made my heart ache with a pain I had avoided during these past days of frantic activity and work.

"I'm not a ghost, Mr. Cutter," she smiled. "I must explain that I come from a family of suffragettes, and I exercise the right of a woman to revolt and demand her privileges. That is, I exercise it on Sunday afternoons when the weather is good. They give me four hours for myself, and I use it to explore the backwaters of the Nile, and I am rapidly becoming an Egyptologist. Now isn't that perfectly silly? I don't know why I said it—except that I feel so good when I am able to get away by myself like this, and there is never anyone around to whom I can say anything foolish."

"I didn't think it was foolish," I said lamely.

"Oh? You are very kind." She waved a hand toward the open crater. "This is our famous Arrowhead Pit, Mr. Cutter. But then I am sure you know that."

I nodded. "I rode out here to see it."

"And isn't it something to see?" She began to walk her wheel across the rough ground that formed the lip of the excavation. "There's something dramatic and exciting about it. I've been out here half a dozen times, I guess, and I never get over the sense of excitement in seeing it. That steam shovel looks so small down there, yet they say it's the largest one in the whole world—larger even than the shovels they used to build the Panama Canal. And those trucks—do you remember, when we were children, what an event the sight of an automobile was! Who ever thought that we would see anything like these Mack trucks—they haul ten tons of coal, twenty thousand pounds—" She was outgoing, ingenuous, and apparently delighted that she had someone to talk to. She was a woman, a mother, with the enthusiasm and the unaffectedness of a schoolgirl who had suddenly become the possessor of a great fund of fascinating information. I tried to estimate her age; she was twenty-seven at the time, but in spite of the three children, I felt that she was much younger. All this struck me even more sharply because on that night when I had dinner at her house, I was left with a

173

sense of a somber, almost tragic person, not in any evidence that I could then put my finger on, but subtly. Now there was no trace of that.

"—doesn't it excite you, Mr. Cutter?" she finished.

"It excites me, Mrs. Holt," I agreed. "It also worries me. It's the object of too much passion and hatred and fear on the part of the miners. That steam shovel does the work of two hundred men."

"But when you think of the old way—crawling into the earth through those black tunnels and bent double to hack away at the coal with the whole world pressing on you— have you ever been in a mine, Mr. Cutter?"

I shook my head. "No—not yet."

"I have been. Ben took me into one, and I was too proud to tell him how frightened I was, and when we were a mile or two underground—I don't know how far, but it seemed terribly far—I panicked and I knew that if I didn't see the outside I would die. Of course, I didn't die, but I never will forget the feeling. I can't believe that it's a good thing for men to work under such conditions, no matter what is said of the pride of a digger in his work. And this"—she pointed to the crater—"this will someday do away with the whole business of tunneling—"

"If it doesn't do away with the miners as well, Mrs. Holt."

At this point, we were approaching a small shack, set back a few yards from the lip of the crater; and as we walked toward it, the door opened and a man carrying a rifle emerged. He had a flat, ugly face, and almost with a snarl, he informed us that this was private property and demanded to know where in hell we thought we were going. I reminded him that there was a lady present and that there was nothing much of any value that we could carry off on our bikes.

"All right, buster, so there's a lady present. Now I give you and the lady two minutes to get out of here."

I stood there watching him, trying to think of some way to retrieve my bruised manhood, but Dorothy pulled at my

174

sleeve and begged me to go. "Please," she whispered. "Please, Mr. Cutter."

I nodded, and we turned away from the place. As we left the mine behind us, she said to me, "Thank you, Mr. Cutter. I live in dread of something like this happening when Ben is with me. Ben would have felt an irresistible obligation to take the rifle away from him and break it over his head."

"Do they always have armed guards here on Sunday?"

"Not so far as I know."

We reached the road, mounted our bicycles, and rode for about half a mile away from Arrowhead. At a place where a flat, white rock lay alongside the road, Dorothy braked her wheel and dismounted.

"Do you mind if we rest for a while?" she asked. I joined her, and we sat down on the rock. "I'm shaking," she said, holding out one hand. "I'm ashamed of myself. But I hate guns. They frighten me so. I'm so ashamed."

"Why?" I smiled. "Because you hate guns? I hate them. They frighten me, and I'm not ashamed."

"You can afford not to be ashamed, Mr. Cutter. Ben told me about your war record. You were a hero—"

"No. No, that's not true!"

"—but you were, and it gives you the right to be afraid of guns."

"Believe me, it's a natural right."

"Then we won't talk about guns. Tell me about your job. Do you like it?"

"I don't know," I answered slowly. "I really don't know, because until today, I haven't had ten minutes to think about it. I'm not even sure that I know what my job is."

"Tell me about it. You know, after that first night—well, I told Ben that I didn't think you'd stay. I was almost sure you wouldn't."

"Why?"

"I don't know, unless it was that you suddenly made me aware of Pomax. You can get used to a place—even a place like Pomax. We've been here a few years and it feels like we've been here forever. But when you came, I suddenly saw it with fresh eyes. Do I sound very disloyal, Mr. Cutter?"

"I can't think of you being disloyal, Mrs. Holt. I don't think you know how."

She smiled, not as before, but with sheer pleasure and gratification, her whole face mobile, the way a little girl smiles, and she told me, "Why that's the nicest thing I ever had said to me, Mr. Cutter, and I don't think you were trying to be artful. I think you said it because you meant it."

"I did."

"Then I'm going to go around in a glow all day. But do tell me about your job."

I told her everything I could think of, and then suddenly, it was late and she was wondering how she could have sat there and let the whole afternoon go by. We rode back to Pomax, and at the edge of town, I left her.

14

I turned over in my mind the question of whether to say anything to Ben Holt about meeting his wife, and the very fact that I should have dwelled upon it perplexed me. I realized then that Dorothy would come home and blurt it out; it was not in her to hide anything, and certainly there was no reason for me to have the slightest trace of guilt. I decided to mention it to Ben in passing, but then one thing piled up upon another so rapidly that I didn't have a chance to bring it up.

Firstly, the International Miners Union threw a picket line around the entrance to the Dakota Pit. This was an Associated Miners colliery, and when their men reported to work, they tried to break through the picket line. There was a bad fight, and five men were hurt enough to require medical attention. The Chicago papers carried banner headlines about the violence at Egypt, and I found myself trying to convince the press that a splinter union was an enemy of the public as well as the great majority of mineworkers. It was not easy—and the more so since Ben and his associates had never properly worked out any real understanding of their relationship with the small Associated Miners Union. For my part, I could form no clear picture of what the smaller union represented. When I spoke to one of our men, I got a picture of vicious reactionaries, labor spies, company men in union clothes; when I spoke to another, I got as earnest a picture of Bolsheviks, anarchists, and Wobblies.

There was a meeting that lasted half the night, centering around the problem presented to us by the big Arrowhead Pit. Although no more than a dozen men were required to conduct the steam-shovel mining and stock-piling that Hans Klingman, the boss there, had pledged to limit himself to, we received constant reports of a steady flow of new men from Chicago. Nor were the descriptions of these men in any way reassuring. They were not diggers; all reports agreed on that; and so far as we could learn, they were the pale, hard-eyed inhabitants of the Chicago back alleys and gutters. I didn't put much stock in the stories that these were full-fledged gangsters, recruited from some of the big Chicago mobs; I felt that it was more likely these were drunks, loafers, petty hoodlums, and perhaps a scattering of flophouse bums; for even bonus wages would not bring mobsters into a strip mine in Egypt. But what was most disturbing was the fact that these men were not needed; they had no work to do; they were fed and lodged at the mine in hastily erected tents; and according to all stories, they were armed. Not only did we hear of rifles and pistols, but there was one not-to-be-dismissed report of two Browning machine guns.

And as fast as these men arrived at the mine, they were given union cards in the Associated Miners by Gus Empek.

Jack Mullen kept pounding on this during the meeting. "Ben," he said, "I been telling you for years what Gus Empek and that lousy mob he calls a union is. We let them get fat on our flesh. Now look what that bastard is doing!"

177

"We know what that bastard is doing," Ben agreed. "He's using his union to break this strike. But do we have to be such damn hotheaded fools as to walk right into the trap he set for us? We already had the worst possible press with the business at the Dakota Pit. What does it get us? Headlines? Cries of violence—the lawless miners! Bring in the National Guard! Break the strike! The hell with that! I want to win this strike and win it legally."

"No. We got to close down that Arrowhead Pit."

"How? They're digging coal, but they're not shipping it out. What should we do? Go in there against their guns? Have some kind of a war? I'm sick and tired of wars. Let's try this one without being killed. We got enough widows in the union already."

"I agree with Ben," Mark Golden said. "This is a trap—just as sure as God, this is a trap."

"And if they start shipping coal?" Mullen demanded.

"We'll face that when it happens."

The meeting went on for hours, but always around the same points and coming to no solutions.

The next morning, a telephone call from Pittsburgh told us that injunctions had been issued, over fifty struck pits opened, and two hundred and twelve men had been arrested. Two of the men in prison had been beaten to death. A few hours later, Ben, Mark Golden, and I were on our way to Pittsburgh.

15

A man named Paul Wassilinski, one of a number of men Golden had gotten released on bail, was brought up to my hotel room for me to take down his story. This was on the third day after we had arrived in Pittsburgh. Golden brought him up to the room. He was a big, soft-skinned Lithuanian, with a broad, cowlike face and a child's blue eyes. One of his arms had been broken and was in a plaster cast and a sling. He was also badly bruised around the face and neck, and an eye was closed, discolored and swollen. I gave him a drink of straight whisky, and then he sat down in the armchair in the room, looking around with admiration. He had never been in a hotel before, or, as he told me, in a room as fine as this one.

"Just try to make yourself as comfortable as you can, Mr. Wassilinski," I said to him. "I'm going to ask you some questions."

"Sure," he nodded. "But you don't call me Mr. Wassilinski, huh? You call me mister, it makes me feel like a boss. With all this pains and hurts I got on me, I don't want to feel like a boss right now. You understand? Call me Paul."

"All right, Paul. How old are you?"

"Thirty-five."

"Married?"

"I got good wife—fine three kids."

"You're not born in this country, Paul?"

"No. I taken here I'm nine year old."

"And how long have you worked in the mines, Paul?"

"Since I'm eleven. That's twenty-five, twenty-four year."

"And how long have you been a member of the International Miners Union, Paul?"

"Long as I work in mine. I tell you something—my papa say to me, in old country, Paul, no union, a man's same as a slave. I come here, I see a union, maybe I don't know nothing else, I know that. Everybody say, Paul, you a dumb Polack. I'm Litvak, but they see you from old country, they call you Polack. So I join union, I got enough sense for that."

"And what is your post in the union, Paul?"

"I'm member strike committee for whole district."

"And where were you working when the strike began?"

"Demerest Collieries."

"And where were you arrested? On the picket?"

"No. They come to home. Some lousy fink tell them who is strike committee. They come to home."

"How many other men were arrested at the same time?"

"I don't know that. They take me Pittsburgh and put me in cell with two other members strike committee, Joey Shine and Alec Vostov. That's all I see, poor Joey and Alec."

"Did they give you a hearing? Did they take you into court? Did they arraign you before a judge?"

"Hell, no. Nothing like that."

"How long did they keep you in the cell?"

"Overnight, maybe whole day. One glass water to drink, one rotten boloney sandwich. Then they take three of us to room in cellar. In room is six cops and table and chair. On table is paper for us to sign."

"Did they let you read this paper, Paul?"

"Tell you truth, I don't read so good English. I don't read so good Litvak either. But poor Joey Shine, he smart. He reads. He tell them it God damn lie what they write there."

It was at this point in the question-and-answer procedure of getting a statement from Wassilinski that Ben Holt entered the room. I paused, while he shook hands with Wassilinski; then he motioned for me to continue, sitting down on the bed and lighting a cigar. I recorded each answer in my own shorthand.

"Do you remember what was on the paper, Paul?"

"I remember what Joey Shine gets so mad about. He gets angry because they say Ben Holt is Bolshevik, agent Moscow, and we got dynamite stashed away to blow up tipples and car. 'Son of a bitch,' he yell at them, 'you got to kill me before I sign this.' So they kill him and Alec. That's right. They kill him."

"You don't remember anything else that might have been written on the papers?"

"I only know what Joey yell about."

"What happened then?"

"They start beat Joey. They push him up against wall and punch him in belly. Two of them hold arms, third punch him in belly. I try help him, they twist arm around my back

180

and break it. Then they put Joey in chair and put pen in his hand. He throw pen at them. Then they beat him around face and head with little clubs. One eye come out. He fall down on floor, and they kick him. Alec try push them away from Joey, they beat Alec around head and try make him sign. Then they beat him more. I try stop them and they hit me in face. I'm no good with broken arm. Then I faint and don't remember nothing until I wake up in prison hospital."

The silence after that was broken by Ben asking Wassilinski whether he'd like a cigar.

"That's nice, Ben. I don't smoke. I used to smoke, wife say it take bread out of children mouths. So I stop smoking. Lose the taste for it."

Ben nodded. Golden stared at Wassilinski moodily, and I said, "You understand, Paul, that I have been putting down the questions and answers. I'll have them typed up, and then we'll ask you to sign it in front of a notary public. You may have to give evidence in court about this. Will you do that?"

"I do it," Wassilinski nodded. Then he sat in silence for a while. I guess there was nothing any of us wanted to say, so we sat there silently, and finally Wassilinski shook his head and said that it was a terrible thing to see two men die. They didn't have to die. "Like they tell me in the old country, you go away to a war and die, but nobody make no sense of it."

"Things don't make much sense," Mark Golden said slowly. "They don't at all. We'll try to get some money for their families, and we have a pretty good chance there. But it doesn't make any sense." Golden seemed to have aged in the time I had known him; the lines in his face had deepened, the dark, deep-set eyes more tired-looking than ever.

Ben Holt spoke crisply and matter of factly to Wassilinski as he said, "You know, Paul, a strike is a rough thing for a union like ours. It always has been. Ordinarily, I would say that what happened to these two union brothers of yours deserves to be taken care of to the fullest extent by the union. But we've been punished. Every day of the strike eats up our treasury, and there's no more coming in. Mark here will sue the city of Pittsburgh and perhaps we can bring suit against certain operators. But that's dubious, and a long-drawn-out process at best. In any case, I can promise that there will be five thousand dollars out of union funds for the two families. That's two thousand five hundred dollars each. It's not much, but it will help them over the hump. You can tell them that. As for yourself, your medical expenses will be paid. I wish we could do more—I just wish we could."

16

The next day, I spoke to Fulton Grove at Pomax, and his news caused Ben and me to take the next train back to Illinois. Briefly, this is what had happened. A miner named Mike Duffey lived three miles from the Arrowhead Pit. He had two sons, one fourteen, one seventeen, and the boys thought it would be fun to sneak up as close to the crater as they could. They were at the lip of the crater when they were spotted, and the guards opened fire. The seventeen-year-old boy was shot through the heart.

According to Grove, the feeling around Pomax about the Arrowhead operation had reached the boiling point. The funeral of the boy was scheduled for the following day, and both Grove and Mullen were agreed that there would be trouble. Already, armed miners were showing up at the Union Building. Grove told me to impress Ben with their feeling that he should return to Pomax before any serious trouble began.

Even before I could sit down with Ben Holt and Mark Golden for some kind of an intelligent discussion of the problem, the news of what had happened at Pomax filtered through to Pittsburgh, and our phone at the hotel was ringing steadily. The reporters wanted a statement from Ben Holt, and I told them he was not there. A half hour later, when he arrived, I continued to maintain that he was not there.

"And if you go back to Pomax," Mark Golden said to him, "the same thing is going to continue. Everyone in Arrowhead holds a card in Gus Empek's union. You are going to be asked to make a statement about the Associated Miners. What are you going to say?"

"What can I say?"

"Stay here and say nothing."

"You're crazy, Mark. I can't do that. I can't hide. Associated Miners is not a union—it's a pack of armed hoodlums at this moment, the dregs of the Chicago flophouses in the pay of the operators."

"So we become a pack of armed hoodlums in response to that?"

"No! But neither can this situation continue."

"Then stay here and let it simmer down," Golden begged him. "Let me finish here and we'll go into the courts in Illinois. This is murder and we'll deal with it as murder."

"The way we dealt with murder in Pittsburgh?" Ben snorted.

"That isn't finished either."

"No? Well, suppose you try to finish it, Mark. Meanwhile, Al and I are taking the next train back to Pomax."

We had three hours before train time, and we passed them at a meeting with the heads of the strike committees of the Pittsburgh area. In those days there was an endless succession of such meetings, the group of ten, twenty, or forty miners, the local leaders, the Slavic, Irish, Welsh faces and voices, the natives who had mined coal time out of memory, the hunger and the patience and the acceptance of men who gave up work and bread because they believed Ben Holt's assertion that miners could live and exist as other people did. And Ben's ringing declaration,

"We are going to win! So long as we preserve our unity, we are going to win!"

By then, already, for all my short experience, I knew that we were not going to win. I had become a part of something that was sliding downhill. I was living at the bottom of a black pit. Up above, in the sunlight of civilization or what passed for civilization, people ate and drank and made love and laughed and sang. They knew nothing of and cared less about the carbon-tattooed men who grubbed in the belly of the earth, nor was it important that they should know or care. For thousands of years, since men first mined in the earth, the diggers had crawled and scraped and died. What the diggers felt or wanted did not matter; their anger did not matter; their deaths didn't matter. They dug out of the earth what civilization needed, and civilization went on.

That was the temper of my thoughts as I sat on the train with Ben Holt, and he asked me what was eating me.

"Just thinking, that's all."

"And what will it get you, Al?"

"Nothing, I suppose. I listen to Wassilinski talk about two men beaten to death. I hear about a seventeen-year-old kid shot through the heart."

"And you're going to weep?" Ben replied coldly. "How many tears do you have? You got one for every man who died in that lousy war that made you such a hero? You got a tear for every man who died in a coal mine? I didn't rate you for a sentimentalist, Al. I didn't rate you for a weeper."

"Thank you."

"So I hurt your feelings—the hell with that! If you're going to stay, you'll stay. And if you're going to walk out, nothing I say is going to change anything."

"Don't write me off!" I snapped at him. "When you want to fire me, just tell me."

"All right. Take it easy. No one lives forever, but if you want to do anything or make anything, you got to live for a little while. Eat yourself up, and you got nothing. Nothing. You become like Mark Golden. He bleeds for every drop of blood that's spilled. He suffers for every blow that's struck.

184

How long will he live? It's destroying him. He'll make nothing."

"And you, Ben?" I whispered. "What will you make out of all this?"

"A union," he said flatly. "A real union. A union big enough and strong enough to shake this whole friggen world. A union that will talk and the world will listen!"

"You believe that."

"You don't."

"No, I guess I don't, Ben," I admitted.

"Because you're involved," he said thoughtfully. "You bleed too. I suppose you think I'm a cold son of a bitch."

"I've had that thought, sometimes."

"I put first things first," he nodded. "I'm in a fight, and I'm going to win. That's all that matters. I'm going to win."

17

About an hour before our train pulled into Pomax, Ben said to me, "You've been through a war, Al. What would happen out there at Arrowhead if our people attacked the pit?"

"What do you mean?"

"Suppose there are eighty or a hundred men inside that crater. Suppose they have the two machine guns and rifles and pistols. Suppose they were attacked by three, four, five times their number. What would happen?"

"It depends."

"Sure it depends. On what?"

"On the way the attack was conducted— No, I guess any way, the crater's indefensible."

"Why?"

"Because of its nature. You can't defend a hole in the ground that's half a mile across. Everyone in it's a sitting duck. And if they try to defend the lip, eighty or a hundred men aren't enough."

"You were out there? You saw the mine?" he asked me.

"I was out there," I nodded. "I met your wife out there one Sunday afternoon—"

"I forgot about that," he grinned. "She told me about it. I'm glad she had some company. That's a bad place."

I agreed that it was a bad place, and Ben continued to grin. What he meant by the grin, I didn't know, but then there never was to be a time when I would know or fully comprehend his changing moods, his swift transitions from calm to anger, from fury to tranquillity, from contemplation to contempt. And now, surely, he could put no interpretation upon my meeting his wife one Sunday afternoon. For myself, at that time no woman interested me or moved me; not yet; all the wounds were too sore and too new. And as for Dorothy Holt, well, I had already made an adolescent decision, that she was a saint of sorts—which, ironically, and regardless of how absurd a judgment it was, still was no judgment that a man makes with total disinterest. So my own motives and feelings were confused; but when Ben Holt smiled that way, it could mean any one of many things. I think he was smiling at the thought of Arrowhead, because he said,

"You saw the mine and you say it can't be defended. Not even with machine guns?"

"Machine guns are overrated, Ben. But you're not thinking of an attack on the mine? I hope to God you're not."

"I'm not. Others are, you can be sure of that." His mood changed again. He seemed to forget me, and stared glumly out of the window until we pulled into the Pomax station. When we got off the train there, a young fellow, Oscar Suzic by name, who was Jack Mullen's assistant, was waiting for us. He shook hands with Ben and me, and then he said,

"Ben, Jack sent me over here to meet you. Gus Empek and Joe Brady are here."

"No!" Ben said. "They have more brains than that."

"They're here."

"Where?"

"Right here in the station, in the baggage room."

"I'll be damned," Ben whispered. "I'll be everlastingly damned."

It came out, from what Suzic said to us, that Empek had telephoned Jack Mullen that same morning and had insisted that he be allowed to speak to Ben. At first Mullen said that it was impossible, that under no circumstances would Ben have anything to do with Empek or Brady. But Empek persisted. He pleaded his case. He said that there was something terrible making up, and that anyone with at least a spark of responsibility had to do something to try to stop it. At first, he begged for a meeting in his headquarters at Cairo, and when Mullen refused flatly even to raise that possibility with Ben, he suggested a midway place. Mullen said, "If you want to talk to Ben Holt, come here and talk." Empek pointed out that such a move could be a lynch sentence, considering the mood in Pomax. Then they worked out a procedure. Brady and Empek would take a train. Mullen would arrange with the stationmaster for their use of the baggage room, and Oscar Suzic would be on hand to meet them as well as us.

As Suzic detailed this, Ben's face darkened. His shoulders hunched, and his big fists clenched and unclenched. "I'm just carrying a message from Jack Mullen," Suzic explained nervously. "He said for you to take it easy. Coming from him, he said don't blow your top—listen to what they have to say. Those aren't my words, Ben. Those are Mullen's."

"I'll listen to them," Ben nodded.

We went into the baggage room. Brady was sitting on a pile of mailbags. Empek was pacing nervously, and he stopped and spun to face us as we entered. In a way, I admired both of them; it had taken courage to come here and talk to Ben Holt, more courage than I would have given either of them credit for. Empek was visibly distraught; Brady fought his own battle to keep his pale face composed and expressionless as he rose to face us. After we entered the room, there was a long moment of silence—broken caustically by Ben,

"You wanted to talk to me. Talk."

Empek licked his lips and nodded. "All right, Ben. You know me five years, Ben. Maybe we disagree five thousand different ways. Maybe I said some hard things about you—so you said some things about me. You think my union shouldn't exist. I don't think any union should be run like yours, one man sitting on top of it like a king and crushing any opposition—"

"Is that what you came here to tell me?"

"I'm putting my cards on the table, Ben. I'm not holding anything back. Whatever you can say about me, I'm not a strikebreaker. I'm not a fink. I'm not a murderer."

"The hell you're not," Ben replied, slowly and flatly. "Who gave your union cards to those flophouse bums in the Arrowhead Pit? Who put a veneer of legality on them?"

"They were miners, Ben!"

"Miners? With machine guns and rifles? What in hell did they ever mine?"

"Ben, if I ever thought that a kid would be killed—"

"What in hell did you think?" Ben roared. "What kind of games did you think we were playing?"

"I'm just asking for a chance, Ben. I want to rescind those union cards. I want to clear the air."

"You want to clear the air, you son of a bitch!"

"Don't talk to me like that, Ben."

"I talk to you any way I damn please! What a hell of a nerve both of you got, coming here with this cock-and-bull proposition! Of all the low, strikebreaking bastards I ever looked at, you two are the lowest—"

At this point, Brady lost control, reached inside his jacket, and leaped toward Ben. Ben hit him with an open palm. The blow, apparently effortless, sent Brady flying across the room, and with two long strides, Ben was upon him, ripped open his jacket and removed a gun from a shoulder holster. He looked at the pistol with disgust, and then tossed it to me. "They stink," he said hoarsely. "Let's get out of here."

Then he walked to the door without looking at them again.

18

People—labor specialists, newspapermen, legislators, and a good many others—have speculated endlessly on Ben Holt's power over the men around him, his hold on them, and the loyalty he finally commanded from tens of thousands of coal miners. By their lights, the nature of the man was obvious; he was part hooligan, part actor, part devil, a shrewd roughneck with a talent for dictatorship and an instinct for the dramatic. What they failed to grasp, I believe, is that he was a man who responded to a situation in the only manner he knew. In essence, he was himself; he was a coal miner with the taste of coal in his mouth and the precise understanding that coal is power—and he lived at a particular time.

Perhaps some of this passed through my mind as we walked from the station around the big square to the Union Building. There were a lot of men in the square today. They stood in little groups, and they were armed. Almost every man carried a rifle or a shotgun, and at least half of them wore one piece or another of old army equipment, a bandoleer, a rucksack, a sheathed bayonet, and here and there, forage caps and tin hats. They were not enthusiastic in their greetings to Ben. They nodded or they muttered a word or two; but back of their minds was plainly the fact that he had made the original arrangement for the Arrowhead Pit to remain open.

As we neared the Union Building, Andrew Lust, the chief of police, joined us. "I want to talk, Ben," he said.

"Come upstairs."

There were at least a hundred men gathered around the Union Building, armed men with quiet, hard faces. The kids

189

were still in school, but later that afternoon, they would be there too. Like the others, these men looked at Ben and speculated about him. They stood aside as we went into the building.

The building was strangely quiet inside, and compared to the streets, it was almost deserted. Grove and Mullen were waiting for us. Lena Kuscow asked me about Mark Golden. Their relationship puzzled me, and I found myself watching her curiously as I told her that he was all right. "But you left him there alone?" I informed her that he wasn't alone, not by a long shot. We moved into Ben's private office. Oscar Suzic carried in some extra chairs. Lust began talking, but Ben interrupted him with,

"For God's sake, Andy, hold it a moment. The world's not coming to an end. Let me call my wife and at least tell her that I'm back here."

We sat there in silence, while he called Dorothy—and I began to understand the relationship that exists on the end of a telephone wire. When would he be home? He didn't know that he'd be home at all. "I just may have to go to Springfield and get to the governor somehow." He was uneasy with us listening to the conversation, but neither could he bring himself to ask us to go and leave him alone. He faced us, scowling, and when Mullen asked about the station incident, he snapped,

"The hell with those lousy finks! I took a gun away from Joe Brady." He nodded at Lust. "Give it to him, Al."

I handed the pistol to Lust, who examined it curiously, pulled out the clip, and emptied it. "What's this?"

"I took that away from Joe Brady," Ben answered morosely. "We met him and Empek at the station. Nothing came of it."

"Anyone hurt?"

"No."

"All right, you got your troubles," Lust said impatiently. "I got your troubles and mine as well. I swear I never seen anything like this in all my born days. We got an ordinance

190

in this town about carrying weapons apart from the hunting season. This ain't the hunting season, and there's an army walking around downstairs. I swear there's seven, eight hundred armed men in town right now. Supposedly for the funeral, but they come from all over the county and they never heard of the Duffey kid until yesterday. What about it, Ben? Just tell me what about it?"

"There's nothing to tell you, because we don't know."

"The hell you don't!"

"Just don't call me a liar, Andy," Ben said softly and dangerously. "Just don't give me any lies, that's all. We didn't organize this. You ought to have enough sense to know that. The word gets around, and you know the diggers in Egypt as well as I do. This kind of thing isn't new down here. It happened before. These damn diggers think with guns, not with their heads."

"But I try to think with my head. I got twelve officers— twelve officers. What am I supposed to do?"

"That's up to you, Andy."

"What can I do?" Lust demanded. "I tell you, Ben, call it off! I'm not going to slaughter my men to protect those lousy finks out at Arrowhead. I can't protect them anyway. So call it off."

"I can't call it off," Ben growled. "God damn you, don't you have a brain in your head? We didn't organize this."

"You went into West Virginia with guns in 1920, didn't you?"

"No! No, I did not! The diggers there took up guns because it was a matter of life and death. This is no matter of life and death. What difference does it make to the union how many finks they put into that crater? Sure it's a damned shame that the Duffey boy was killed, but do you think I'm so brainless that I'm going to organize a slaughter on top of that? Do you really think that, Andy?"

The chief of police hesitated, then shook his head. "No. You don't work that way, Ben."

"Thanks. All right, just cool off, Andy. We'll go out to

Arrowhead and talk to Klingman. If he agrees to clear out and take his bums with him, will you give them police protection?"

"What I can, I'll give them, Ben. I got twelve men."

"I understand. Still we can do it. We'll offer them cars to drive them right out of the county. We'll offer it tonight."

"And when do you want to go out there, Ben?"

"We'll go right now. Get your squad car, the one with the green light on top, so we can look official and not have some nervous hooligan pop off at us. We'll meet you downstairs in five minutes."

He left, and Ben looked at us, his eyes going from face to face. "Any better idea?" he demanded.

"You made up your mind," Grove said. "You didn't ask us."

"I'm asking you now."

"You can talk to those men in the street, Ben. You got the force of the union behind you. You can ask them to turn in their arms."

"And they'll do it?"

"They're going to kill every last man out there in Arrowhead," Grove cried. "Don't you know that?"

"I don't know anything. I don't read the future."

"Then maybe it's time you did read the future, Ben. It's plain enough."

"You read it, Fulton."

"I do. And if I was in your place, I'd call in the militia and disarm this mob."

Ben smiled thinly. "I know you a long time, Fulton, but I never thought I'd live to hear you tell me to call in the militia against the members of my own union. I never thought it. I've heard of unions that were broken and died, but they died decently. They didn't die because the president of the union turned the militia loose against his own membership. I never heard of that, and I don't intend to be the first."

"Just to be fair, Ben," Mullen put in, "we heard you tell

your wife that you might go up to Springfield and see the governor."

"Yes. To ask him to clean out that Arrowhead crater before it became a grave. But that wouldn't work. In the end, we'd get the militia—not the owners. Believe me, Jack, there's only one way—to talk Klingman into getting out while he's still alive."

19

In a few minutes, we were on our way out to Arrowhead, Andrew Lust sitting next to the uniformed driver, and squeezed tightly into the back seat, Ben Holt, Jack Mullen, and myself. I think it was at this point that I first began to sense Ben Holt's need for me, for my presence, for whatever he felt I gave to him. Just what that quality was, I still do not wholly understand, nor was it simple. He needed a balance, as if he knew that, brooking no interference, he tended constantly toward the brink of disaster. Yet it was not that entirely. He had a vast confidence in himself; his essence was wild and headstrong; yet he had a deep feeling of something missing. We were as different as two human beings could be; I came hard by judgments, he judged easily; he lived in a world of black and whites, I lived in a world of grays; he simplified, I saw nothing simple, nothing easy; he was as certain as I was uncertain, and I hated power as much as he loved it and needed it. Yet his deep need for someone like myself was evident—and basic to our working together.

On our way out to Arrowhead, he said to me, "Al, how would you put it to Klingman? You're new to this."

"Tell him he's going to die if he stays there. That ought to be convincing enough."

"No. No, it won't be. We're facing arrogance. There's nothing in the world as arrogant as a coal operator. Even small potatoes like Klingman. Why, I have known operators to tell me to my face that God appointed them stewards of

193

the earth's wealth—and that they knew better than I did what was good for their diggers. I tell Klingman he's going to die if he remains there, he won't believe me. He just won't."

He didn't. We drove up to the mine, and the day was as clear and bright as the last time I had been at the Arrowhead Pit. As we drove toward the road that led down into the crater, two men with rifles stepped out from behind rocks. When they saw that it was a police car with a uniformed driver, they let us pass, and we turned toward the entrance. It was true about the machine guns; at either side of the entrance road, at the lip of the crater, there was a nest of sandbags, each holding a Browning water-cooled gun and three men to serve it. Yet the emplacement was childish and thoughtless, as I pointed out to Ben.

"Why?" he wanted to know.

"Because it can be enfiladed, from the side and from across the crater. A machine gun is no good if you can get behind it. They're trying to defend a circle, but the way they're placed, the arc of both is only eighty or ninety degrees effective."

"We won't discuss that with Klingman. The hell with him. If he won't move, let him depend on his goddamn machine guns."

We were driving down the road that made a circular ramp inside the crater. Inside the crater, a whole village of tents had been constructed, as well as several shacks. As it turned out, ninety-two men were living there, all of them well armed, and there were six professional women, brought down from Chicago to ease the boredom of the nights. There were two big tank trucks to serve as the water supply, piles of canned goods in corrugated boxes, piles of smoked ham and sides of bacon, and at least fifty bushel baskets of potatoes and onions. No expense had been spared to make these Chicago imports comfortable, and indeed there appeared to be more food in that pit than in all of Pomax. A bar had been set up on two barrels, and a certain amount of bootleg whisky was sold there. For all that, there was no sense of

194

order or discipline about the place. It stank of excrement and swarmed with flies. The cots in the tents were unmade, and there was filth and refuse everywhere.

As we approached the cluster of tents, dozens of men with rifles moved toward us, but again, as up above, when they saw the police markings, they fell back. We parked at the bottom of the road, fifty feet or so from the tents, the giant steam shovel looming over us, and waited there as Klingman and his foreman, a freckled, redheaded man named Babe Jackson, well hated by everyone I heard speak of him, pushed through toward us. Each of them wore a revolver belted around his waist, and Klingman affected a wide-brimmed western hat, which he took off now to wipe his brow. The day had turned hot, and he was sweating.

We climbed out of the car. No one shook hands. There were nods of recognition, and Klingman said,

"You took a hell of a chance coming in here like that, Andy. This is private property. You got a warrant to come in here?"

"No warrant," drawled Lust. He too wore a gun at his hip; he was skinny, snakelike and dangerous, and he didn't frighten. "I just took a chance."

"Well, if you're looking for the man who shot the Duffey boy, you won't get him. Matter of fact, we don't know who he is ourselves. Them Duffey kids were trespassing, and a dozen men shot at them."

"I figure to find out who he is," Lust said lazily. "All in good time. Right now, we want to prevent some murders." He turned to Ben. "Tell him about it."

"Just this, Klingman," Ben said. "There are almost a thousand armed men in Pomax right now, diggers, and more coming in every hour. You know the kind of men who live in Egypt. They don't wave guns for excitement. They never touch a gun unless it's hunting season or they're very angry. Right now, they're very angry. They don't like the murder of a kid who wasn't doing any harm—just a curious kid. They don't like this kind of Chicago scum brought down here to

195

break a strike and given machine guns and rifles. They don't like it a bit, and I imagine they plan for something to happen out here. If it does, not one of you will leave this pit alive. I don't want that. Andy Lust doesn't want it—and I don't think you want it. So we're here to tell you to get out. We were ready to furnish cars, but you have enough trucks to do it yourself. We want you out of here and out of the county before dark."

Jackson, the foreman, grinned and said, "Listen to him talk, Mr. Klingman."

Klingman said, "Don't make me laugh."

"We wouldn't try to make you laugh," Lust said.

"No? Well, let me tell you this—and it goes for you, Andy, and for Ben Holt and that whole goddamn Bolshevik union of his. This is private property. We are on this property, and we have the legal right to defend it from intrusion. Don't try to frighten me with a pack of ignorant diggers with shotguns. We have two machine guns, and a hundred well-armed, trained men. We're not moving. We stay here and we mine coal. So save your breath and get moving. And if you want your diggers to pay their union dues, keep them away from here!"

"That's it?" Ben asked.

"That's it."

"There might be one other way," the chief of police said. "You turn over to me the man who shot the Duffey kid, and I might have a fifty-fifty chance of taming those diggers. Maybe I can persuade them to legal ways if I can show them that there's some legal way to enforce a law against murder."

"I told you there's no way of ever finding out who fired that shot. But let me tell you this, Andy. If there's going to be trouble, you got an obligation to prevent it."

Lust grinned and shook his head. "No, sir. This is outside of town limits. Anyway, it would take the National Guard to protect you, Mr. Klingman, and then some."

"Don't feel sorry for us. We'll get along," Jackson said.

"You damn fools," Ben whispered. Then we got into the

196

car and drove up the ramp and back to Pomax. Lust said nothing on the way back. I suppose it hurts the ego of a chief of police to walk into a place that shelters a murderer and not to be able to do one blessed thing about it; and it probably hurt Lust more than the average. He was a man who was used to getting his own way with things, but then so was Ben Holt.

20

Things are only simple when you look at them in retrospect; when you are a part of a thing and you know that it will happen, you can also know the hopelessness of trying to prevent it from happening. But that isn't easy to explain. People make up their minds, and then they close all the shutters. Pomax was full of people who had made up their minds.

I had missed my lunch, but I didn't feel hungry. When we returned to the Union Building, Ben and the others went upstairs. I remained on the street. The first few days of a strike are good copy, but after a week or so, the newspapers have pulled out all the reporters; for the tedious business of maintaining a picket line and becoming hungrier is nothing the public is very interested in. There were no more reporters for me to persuade or to tell lies to, and a press release would have to wait for the rest of that day.

I walked down Lincoln Street, past the knots of armed men and past the Pomax House. The Civil War monument, occupying a corner of the main square, was surrounded by a low granite wall, and now every inch of this wall was occupied by armed miners who sat in a circle, knee to knee, and simply waited. In their blue jeans and long-sleeved blue work shirts, they were like a shabbily uniformed platoon, their faces bleak, their eyes hooded. The shaft over their heads contained the names of the men from Pomax who had fallen in battle—twenty-two names, as I once counted them, a great many, considering how small a town Pomax had then been; but even then, a mining town, where miners had volunteered and formed their own regiment and marched away. The whole train of thought engendered here made me feel sick and empty, the guns a symbolic signature underlining my existence. If I felt no closeness and relationship to these diggers, neither did I feel it toward anyone else; but neither did I believe that I could cure myself by leaving Ben Holt and the Miners Union. In a world of hatred, violence, and behavior that would shame animals, there were islands of repose and gentleness; but my desire for such refuge had disappeared.

Turning away from the square, I walked down a tree-shaded street, lined with old houses badly in need of paint. The children were coming home from school now, and the good weather had brought the women out of doors, but there were no men. I saw kids go into the houses and then leave the houses and head for the square.

The First Baptist Church was not a handsome building. Like the houses, it needed paint; it bore the soot-brand of Pomax; and unlike most churches in the East, it had neither a tower nor stained-glass windows. A man in dark trousers and shirt sleeves was turning the borders of the front walk, and when I stopped by him, he smiled apologetically and explained,

"I try to put in some flowers around this time of the year. They're the least expensive type of decoration. Mostly zinnias. We dry our own seeds." He was a tall man with a low-slung chin and large, sad brown eyes.

"Are you the pastor?" I asked him.

He nodded. "George Frayne," offering his hand. I told him my own name, and he said, "Oh yes—you're the new man at the union. How do you like it?"

"I'm afraid I never thought of it as anything I like or dislike."

"Oh?" He stared at me for a long moment, and then he observed that since it was so warm outside, I might care for a cool drink. I said I would, and he led me into the parish building, a small house alongside the church, no larger nor in any better condition than the miners' houses up the street. I was introduced to his wife, a woman of fifty or so, gray-haired, shy, retiring, and then we sat down on the back porch and she brought us some lemonade.

"You know what's going on out there?" I said to Frayne.

"Yes," he answered slowly. "I know."

"They'll probably attack the Arrowhead Pit tonight. I don't know exactly what will happen, but I do know that the men down in that crater haven't a chance. A lot of men are going to die, miners as well as the hoodlums they brought in from Chicago."

"That would be a terrible thing, wouldn't it, Mr. Cutter? But why do you bring it up here? Do you think I can do anything about it?"

"Can you?"

"Then I must ask you first why Ben Holt doesn't put a stop to this?"

"He tried," I said listlessly, now regretting whatever impulse brought me to beard this sad-eyed man. "I was out to the mine with him earlier today. He practically begged Klingman and his men to get out before anything started. They refused."

"That's all?"

"What else could he do?"

"He could have the miners call it off. He could stop them."

"How?"

"By talking to them. By putting himself against them and what they intend to do. They respect him. Many of them love him. They don't respect me, Mr. Cutter. They don't love me. Last Sunday, I preached to eleven people—eleven people, Mr. Cutter."

"I don't think Ben Holt could stop them."

"You mean he wouldn't stop them, Mr. Cutter. You mean he won't risk separating himself from them, turning them against him. He won't risk shaming them, because men never forget when they are shamed. Isn't that it?"

"No. I don't think so," I said.

"How old are you, Mr. Cutter?" he asked, almost apologetically.

"Twenty-six."

"I am fifty-one, Mr. Cutter. When I came here, fourteen years ago, I was a young man. Oh, I know—thirty-seven doesn't seem so young to you, but when you are thirty-seven, you will not feel very old, believe me. I felt young, and I was filled with confidence and hope. I am not a fire-and-brimstone preacher, Mr. Cutter. I believe in a God of love and compassion, and I came here to Pomax out of choice. I knew that Pomax had the reputation of a bleak and unlovely place, and I felt that such a place needed hope and faith. But, do you know, Mr. Cutter, there was nothing I could give to Pomax. You cannot win love or respect from hungry men unless you feed them, and you cannot read a funeral service over a dead miner and ignore the conditions that killed him. I can do nothing to stop what is going to happen. After all these years, I am alone in Pomax. I have spent many years brooding over whether that is my fault or the fault of what I try to teach. I am alone but Ben Holt is not alone. We both minister to a sick world, and my medicines are useless. It is up to him, Mr. Cutter, not to me—and I cannot tell you how ashamed it makes me to say so."

21

By five o'clock, the streets of Pomax were empty. The Duffey boy had been buried and the armed miners were gone. A disquieting stillness hung over the town. In the distance I heard the mournful wail of the five-fifteen train from Chicago, and it was answered across the fields by the faint cry of crows. From the Union Building, the only human being visible was Shutzman, the butcher, who stood in front of his pork store in his blood-stained apron.

Upstairs, in the outer office, Oscar Suzic and Lena Kuscow stared moodily at each other. When she saw me, Lena said,

"Join the wake, Brother Cutter. We got almost enough now for a poker game."

"I'll buy you some supper," I said to her.

"I'm not hungry." She pushed a bag of pretzels toward me. "Help yourself. Be my guest."

I munched the pretzels and asked them where Ben was.

"He and Grove and Mullen drove over to Cairo."

"What? Why in hell's name did they go to Cairo at a time like this?"

"Al, grow up," Lena said tiredly. "It's going to happen tonight if it's not happening already, and Ben can't afford to be here when it does happen. There's nothing he can do now to stop it from happening, and it's best for everyone if he's not here."

"If he's not here? He's the only one who can do anything."

"What? What can he do?" Suzic demanded.

I shook my head hopelessly.

"I'll tell you what he can do," Lena said flatly. "Just what he's doing. Keep clear of the whole thing. Not be implicated. This isn't the end of the world. There's still the strike. There's still the union."

"All right. But I'm going out there," I said.

"Why?"

"Because one of us has to see what happens. Otherwise, we're blind."

"Al," Lena said, "if you go out there and try to interfere, they'll beat the living daylights out of you. Don't you understand that? You're new here. Even after five years, these diggers wouldn't trust you. As it is, they think you're some kind of a company spy."

"I'm not going to interfere. I just want to see what happens."

"Ben said we were to stay here in the building," Suzic insisted.

"You stay here," Lena said. "I'm going with Al, because at this point it would only complicate things for him to get his head broken. We'll get back as soon as we can."

Lena had an old Model T, which she drove with great competence and which she kept in the livery stable behind the Pomax House. In a few minutes, we were on the road out to Arrowhead, and halfway there, we heard the distant sound of rifle fire. I asked Lena where Police Chief Lust and his force were. "In the station house, where they will remain, you can be sure. There must be a thousand men out at the mine now, Al. Not just miners, but farmers too. The farming around here is nothing to write home about, but the farmers make out by selling their produce directly to the miners. Now there's no money to buy anything."

A half a mile from the mine, some trucks and cars and wagons were grouped on the side of the road. There were also more than a hundred bicycles, and a good many youngsters and about a dozen women. They had fires going, heating cans of coffee, and on a trestle table they had set up, they were making sandwiches. A steady trickle of miners moved back and forth, from the crater to the camp and from the camp to the crater. The firing was very heavy and very close now, but the people in the camp, sheltered by a fold of rock, paid little attention to it—except for the women screaming dire threats at any kid who showed signs of wandering.

Lena parked by the other cars, exchanged greetings with some of the women and some of the miners, and then followed me toward the lip of the open mine. A few hundred feet from the edge of the crater, we saw a dozen or so miners running toward us, and then, behind them, there was a tremendous explosion, a lifting mushroom of rock and dirt and a cloud of smoke. At the sound of the explosion, I flung Lena down, myself next to her, the reaction on my part being instinctive and going back to that experience in my life which had left its deepest mark on me. Dirt and rocks pattered around us. We sat up, unharmed, and the miners who had been running toward us were grinning and smacking their hands with delight. As more and more miners converged on where we were, one of those who had run toward us shouted for them to get back to the road and stay there. Among all of them, I saw only one wounded man, he with a bandage around his arm.

If the miners mistrusted me, they talked readily to Lena, and we learned what had happened. Almost half of the miners had seen service during the war, and they were not impressed with machine guns. They had divided their forces in half, and had sent one half around to the opposite lip of the crater. The sun was low by then and to their backs, making it almost impossible to see them clearly at a distance of six or seven hundred yards, and when they had taken their positions, they opened heavy fire on the rear of the machine-gun emplacement. Under this provocation, the men in the machine-gun emplacement turned their guns completely around to sweep the opposite edge of the mine, and no sooner had they altered their position than a miner raced down the road and threw a bundle of twenty sticks of dynamite with a short fuse between the two nests. They didn't see him until he had started back, and then, apparently unaware of the dynamite, they opened fire on him with side arms. As he was running and leaping from side to side, the pistol fire missed him completely. A moment later, the dynamite went off, destroying the machine-gun emplacement, the men in it, and a section of the road. The miner who had thrown the dynamite suffered no other damage than bruises when he was flung on his face by the concussion.

To understand what was happening and what would happen, one must realize the frustration and bitterness of those miners of the Pomax area. Hungry, desperate, and with a growing awareness that their strike was hopeless in the face of the river of coal flowing north from the southern pits, they were filled with an increasing anger that had no outlet. They were not for the most part, as in the East, immigrants or a first generation. The majority of them stemmed from the pioneer population movement into Illinois in the early years of the nineteenth century, and now they were full of a sense of being singularly dispossessed, of being those who had planted seed but had no harvest. Unlike the West Virginians, they had not lived their generations in a mountain fastness that the world passed by; they were no backwash, but squarely in the center of the great basin of middle-western wealth, from which they gleaned only the scrapings, and their anger against the operators was part of their anger against the cities, against the vast Chicago complex to the north, that owned in absentia and squeezed blood in absentia. The big strip mine that continued to dig coal in a place where every other pit was closed down by their strike had been for weeks the focus of their attention and hatred.

It was no new thing for thugs and hoodlums to be brought in to break strikes, but in Egypt it was new; in Egypt, the miners had guns, and always their guns had been an unquestioned part of their existence. They hunted small game in the canebrake and the worthless second-growth scrub, but even if they had never hunted, they would have considered the guns a normal part of their existence; and when a seventeen-year-old boy was shot and killed by the men in Arrowhead, something inside of these Pomax diggers exploded.

During all the years that have passed since then, I've turned over and over in my mind the question of whether Ben Holt could have stopped it. I don't know; I didn't know then, and I still don't know. I made one poor effort of my own, talking to a leader of the miners during the attack. He replied to me,

"Cutter, it's time for this. You can't stop a thing when it's time for it. You're here, but so help me God, don't interfere with us. Leave us alone."

We went up to the lip of the crater, where the miners were sprawled on their bellies, shooting down into the cluster of tents and trucks. Where the machine-gun emplacement had been, there was now a hole in the road and six mangled, shattered bodies. The sun was dipping below the farther rim of the crater when we got there, and all of the bottom of the mine was in deep shadow, but we could see darker shadows here and there where dead men lay. From the mine itself, there was a certain amount of firing, and as the darkness increased, you could see the pinpoints of light; but this firing from the bottom of the pit had no effect, and it was only by chance that one or two of the shots from below took a toll of the miners. Klingman and his Chicago gunmen had chosen an utterly indefensible position, a stupid, thoughtless position, in which they had no cover at all and faced an enemy whose cover was excellent and whom they could not see.

Gradually, the miners spread out around the whole rim of the pit. They were in high spirits, released from the tension of inaction, facing something they could see and hate and kill; and in the deepening twilight, their voices echoed back and forth. It was like a shooting match, with pinpoints of light down below as the targets. At this time, the men from Chicago had taken refuge beneath the trucks and the steam shovel. We could hear their voices clearly as they cursed the miners and flung up their empty threats, but by now it was almost impossible to see them. Then we heard a motor started, and the lumbering tread of a piece of machinery. I guessed that it was something on a caterpillar carriage, and in a few minutes a bulldozer, its blade held high, appeared as a blurred image on the road out of the crater. Immediately it became a target for a hundred guns, and we heard the scream of a man who was hit. Then the miners dropped a bundle of dynamite over the crater edge, and with a roar, tractors and road went up in a fountain of rock and smoke. The explosion echoed and re-echoed back and forth across the crater, while from the darkness below came the screaming hatred of the men trapped there.

Night fell. From below, there were no more shots and no sound of voices, as if they had finally realized that their only hope was in the darkness. In the black bottom of the pit, one could still make out, although vaguely, the lighter blurs that were the tents and the darker blurs that marked the trucks and machinery, and from around the rim, there was intermittent fire at these targets. Then a miner came by and told them to stop firing until they got the signal, although what the signal would be I didn't know. Silence settled down over the mine, broken only by the voices of the miners and the sound of their movement in the darkness. I noticed now that opposite the place where the road debarked from the crater, miners were gathering brush and deadwood together into two large piles. At this point the man who had spoken to me before came back and said,

"What do you intend to do, Cutter?"

"What can I do?"

"That ain't what I asked. What do you intend to do?"

"I'll tell you what I think," I replied with disgust. "I think you've had your pound of flesh. There are maybe twenty, thirty dead men in that pit now—"

"Why don't you shut up, Al?" Lena snapped at me.

"—yes, twenty or thirty. That's enough, isn't it?"

"Let us decide when it's enough, Cutter," he said coldly. There was a circle of miners around us now, listening. "What in hell's your position that you talk so big?"

"I work for the union. That's my whole position."

"We don't work—we're on strike, remember? How many strikes have you sat through, Cutter? How many kids have you watched starve? You ever been hungry, Cutter?"

"Oh, leave him alone," Lena said. "He's all right. Maybe what he says makes some sense."

At that moment, one of the wounded men in the mine began to scream. We stopped talking, held momentarily by that wild wail of pain. I felt my stomach contract with horror. Less than five years ago, I had stepped off the train at a tiny coal town in West Virginia, and since then the story of coal had been for me an unremitting procession of terror, blood-shed, and death. I had seen cruelty and insanity compounded and then compounded again. Without mercy or logic, an endless war went on for the black gold that was the food and blood of what we so lightly called civilization. It had brought me a woman to love and then had taken her; it had given me hope and despair, and now, in a night as savage as any in the so-called Dark Ages, it was placing an added fillip on its bloody history.

"How can we leave him alone?" the miner said. "Look when he's seen. Do you want him to testify against us?"

"He won't testify," Lena said.

"Talk for yourself, Cutter."

"Don't threaten me," I said. "I didn't come out here to testify. I came out here because I still think the only hope in this whole rotten business is the union—if there's any union left after this."

"It would be a lot easier to kill you."

"Sure. Who else? You'd have to kill her too. Where do you stop? Why don't you use your brains? Why don't you think?"

Another miner said, "Leave him alone! For Christ's sake, don't get us started against each other! Leave him alone!"

That broke it up, and they moved away. I took Lena's arm, and she was trembling all over. "Oh, my God," she whispered. "Oh, Holy Jesus—I never want to get closer to dying than that. Let's get out of here, Al. Please—please, let's get out of here. You be a hero sometime all by yourself. For me, this hero business is overrated. Just let's get out of here."

"All right," I agreed. "I've seen enough."

At that moment, a flare exploded. It was an army flare, part of the surplus that was still sold at that time in the army and navy stores, and someone had fired it up over the pit. A second flare followed and then a third, and like a chain of blazing diamonds they drifted down into the crater. Night turned into day, and suddenly, the whole bottom of the crater was visible. The Chicago hoodlums had come out of their hiding places under the trucks and equipment. Some of them were standing around in little clusters; others were sprawled on the ground; still others had made their way in the darkness to the wall of the crater and were slowly and painfully climbing up the rough shelving in an attempt to get out of the crater and escape. The flares caught them where they were, blinded and frozen in bewilderment and uncertainty—but only for an instant; then they broke and ran wildly for cover, all, that is, except those on the inner face of the mine. They could not run. They were frozen where they were, like beetles pinned on a board.

And then, from the whole rim of the crater, the miners' rifles blazed out. The roar of gunfire was like the sound of a full-scale battle in progress, and as the first flares faded, a fourth and fifth and sixth arched over the pit. The men on the side walls fell, some of them clawing at the rock edges and dirt, others rolling down like bundles of rags. Of the men on the mine floor, some gained the safety of the trucks and machinery; others rolled over and lay where they dropped.

Lena was pulling at me, and I went with her now. As we stumbled through the darkness, I could feel her reaction, a convulsive sobbing that the gunfire muted. The car wasn't hard to find. There were fires blazing at the parking place, just as there would be fires blazing at the top of the road, in case anyone should be alive to make his way out of that hole, and here women still dispensed food and coffee, good women, their faces drawn with toil and poverty and the premature aging of the miner's wife. Lena asked me whether I could drive a Model T, and when I said that I could, she sighed with relief.

We drove back toward Pomax. We must have gone more than halfway before the gunfire was reduced to the sound a crackling fire makes. Then Lena burst into tears. I pulled off the road, stopped the car, gave her a cigarette, and took one myself. She drew in the smoke hungrily, trying to control her sobbing. I offered her my handkerchief, and after she had dried her eyes, she sighed and said slowly,

"You know, Al Cutter, you're quite a guy."

I've had very few compliments in my time. This was one of the best.

208

22

About ten o'clock, we pulled up in front of Ben Holt's house. Dorothy must have been watching, because she had the door open as we came up the steps. She was distraught and magnified her own fears about Ben, and she begged us to tell her what had happened. Very briefly, I did, not in all detail but in the general sense that there had been a fight between the diggers and the strikebreakers brought down from Chicago, and that their fight still continued although there was no question about its outcome.

"Then why isn't Ben here?" she burst out.

"You know that, don't you? You know where he is."

"He's in Cairo. I know that—but he should be here."

"He's not here, Mrs. Holt," I said, "because he can't be implicated in all this. If he is, that's the end of the union. Completely the end. I guess he did the only thing he could think of doing. Have you heard from him?"

"He called about a half hour ago."

"Where's he staying?"

"At the Parker House."

Lena told her that I hadn't eaten all day, and she led us into the kitchen where she poured milk and made sandwiches. I had no appetite until I began to eat, and then I found that I was ravenous. Dorothy watched me, and after a while she said,

"You weren't telling me the truth, were you, Mr. Cutter?"

"What do you mean?"

"About what happened out there at Arrowhead. It was a slaughter, wasn't it?"

I shook my head. "I don't know, Mrs. Holt. We didn't stay until the end. I just don't know."

When we finished eating, we left, to put Lena's car away for the night, and then to go back to the Union Building.

Lena said to me, "How do you suppose a woman like that came to marry Ben Holt?"

"I never thought of it. Maybe she loves him—did you ever think of that?"

"Don't jump all over me, Al. It's a funny world where mostly you don't end up marrying someone you love."

Lights were on all through the Union Building, the doors open, and quite a few miners there now. Whether they were men who had come back from Arrowhead or never gone there, I didn't know; but whispers of what took place had preceded us. There are winds bad news rides on; I have never known it to fail.

Going up the stairs, we met Andy Lust on his way down, and he stopped me and said, "This is a hell of a business, Cutter, with everyone gone. Where in hell's name is Ben Holt and the others?"

"I don't know."

"My uncle's elbow, you don't know! Where is he, Lena?"

"He didn't tell me."

"Were you two out at Arrowhead?"

"We just finished having dinner with Mrs. Holt," I said.

"You eat dinner late, Cutter, don't you? You're full of fancy ways. The way I hear it, there's been a slaughter out at the Arrowhead mine, but you don't know a God damn thing about it, do you? Well, just in case you talk to Ben Holt, tell him I got my neck to think about. I can't sit on this. If I don't call upstate now and ask for help, I'm finished."

"I can't help you, Chief."

He stormed on down, and we went into the outer office, where Oscar Suzic and Dan Jessup, a dry, thin-faced man of sixty or so who was president of the local union attached to the International, faced the mayor, newspapermen from nearby towns, two members of the council, and three or four others who were strangers to me. He threw us a hopeless, desperate glance, but we pushed past him without stopping and into Ben's private office. Oscar joined us there, and said

210

to me, "This your job, Al. I don't know what to tell them. So help me God, I don't!"

"Poor Oscar," Lena said. "Oh, what a fine bunch of representative trade-union characters we are! Al here was almost shot by a firing squad, and I've had the shakes for two hours now. Doesn't Ben keep a bottle somewhere in his desk? I need a drink like I've never needed one." She found the bottle in the desk, and poured liquor into paper cups. It was plain bootleg sugar alcohol, raw and hot, but it tasted good that night. I told Suzic that I knew no better than he did what to tell the people outside. "This is nothing," I added. "Before the night's over, the whole world's going to move in on Pomax. This town is going to be famous. But right now, the thing to do is to try to get some medical aid out to the mine, just in case some of them survive." But we couldn't solve that. There were two doctors in Pomax and we called both of them. Both of them refused to go out to Arrowhead at this time of the night. They knew what was happening out there, and they didn't want to be involved. They didn't want to be put on a witness stand to name the miners they had recognized.

Oscar and Lena went back to the outer office to try to answer questions and divert questions, and I called Ben at the Parker House in Cairo. He was there, and I suppose he was waiting for me to call. I told him what we had seen, and he promptly told me what a damn fool I had been to have gone out to the mine at all. But I was in no mood to listen and I told him that at least I had seen what happened there, which was better than trying to operate on the basis of rumors and secondhand stories. He softened somewhat and said to me,

"Al, I just can't believe that they were all killed. There were almost a hundred men in that pit. What about the women?"

"When a thousand crazy men are shooting in the dark, they can't bother to be chivalrous."

He said that he and the others would be back by nine in

211

the morning. When I asked him what our position would be, he replied that our position was plain enough. The union leadership had done everything in its power to persuade Klingman and his men to leave the mine. They had refused. The union had absolutely no part in what followed. Then he said, "Wait a minute, Al." I heard a whispered conference at the other end, and then,

"Al, what about the communists?"

"What about them?"

"Do you suppose they were involved?"

"Ben, I don't know any communists. I didn't know there were any in Pomax."

"All right," he agreed. "Play it carefully and cool as it comes. Don't make any statements. Tell the press that I'll have a statement and put them off."

"I'll try," I said. "Ben, I'll try."

Then he offered a few words of praise. That too was in the nature of Ben Holt. A few words of praise from him made you forget all that had led up to the praise. You felt proud and rewarded—or at least you felt that way if you were young enough.

Lena came back into the room, to tell me that she had disconnected the switchboard for the moment. Calls were coming in steadily by now, from Springfield, from the state police, from Washington, from the United Press and the Associated Press. She didn't know what to do. Did I?

"No, I don't," I admitted. And then I asked her about the communists.

"Not in Pomax," she said. "Not that I ever heard of, Al. There are a few in the union, but not enough to even make a ripple. Why do you ask?"

I shrugged it off and said that we'd have to open the switchboard and try to do something with the calls. Then I got Oscar Suzic aside and told him to keep his mouth shut about Lena and myself being out at Arrowhead. As far as he was concerned, he knew nothing about it.

From then on, it got worse and worse, and it was three

212

o'clock in the morning before we were able to close up the building and get some sleep. By then, we had managed to get an ambulance from the county hospital out to Arrowhead, and we had also learned that three men and one woman had survived. They were all badly injured, and it was not believed that the woman would live through the night. She died the next day, as did one of the men. Two of the men, both of them drifters from Chicago, flophouse alcoholics, survived. Klingman and his foreman, Jackson, both died in the crater.

Back in the hotel, I left word to be awakened at seven. Then I fell on my bed, too tired to take my clothes off, and for a few hours slept the sleep of utter exhaustion.

23

As I walked from the hotel to the Union Building the next morning, I saw the first detachments of the National Guard debarking from the train at the station; by midday, Pomax was a town under military occupation and the Pomax House host to an increasing congregation of reporters from all over the state and many more from outside the state. By nine o'clock, Ben Holt, Jack Mullen, and Fulton Grove were back in their offices, and by ten, Fulton Grove was telling an audience of reporters that the bloody slaughter out at Arrowhead was the work of communist agitators. When I put it to Ben and asked him how he could allow that kind of tripe to be handed out by Grove, he replied that so much was said about the communists already that a little more couldn't possibly hurt. I refused to include the charges in my own press releases, coming officially from the union, and we had a bitter argument about it. The argument was never finished, for that was a day of unending turmoil. Several of the newspapermen had somehow gotten wind of my being out at Arrowhead the night before, but I refused to affirm or deny this. Meanwhile, the bodies from Arrowhead were brought into Pomax, where an empty barn was converted into a mortuary. Rumor had it that two of the miners had been killed and several more wounded, but the bodies of these two were buried quietly and not publicly identified until months later.

Through that day and the days that followed, the union held firmly to its position, that we had tried to prevent trouble in the only way we knew, and that, failing there, we had no part in what followed. Police Chief Lust insisted that he had no knowledge of what happened at Arrowhead until it was over, that no calls for assistance had come into the police station, and that if, in any case, he had tried to stop the incident, he would have been leading his men into disaster as well as violating his territorial restrictions, since the mine was well out of the town limits. This last was debatable, since Lust had certain county privileges in an emergency, but he stood on it because it helped to support his general position.

Strangely enough, the chief effect of the Arrowhead Slaughter was felt outside of southern Illinois, particularly in Pennsylvania where it led to an immediate and brutal assault on the striking anthracite and bituminous miners, an assault that eventually smashed the strike and broke the power of the union in Pennsylvania. In those weeks that followed, Ben and I went to Pennsylvania five times, but we could only be witnesses to deepening poverty and increasing brutality. One after another, the pits opened, some with union miners who left the union, some with strikebreakers brought in from the South.

In Egypt, the strike held much longer, the miners drawn together in a dark and bitter unity. From the first day, they shared the guilt of Arrowhead and swallowed it among themselves and pressed it deep into their flattening bellies. Reporters and investigators roved town, but they could find no one who knew anything of what had happened the night before, or who had taken part in it, or who had spoken to anyone who had taken part in it. So far as the people of Egypt were concerned, the Arrowhead Slaughter had never happened, no one had killed anyone, and if there were dead

214

men, the cause of their death could not possibly be ascertained; so far as the miners were concerned, they had been home with their families, as the women and children testified.

Angry and frustrated, the newspapermen turned on me. I spent almost an hour at the mortuary because both Lust and Colonel Sevard, who commanded the National Guard detachments, insisted that someone from the union be there. I was supposed to identify bodies, but the only two I could recognize were Klingman and Jackson, and when they forced me to stare at the shattered remains of the men who had been blown to pieces by the dynamite, I mentally cursed Ben Holt and the day I had ever met him. The newspapermen were there, and they said to me, "Come on, Cutter, you were a working newspaperman, so give us a break and open up this goddamn business. What do you want us to do, take it all out on the union! Someone killed these men." I agreed that someone had killed them. The National Guard colonel was hating my guts, and he said that if he had his way, I and Ben Holt and the rest of the union officers would be hanging from the rafters of the same barn.

As yet, no one had come forward to identify bodies, or claim them or swear out a warrant for the arrest of anyone. Klingman lived in Chicago; whether he had relatives or not, I don't know; Jackson was out of state; almost all of the others were drifters and the kind of women that don't have families. It was a heartbreaking and terrible thing to see the bodies laid out as they were, but sadder to realize that in death, these people were as alone as they had been in life. They were strikebreakers and hired gunmen and flophouse drifters, but they were also the flesh of what had once been human, and I had no defense or retort when Sevard snarled at me, "Why don't you look at the women, Cutter? I want to see your face when you do. All the little birds around here say that you watched it happen. Did you lead it, Cutter? I'm told you were a big man in the war. Is this your idea of war, Cutter?"

Five weeks later, in Pennsylvania, thirty miles from Pittsburgh, I stood looking at the bodies of five miners beaten to death by coal-company police. But one didn't cancel another. Ben and I stood and looked at what had been a miner's family—that was a year later—and five children were skin and bone, dead from starvation in the United States in 1925, but still nothing canceled. Mullen roared at me that same evening, "For Christ's sake, those dames were hookers, the lowest kind of hookers!" It didn't balance any better.

I got out of that place of death, with the reporters crowding around me and pleading for a break, and I don't know whether I hated myself in my present position any more than I hated what I had once been—a working member of the press. The man from the Chicago *Tablet* said, "Let me tell you this, Cutter—you give us nothing, we give you nothing, not one inch. We'll cut your goddamn heart out—you and that lousy union of yours."

They did. That evening's *Tablet* carried the banner headline: MASS MURDER IN POMAX, and below: OUTRAGE WITHOUT PEER IN AMERICAN HISTORY, and the story under this read:

Last night, in Pomax, Ill., in an act of savage revenge that has no equal in our past, the miners of Pomax County gunned down a hundred miners of a rival union. The men who were killed, in a slaughter reminiscent of the Indian wars, were trapped in the Arrowhead Pit, an open-strip mine about five miles outside of Pomax. Of the hundred, only two survived. Five women, trapped in the pit with the miners, were also shot to death.

Local sources say that over two thousand armed miners took part in the attack, which adds the bloodiest chapter to the already bloody history of that part of the state known as Egypt. Almost every dead man was found to be carrying a membership card in the Associated Miners Union, a rival union to the larger International Miners Union. So far no clear-cut evidence has been unearthed to prove that the attack was mounted and carried out under the aegis of the International Miners Union, but the implication can hardly be avoided. Highhanded, powerful Ben Holt, president of the International Miners Union, who has already gained national notoriety in his constant defiance of law and order, disclaims any and all responsibility. Vice-President of the IMU, Fulton Grove, charges communist inspiration for the outrage. But it is more likely—

And so forth and so on. The other papers took the same line, some more strongly than others in the matter of direct accusation. A New York City tabloid said:

Justice can only be served by the indictment of the entire Pomax County membership of the IMU, on charges of murder in the first degree. Force must be met by force—if it means an armed federal invasion of Pomax County.

Another Chicago paper limited its charges to Ben Holt and the union leadership, thus:

"Ben Holt and the men around him must be made to stand trial for murder, and to prove under oath that they are innocent of this dastardly and heinous crime."

Thereby reversing the stipulation that a man is innocent until proven guilty.

At that time, I would have said that anything could happen as a result of this and I was pretty certain that a great deal would happen. The last thing in the world that I looked forward to was for nothing to happen, so far as Pomax and the miners of Pomax were concerned. But nothing happened. The state government was in an uproar over a series of scandals that had been coming to light during the past three years; the local judge and district attorney were up for re-election, and in Egypt, nine men out of ten who voted were miners. No indictment was ever brought forward, nor—not so strangely—did Gus Empek or Joe Brady make any statements or accusations. They were too deeply involved, and they preferred to wait their time. In any case, having so few members to begin with, their union was perishing more quickly than ours.

217

For a few weeks, the papers made the most of the Arrowhead Slaughter, and then other news became more important. It is surprising how quickly the whole matter was forgotten, but then other things were also forgotten. I once did some calculation on the decade of the 1920s, totaling up the number of miners killed by police, company police, private detectives, and strikebreakers. This total came to three hundred and forty-seven men, apart from those who died in mine accidents, or from rotten lungs or plain starvation. This too was forgotten in a surprisingly short time.

24

I guess no day was as long as that first day, yet it ended. Pomax had become a peaceful, quiet town, most of whose inhabitants remained indoors, and toward evening rain started. Both the local district attorney and Police Chief Lust testified to their ability to maintain law and order, and by nightfall, an order had come from upstate for the National Guard units to be withdrawn. At the same time, other National Guard units were moved into the eastern part of the county, where three collieries, with the assistance of more than two hundred armed private police, began to mine coal. It was the first major break in the strike in Egypt, but not the last.

Early that evening, during the first lull in the day's excitement, Ben Holt called me into his office, asked me to sit down, and offered me a cigar. His desk was covered with newspapers, releases, telegrams, the remains of a sandwich, and half a container of coffee; and he himself was disheveled, his suit rumpled and shapeless, his shirt gray and limp with two days' wear. For some reason, I felt the beginning of age in him, noticed the increasing streaks of gray in his hair and the first fold of a paunch around his waist—very little as yet, but beginning. We lit our cigars, and then he leaned back in his chair, put his feet up on the desk, and stared at me in a moody, quizzical manner that was not without humor.

"Well, Al," he said, "nothing but trouble since I first laid eyes on you. If I were superstitious, I might say you were bad luck."

"You could say that, Ben," I nodded. "You could also say that this whole rotten business of coal mining is bad luck— to anyone who touches it with a ten-foot pole."

"I could but I wouldn't," Ben sighed. "Hell no, I wouldn't. Was it Bobbie Burns who said that there is drama and meaning in the lives of kings and shepherds and not much of either in the lives of those who live in between? Or something of the sort. Don't knock coal, Al, because the dirty, filthy stuff is all the power and the glory that makes sense in the world today. I wouldn't want any other life."

"You might think differently if you spent a little while at Flexner's barn, where the bodies are. Did you see that, Ben?"

"I don't have to see it, Al," he replied softly. "I got just so many tears, and I'm not going to waste them on strike-breakers and hoodlums. I never liked Klingman alive, and he's no more to my taste dead. You could have all kinds of feelings about what happened out there at Arrowhead, but remember one thing, Al. The operators have their money, the police, and the National Guard and a cellar full of groceries at home. The miner's got only one weapon that counts, the strike, and when he sees that strike being broken, he's going to hit back. All right. What did happen out there at the mine? Tell me the whole story, all of it. Don't leave anything out."

I told him the story, all of it, every detail, and he listened without interrupting. When I finished, he sat in silence for a while; then he said to me, very quietly and directly,

"Do you think I could have prevented what happened out there, Al?"

I thought about it for some time before I said, "I don't know."

"But you're not sure that I couldn't have stopped it?"

"That's right, Ben. I'm not sure."

"I guess I could have stopped it," Ben said thoughtfully. "Maybe even short of bringing in the militia myself. I could have fought it out with the local leadership here. I could have threatened them, bullied them—and I could have gone out to the mine last night and fought it out on the spot. Oh, I don't say that I could have kept anything from happening. This isn't Pennsylvania. You can't come in here the way Klingman did and murder a miner's kid and walk out scot-free. It just isn't in the cards for Egypt, and things don't work that way. There would have been violence, but less of it and not the way it happened. But if I had thrown myself into it to stop it, all that would have been the end of my position here. You have to know miners to know about that —and you will, someday, but I don't think you do yet. One act of betrayal, one single act, and you're finished."

If I had known him longer, better, I might have asked him why he needed the leadership of that union so desperately—what it meant to him. If I had been a little older, I might have carried out my original resolve, that I would walk into his office and resign. I did neither.

The following evening, the same question was brought up somewhat differently. I was eating dinner alone at the Pomax House, when Mark Golden, who had just returned from Pennsylvania, and Lena Kuscow came in and asked whether they could join me. As I dislike eating alone, I was pleased and begged them to sit down. We talked for a while about the incident at Arrowhead. Golden had already spoken briefly to the district attorney and would see him again the next day, and I was relieved to hear that a possibility existed that no charges would be brought against anyone. "It's a very complicated business," Golden said. "Not only the boy being killed by the guards around the mine, but for a week before the actual attack on the mine, the guards had fired at anyone whose appearance they disliked. The laws of trespass do not include the right to shoot indiscriminately at any passer-by. The whole question of self-defense enters into it, and there are some interesting local statutes here that go back to the pre-Civil War days. Lena told me what happened out there, and that's one thing that can't be changed. But to let it destroy the union and everything these miners have fought for, well, that's something else entirely."

"Why is the union so important to you?" I asked him. "I mean that seriously—I mean I'm asking it because I'm puzzled. I don't really understand. I do understand to a certain degree about Ben and Mullen and Grove and Suzic— they were miners. I've listened to Ben talk about his life, his experience as a breaker boy, what he's seen in the mines —but you and Lena here, you're not miners—"

"And what about you, Al?" he interrupted. "Did you tell Ben you're leaving?"

"I'm not leaving."

"Then what keeps you here? Pomax is the bottom of creation. Your pay is miserable. What keeps you here?"

"That doesn't answer my question, because my own reasons are too complicated. It has to do with my wife and who she was and how she died, and with Ben and with other things. I'm younger than you are, Mark—and I stay on this job from day to day. I don't like to walk out of anything when the going gets rough. Maybe I'll be here next week and maybe I won't, but I don't feel about the union the way you do."

"No, I don't suppose you do," Mark nodded. "You see, all of us—Ben, Lena, and myself—we came out of the bottom. We came out of the hopelessness of poverty, and what is worse, out of the hopelessness of ignorance. It's hard to describe that to someone like you, Al, not because you had so much—I can pretty well guess what your background was like—but because you were a part of something that made sense and had meaning, with roots in the past and some kind of connection with the future. We didn't have that. No roots in the past, no connection with the future. I was born in 1878, on Hester Street, on the East Side of

New York, and I was born at home, in a lousy, ancient wooden tenement, because there was no money to pay a midwife, much less a doctor. I don't intend to bore you with my life history, and I don't know how much sense it would make to try to explain what it means to be a Jew in an East Side ghetto, with a father who died over his machine when I was ten years old and a mother who coped with five children and tuberculosis. Like Ben and the others, I survived, I got an education, I went through City College and I became a lawyer. But I didn't relish the law of survival. Three of my brothers didn't survive. That's not unusual, Al. Lena here was one of a family of seven children. Three survived. Her father worked in the slaughterhouses in Chicago, and sometimes he didn't work. One of her brothers starved to death —yes, in Chicago. So survival isn't all that it's cracked up to be. I survived and read law and passed my bar, and I eventually became a part of a very estimable and successful firm of lawyers. In 1912, I made over thirty thousand dollars, and I was beginning to collect a fine portfolio of securities, as well as other investments calculated to make certain that I never slid back into the ghetto I had climbed out of. I also acquired a wife, who had never been faced with the necessity of putting the law of survival to a test. She was a beautiful woman, and I suppose that for a while she loved me, but my own trouble was in the past. I couldn't forget and I couldn't adjust, and because of this a number of things happened. My wife left me, and I left the law firm. My wife was well taken care of, and she bears me no malice and I bear her none. Indeed, I am grateful to her for curing me of the beginning of a penchant for collecting things. I took this job with Ben, because it's the first job I ever really wanted, and probably the first time in my life that I have ever been at least partly content. As for the union, which started this long outburst of mine—why, Al, to me it's simply an instrument for human dignity as opposed to the old-fashioned law of survival. I don't idealize it, I don't glamorize it, and in many ways, the men who were my partners in the law firm in New York were as decent and honorable as the men who lead this union. It's just that I sleep poorly as a part of a law firm and I sleep well as a part of a union."

"And what happened at Arrowhead doesn't disturb you?"

"Of course it disturbs me, Al! It's a nightmare! I hate violence, I loathe violence! I think there's no cause that honors or justifies murder, whether it's illegal murder that's called crime, the judicial murder they call execution, the social murder called poverty, or the political murder that is so euphemistically called war and filed under the heading of patriotism. I look at all of them with equal loathing. But what happened at Arrowhead is an effect that is not without cause, and a precedent of cause and effect that reaches back through the whole bloody history of coal mining. That doesn't lessen or efface what happened, but it does put it apart from sheer barbarism and savagery, and it allows for understanding. The only way such things will stop happening is for the miners to have a union strong enough to allow them the dignity of living like human beings. I know as well as you what Ben's role in this was, and maybe I know Ben Holt a little better than you do. I don't judge him. He wants a union, I want a union. Men like myself don't build unions and lead others; men like Ben Holt do."

25

For three weeks, I was in western Pennsylvania with Ben Holt, and for part of the time Golden was with us. Lena came down for a week to help us take depositions, and I remember one pleasant day the four of us spent in Pittsburgh, sharing a good dinner and then an excursion trip up and down the rivers in a tourist boat. It was a few hours of pleasure in what was essentially an unpleasurable time. Yet those days brought me very close to Ben Holt. I was with him constantly, day and night. We shared the same room in a miner's shack, and for twenty-four hours once, we shared the same cell in the Iron City jail. We worked together, which is, I suppose, the best way to know a man. A newspaper story of the time referred to me as Ben Holt's errand boy, and it was not without truth. I ran errands, but I also arranged interviews, handled the press, carried on correspondence, developed my diplomatic faculties with every type of law-enforcement agency, from policemen to company detectives, hired halls, and arranged meetings. It was a curious job, but there were times when I enjoyed it, and I prided myself that I was getting better at it. Among other things, at that time, I arranged for Ben to see an important coal operator in Pittsburgh. It was Ben's feeling that if one strong and powerful operator were to sign an agreement with the union, it would make an important opening wedge, and unlike some trade-union leaders of the time, he was not averse to talking with the owners. Every conceivable accusation has been thrown against Ben Holt except one—that he would make a deal with an operator to sell out his union; and because the thought itself could not take shape in his mind, he met with the operators frequently, argued with them, swore at them and denounced them in their own living rooms. In this case, the meeting was to no effect; but arriving at the man's offices before Ben did, I was invited in and had a few minutes alone with him. He asked me what my job was, and I tried to explain it to him.

"In other words," he said, when I finished, "it's up to you to make the union taste sweet in the public's mouth and to keep the horns off Ben Holt's image?"

"Yes, that's part of it."

"I like that, but you'll have one hell of a time. How would you like to work for me? Do for me what that cookie in New York does for John D. Rockefeller. I'll even give away the dimes."

I shook my head.

"I'll double your pay."

"No, thank you. I have an obligation to Ben Holt that I haven't worked off yet."

224

"When you work it off, come and see me," he grinned.

But a few minutes later, he and Ben were shouting at each other and threatening each other, and I think we both forgot his offer.

Back from Pennsylvania, I plunged into my work at Pomax. The strike did not formally end; bit by bit, it disintegrated, and one after another, the various locals of the union voted to abandon the strike and return to work. Summer came, as hot and bleak in Pomax as anywhere in the country, and Ben left for Colorado to attempt to salvage what remained of the union in the West. Life at Pomax consisted of hard work, dull evenings, and very little to look forward to; but in that same process, I learned a good deal about the coal industry, its history in America, its manner of development, and the attempt of its workers to create a union of some strength and consequence. I came to know the miners, and I had the feeling that after the Arrowhead incident, they began to trust me just a little.

As for the men who worked with me, I could never penetrate the strange shell that enclosed Fulton Grove or decide whether it was compounded out of reserve or stupidity. I fell into a working accord with Jack Mullen and the beginning of what was to be a long friendship with Oscar Suzic.

A month after the Arrowhead incident, when it became apparent that the union would not win the strike, the National Confederation of Labor denounced Ben Holt and the Miners Union. The denunciation was couched in insulting and angry terms, and I begged Ben to answer it in kind. Fulton Grove opposed me, and we had our first serious argument. The denunciation remained unanswered, and Grove and I continued on the coldest terms of forced cordiality.

I suppose that this period of my life was an important time of growth and change, even though so little happened. Yet there was one thing, and I can hardly avoid it. If this is a story of Ben Holt, it is also myself doing the telling.

Almost every Sunday, I was out on the bicycle, which Abner Gross had practically surrendered to me by the right of sole usage. I think I explored every road and track and path within ten miles of Pomax, but not until mid-July did I find Dorothy Holt again. I suppose there was never a time when I rode out without having in mind the possibility and hope that I would see her. This, I rationalized to myself. She was a charming person, and I was desperately lonely —and it was no more than that. I met her this time alongside a little pool or lake which, for all its stagnant and motionless water, made a shadowed and pleasant spot in the generally unlovely countryside. She had dropped her wheel, and was standing pensively by the water when I rode up; and she turned to me, and smiled, almost as if she had been expecting me. She had a quality of calm acceptance that never failed to astonish me, and although we had not seen each other for weeks, she simply nodded and said,

"How nice to see you again, Mr. Cutter."

"It's all my pleasure." I don't know whether my appearance showed it, but I felt as excited as a schoolboy.

"It does seem that the only way to meet each other is to resort to bicycles. It's been so very hot, and this place is cool and delightful, don't you think?"

"It's a very nice place," I agreed. "I didn't know it existed until today."

"Neither did I. So it does seem that fate is determined for us to meet each other. Tell me what you have been doing all this time."

We sat down on a fallen tree trunk, and I talked more than I had in a long time. She listened well, as if truly interested—which she might have been—while I poured out my experiences. At last, I paused to protest that certainly I was boring her to tears.

"No, you're not boring me," she said softly. "Not at all, Mr. Cutter."

"You never talk about yourself."

"No? I suppose I don't. I lead a very uneventful life, Mr. Cutter, which is mostly occupied with the raising of three children."

"Still, you're Ben Holt's wife—"

"Yes, I'm Ben Holt's wife, as you put it, Mr. Cutter. And Ben is in the way of being an idol of yours, isn't he, Mr. Cutter?"

"Well, I wouldn't put it just that way—not an idol exactly. I think he's quite a man—"

"And therefore, his wife must be quite a woman?"

"You're laughing at me, aren't you?" I said.

"No, not laughing, Mr. Cutter. I have nothing to laugh at, not even your attempt to bestow some glamour upon me as the wife of Ben Holt. When have you last seen Ben, Mr. Cutter?"

"A week ago, just before he left for Colorado."

"That was when I saw him—and before then, not for weeks, and when he's here in Pomax, Mr. Cutter, if we have two hours of Ben at dinner, we are fortunate. Do you feel that I shouldn't speak of this to you or to anyone else? That it's an act of betrayal toward Ben?"

"No—well, no. I mean—"

"I'm a very lonely woman, Mr. Cutter, and I don't talk about myself because there is nothing that I want very much to discuss. I married a trade-union leader, and I live in Pomax, Illinois, and all of this is of my choosing and I should have nothing to complain about. At least, that is the way I see it, and at this moment I thoroughly despise myself."

"Why?" I cried. "For heaven's sake, why?"

"Because I am so delighted to have you here with me—to have the companionship of a man and a human being, even for a few hours."

We were both silent for a while after that. She was not the type of woman who resorts to tears, and I don't know that I have ever seen her weep. After a time, I said,

"If that's the case, do you suppose that you could call me Al? And that I could call you Dorothy?"

Turning to me, she smiled and asked me, "How old are you, Al? I knew, but I've forgotten."

"I was twenty-seven last week."

"I'm only six months older than you, but it feels like so much more. You're very nice, you know."

We walked most of the way back to Pomax, wheeling our bicycles, just slowly and talking about one thing and another as if we had known each other a very long time. We made a tentative appointment to meet a week later and ride together.

26

The following Sunday, we rode out to the Arrowhead Pit. At one time, I had been certain that I would never want to see this place again as long as I lived, and now something drew me back there. I think Dorothy felt the same way, because she made no protest when I suggested that we go there. When we came to the mine, we wheeled our bikes up to the edge of the crater, looked at it for a little while, and then turned away. It had not changed very much. The road had been repaired, and the mine was being worked again, and there were more trucks and a second steam shovel down at the bottom. Non-union men were working the mine, and as far as this place was concerned, the strike was over.

As we walked away from there, Dorothy said, "I don't feel anything. That's strange."

"Not so strange. I don't feel anything much. It's just like a dream, that's all."

"Is a great deal of life just like a dream, Al? I feel that way sometimes."

"I don't know. I wonder."

"I've never asked you about your wife, Al. Is it something you don't want to talk about?"

"I don't like to talk to most people about it. As far as you're concerned, Dorothy—I don't think there's anything I couldn't talk to you about."

"You loved her very much, didn't you?"

"Yes, I did. Very much."

"Ben told me about how you met—how she was hurt and you took her through that roadblock to the hospital. I'm ashamed of the way I complained last week. You must be lonely."

"No. It's been lonely, but I'm all right now."

"What does all right mean, Al?" I glanced at her sharply, and she added, "I want to know. Maybe I want to say that I am also all right now."

"Well—it means—I don't know. I suppose it means that I've learned how to live with myself, how to be alone."

"Philosophically? Is that it, Al? Do you look forward to long, comfortable years of being alone?"

"No," I snapped.

"I'm sorry, Al. We'll forget that we ever spoke about this."

Now I tried to apologize and persuade her that she did not understand.

"What don't I understand, Al?"

Of course she knew. She knew and she was pushing me toward it, and that was because she couldn't help herself any more than I could, and she was pressing toward the point where I would say, "Because I love you, Dorothy Holt. Because I am caught in something that makes me sick with shame and guilt, for it seems to me that all at once I am betraying a man I have come to consider the best friend I have in the world, and betraying my wife's memory too." And it was in no spirit of virtue that I refused to be pushed the last bit into an open expression. It was because I knew that at such a point, it would be over between us.

Then, after that, I lived with Dorothy Holt more than I lived with Laura. Laura was dead and Dorothy Holt was alive. But it was a question of dreams, and I lived with Dorothy Holt nowhere else but in my dreams, quite sensibly aware in my waking moments that she was the wife of Benjamin R. Holt, the mother of three children and the last person in the world who could make any constructive difference in my life. Or perhaps my waking approach was less sensible than hopeless.

I was glad that the work I did was demanding. As the summer drew to a close, the strike in Pomax collapsed, and at a meeting of the International leadership and Egypt's local leadership, it was decided to vote a back-to-work order and see what could be salvaged of union membership. At this point, the beginning of an increasing despair that was to continue for years to come, only Ben Holt remained confident and unshaken. His ferocity and brutal handling of all opposition changed into something almost as gentle as it was enduring. He coaxed, supported, and had faith. In southern Illinois, the heart and strength of the union movement, we had lost 50 per cent of our membership. What it would be in the rest of the country, we could only guess—and expect the worst. But when Fulton Grove raised the question of the total destruction of the union, Ben, without anger, replied,

"That never happens—not any more. They may get rid of you and me, Fulton, but not of the union. It will survive."

It survived. By November, we had completed a national membership-and-dues drive. From better than three hundred thousand members, the union had shrunk to a total national membership of a hundred and six thousand. And of those, almost half were black-listed, locked out of work.

I saw Dorothy during that time, but only once when Ben was not present, and that was when some business took me to her house, and I stayed for supper and spent the evening playing with the children and then talking. Nothing passed between us.

Christmas at Ben's house could have been bleak and dismal, but he was determined that it should not be so—even though he had just begun that fight for his life, as leader of the International Miners Union, which lasted through 1925 until January of 1926. This night, he had invited Mark, Lena, Jack Mullen, and Oscar Suzic and myself to be with him. Grove was also there. He was to leave for Chicago the following day to make, as we learned later, final plans

230

to leave the Miners Union for a good-paying job with the National Confederation of Labor. For the first time I met Mullen's wife, a shy, pale wisp of a woman who always moved quietly in the background of his life. It was a good evening, even though we had all of us recently taken a 50 per cent pay cut, and it was the time when Ben Holt was at his best. Whatever went on within him, on the surface his heart was high. To his children, he was the big, shaggy giant who, if they saw him only infrequently, was nevertheless a wonderful person to have at home with them on Christmas, playing with them and singing carols.

At dinner, we toasted each other from a bottle of bootleg wine that Mark Golden had provided, good, imported French wine. "Nineteen twenty-five," Ben said. "The best year— the year we win!"

Outside, snow fell, a white blanket over the scarred and barren plains of Egypt.

PART IV

January 10, 1959

MY DEAR ALVIN:

I have read all that you have written, and what am I to say?
It is almost thirty-five years that we have known each other,
and if I ever had any doubts that Alvin Cutter was a person
of honesty and integrity, they have long vanished. So I know
that you wrote honestly and as well as you knew how, and
it makes me wonder whether any story of a man, written
after his life has been lived, bears more than a shred of validity.

I must hasten to add that I question nothing you have put
down. When I sum up the facts you have recorded, they are
true enough, but the scholars will also do that and perhaps
better than we could. We are not afraid of the facts, no
matter how awful they are, but for some strange reason, we
are afraid of people, who at their worst are still a little noble

233

and a good deal wonderful. Or don't you think so? It is so easy for us to spell out a thing like the incident at the Arrowhead Pit and to put it down on the record and to rest on the security of the past; but where the people in the incident are concerned, we prepare a host of reservations and are prepared to swear by them.

What traps us? I don't think it is the bright public glare of a book in print, for it seems to me that these memoirs you are putting together will never be published, or at least not in our lifetimes—which are almost over anyway. Are you protecting the people concerned? But they are almost all dead, Alvin; Ben and Jack and Mark and poor Fulton Grove, who was never enough of a man to be a villain—and so many others whom we knew and worked with. Or are you, perhaps, protecting me? That too occurred to me, and it would fit in with that strange, Victorian sense of propriety which you brought with you to Pomax, but I want no protection, Alvin, and the union needs none.

Reading what you have written makes me wonder why so few, if any, have been able to make human beings out of the men who lead labor—that is, in books, yet in books the people on the other side of the struggle, the owners and operators, loom like giants, or, even better, like people of flesh and blood. Why are we like shadows, who look back at other shadows?

I think of Lena Kuscow, and that night you went with her to see what was happening out at the strip mine. Did it never occur to you that Lena wanted you so desperately that she would have gone to the edge of a live volcano to be with you? But of course that did not occur to you—because you never saw Lena, that strong, beautiful, and wasted vitality, full of hate and resentment and frustration. The union had meaning to her only in terms of what she was, what she had lost, and what she needed so desperately; and in that way, she was not so different from Benjamin Renwell Holt.

You didn't know that she was the first person ever to

speak to me about you—knowing the two of us and what our thoughts were; something not so difficult to know. Ben also knew. Lena had begun to despise me, and perhaps there was a beginning of the same thing with Ben.

It happened that same Christmas Day, that day you wrote about at the end of the manuscript you sent me, when Lena and I were alone in the kitchen, the rest of you inside, and Lena turned to me and said,

"You're a fool, Dorothy. I guess you know it."

I told her that I didn't know what she meant. You see, your idealization of me translated my fear and uncertainty into a virtue, and we were still in the pre-Freudian days then. I was a prim and, as I have often suspected, a none too wholesome woman. It terrified me to face things like that, and I suppose Lena also terrified me somewhat. So I retreated into ignorance, the beclouded ignorance that used to be a woman's refuge, but had already worn thin in the 1920s.

"I mean Alvin Cutter," Lena said.

"Well, what about Alvin Cutter? I really don't know what you're talking about, Lena."

She had too much to drink that evening, but so had I; so had all of us; and even your own memory of the evening is beclouded, an alcoholic haze obscuring what really happened.

"Have you ever looked at life, Dorothy?" Lena demanded. "Have you ever faced up to it and examined it? Did you ever let yourself think of what kind of a joy ride it is to be Mrs. Ben Holt? Or did you ever take a good, long, clear look at Ben?"

I told her that it was none of her business and that it had nothing to do with Al Cutter.

"Dotty, this is Lena. Stop being a damn fool and a prig. Al is in love with you. He's so much in love with you that he can't sit in the same room with you and not let everyone know it."

I said something about her having a nasty and inventive

235

mind, protesting that I had never touched you, that you had never touched me, that we had never even kissed. "And," I added, as a final touch, "he loved his wife. Maybe it was the kind of love you don't understand, but he loved her. He worshiped her."

"You don't worship women," Lena answered tiredly. "These days, people don't even worship God—and as for his wife, she's been dead almost a year. He loves you and you love him— Oh, Christ, what am I wasting my breath for? I must be drunk. The hell with it!"

But things change; and if they say that people never change, they could also say with as much certainty, that people never remain the same. I suppose there was no woman I was ever as close to as Lena, but that took time. It took a basic revision in my own standards of morality, or of what passed for morality in a person like myself. Most importantly, it took a desire to understand Lena.

She lived with Mark Golden on and off for almost fifteen years; she left him and returned to him, and she loved him and hated him, as you well know. Dedication wears thin, and like war, it is interspersed with a good deal of boredom. She never had anything to do with Ben, because she did not like Ben and because adultery was not one of Ben's failings. Mark was much older than she was, and in a way, Mark was the most tragic figure of all—but that was my opinion and not Mark's. Years after this Christmas night of which I speak, Mark and I talked about it. He was so old then! Somewhere, youth had passed him by, somewhere far, far back in his life, but when we talked, he said that all in all, he considered that his life had been a useful and fruitful one.

"I did the kind of work that, for the most part, I'm not ashamed of," he said to me. "After all, Dorothy, the most frightening thing about growing old is neither the nearness of death nor the infirmity age brings, but rather the realization that time is an illusion, and that the eternity of days and years that faced our youth is no more than the blink of an eye, only a moment, an elusive, fleeting moment. It's a hell

236

of a thing to look back shamefully and regretfully, and at least I can say that I've had good years and some moments of happiness. All in all, it's on the black side of the ledger."

Lena was there then. She said something about Ben Holt being remembered, while few would remember Mark Goldman.

"Why not?" Mark smiled. "The memories belong to him—God knows, he worked for them. Practically speaking, it doesn't matter to the dead whether they're remembered or not—not one single iota."

That was years later. On the Christmas night I spoke of, I had little love for Lena; or, to tell the truth, for anyone else at our house. I can number and remember them, too. I was, for the moment, heartily sick of Alvin Cutter and his adolescent worship of me. I was tired to death of remembering not to be caught in a hallway or behind a piece of furniture with Fulton Grove, with his damn, roving, feeling hands and his dirty, little-boy lechery, and the sight of Jack Mullen's poor ghost of a wife, let out of captivity and allowed to take her marital position in the sight of mankind for one brief night, while her stud of a husband restrained himself, was more than I could bear.

I too had had some discussions with Mark Golden about the trade-union movement and how the heights of Jerusalem were always scaled by Class C human beings. Perhaps I was slower than most to learn a lesson of history, for after all, it was eight years since I had married Ben Holt and long enough that I had been living in Pomax; and my dreams of glory fractured slowly. Even the sight of familiar objects changes with time, and one falls into a pattern of observation that can only be forcibly shattered—as it was for me that evening as I watched Ben undress, watched this giant of a man with his thickening waistline sit on the edge of his bed, pull off one sock slowly, then the other, dropping them, leaving them there on the floor. I said to him,

"You could put them into the laundry bin as easily as I could."

237

"Oh? I thought I'd wear them tomorrow."

"The same socks?"

"The same socks. Yes, my dear. I'm just a lousy, uncultured miner who wears his socks two days in a row."

"You're not a miner," I said. "I'm sick of having you call yourself a coal miner every opportunity you have."

"What?"

"I said you're not a miner. You haven't been for eight years."

"What the hell are you getting at, Dotty?" he asked thickly. "What's eating you?"

"I just think that you've been out of the mines long enough to change your clothes when they're dirty."

"What a cheap, lousy thing to say! If I didn't make allowances for your background—"

"What kind of allowances? What about my background?"

"The hell with it! Go to bed."

"I want to know what kind of allowances you make?"

"Look, Dotty, this is no time for a philosophical discussion. I'm tired and you're irritated, so why don't we just both of us go to bed."

"What is the time for a philosophical discussion, Ben, or any other kind of discussion? Morning, noon, night—perhaps in those good comfortable after-dinner hours that a man spends with his wife and family? But since this is the first evening you've been here in two weeks, I think this is it. I'm a little drunk, therefore I am also a little philosophical."

"Knock it off, Dotty!"

"Not for the world. I want to know what kind of allowances you make for me."

"All right." He stared at me thoughtfully, his eyes tired and bloodshot, and as he looked at that moment, so help me, I had it in my heart to throw away the whole charade and be only pleased with the fact that we were together this night. But I didn't, and Ben said, "I make allowances for the fact that you were a spoiled brat brought up with a

238

silver spoon in your mouth, and with not enough sense or perception to know what it means to be a worker or to try to build a trade union."

"Why did you marry a spoiled brat, Ben?"

"Because I loved you."

"Or because you couldn't bear the thought of a miner's daughter? Which is it? And if you ever did win a decent life for the miners, I suppose you'd look at them with contempt because they could give their children some decent clothes and an education and three meals a day—which to you is a silver spoon in a kid's mouth."

"God damn it, don't twist my words!"

"Then don't twist the facts. Don't call me a spoiled brat. You know better. I had a maid for a while, but now I'm running this house by myself and raising three children and doing the cooking and cleaning, and without any expense accounts and steaks in hotel restaurants and bootleg whisky and Pullman compartments and all the rest of what goes with the good fight, as your friend, Fulton Grove, loves to call it. And furthermore, you can tell Mr. Grove that the next time he tries to paw me—"

"That son of a bitch! I'll—"

"Hold onto your hurt pride, Ben. For once, you listen. Because on top of all that, I've managed to spend almost an hour or two every day at the Central Soup Kitchen since this strike began, and I know something about people, which is almost as important as knowing about miners, because they're also people—which I think you've forgotten. Just as you so conveniently forgot that those poor devils in Arrowhead Pit were people—"

"Oh no! Damn it, no! You're not going to bring up this Arrowhead thing—not tonight at an hour past midnight. It's Christmas, Dotty. Can't you get it through your head that this is Christmas?"

"I can't get it out of my head. I'm full of carols. This is the one day of the year when the human race gets together on the proposition that we stop being animals for twenty-four hours. But it's past midnight, so we can return to being ourselves. And as for Arrowhead, I agree with you. Put it away. Put it away, Ben Holt, and forget about it—"

I said it was shattered. It's shattered and pieced together again, and people go on living. I went on living with Ben, and people admired us. You see, there was one fact about Ben that was inescapable: he never looked at another woman, and thereby, through all of his life, no breath of scandal was ever whispered about him. That's how the smart designation came into being, Caesar and Caesar's wife. It's a peculiar measure of morality that marks us. He said about Lena once, "She's a tramp." Ben lived in a world of good women and tramps, and you fell into one category or another, and I suppose he demonstrated some kind of profound wisdom in marrying someone who would remain a "good woman."

I don't find the truth painful any more, and I am ready to admit that during those years, I wanted the union to die. I wanted it broken because I had a dream that if it were ever to be broken, Ben and I would be released, and we could leave Pomax and I could forget that I had ever seen a coal mine. So year after year, '25, '26, '27, '28, and '29, I watched the membership shrink—I watched it go down from a hundred thousand to forty thousand, yet by then I knew that it would make no difference. I knew that if there were five coal miners left who were ready to sign cards in the Miners Union, Ben Holt would be on the scene to lead them.

It would be wrong to say that I felt nothing for him, no sympathy, no love; the truth is that I felt a great deal indeed, and there were moments of great warmth and closeness between us. A marriage like ours is composed of ten thousand rivets and strings and knots, and when one breaks, another takes over the strain, and when something snaps, something else adheres. If I just pluck memories out of a grab bag, I can find moments again and again. If the steak in the Pullman dining car cost eight dollars, there were other times when he spent his last penny to buy some toy for the children, or some piece of inexpensive costume jewelry for me. He was a sentimentalist and Lena once characterized him as a "slob." It was cruel but in some ways true; he was also a strong man driven by some wild urgency which I never understood. To you, Alvin, finally, it was his lust for power. I wish I could explain it that easily. In the past I did. But now I doubt much that I knew then.

Also, during those years, I had no time to brood over things. To raise three children, as I did, and to keep a home going, meant a state of utter exhaustion at the end of each day. The days and the months went by—and always, it was Ben Holt fighting for his life. In 1927, a reporter from a St. Louis paper came to Pomax to interview me. She was a bright, sharp young thing, and I remember that she began the interview by asking me how it felt to be Ben's wife. I was supposed to answer that in one short, specific sentence.

You will remember that I spent the summer of 1928 at Father's house in Ringman. I brought the children with me. Ben had to borrow the money for our train fare to Pennsylvania, and while such a summer was a good thing for the children, the plain truth of it was that we couldn't figure out any way to stay alive in Pomax. At that time, you were in Chicago, preparing for the union's national convention. Ben put us on the train for Pennsylvania, and then went on to Chicago.

I am sure you read Kingsley Rowe's article in last month's *National Post*, about Ben and those years in the 1920s. Just in case you missed it, I am enclosing a cutting about the time I speak of. Rowe isn't very dependable when it comes to facts, nor did he take the time to ask me to verify anything. But I thought you would be amused by it, as an example of the reality versus the historical hindsight. Also, there is a real disposition to be kind to Ben, now that he is dead. Could that be part of a national disposition of ours—to ennoble when dead those we hated most alive? Anyway, here is the article:

That was the year when Ben Holt, president of the International Miners Union, faced the daily fare of his union members during the era of the twenties—starvation. As far as his own pantry went, he was no better than a miner. It was empty. Like any miner, he had to contemplate the pinched faces of his own children and hear them whimper for food. But in one way, at least, his own situation was better than most, for he had the unwavering support of his loyal and devoted wife, Dorothy Holt.

There were few families like the Holts, close, tight, inseparable. Whatever arrows his enemies hurled against him, they admired his family and admitted his position as a family man and a good father. So it was not with an easy heart or without denting his hard core of pride, that Ben Holt made the decision to send his family to his father-in-law's home at Ringman, while he went on to Chicago alone. At least there, they would have a roof over their heads and find nourishment.

Once in Chicago, Holt faced the most critical situation of his entire career. Never before or since that summer convention of 1928 was Benjamin Renwell Holt closer to losing his place as the leader of the International Miners Union. For three years, his once powerful union had been torn by strikes, lockouts, and internecine warfare. Its great membership, shortly before close to four hundred thousand, had shrunk to less than fifty thousand. Its various locals had asserted their autonomy, bringing additional disunity into the union. Its treasury was bankrupt—indeed, money had to be borrowed to pay the expenses of the convention.

Fulton Grove, already embarked on his quick climb to power in the hierarchy of the National Confederation of Labor, led the assault of that strong organization against the Miners Union. As his allies, chartered by the National Confederation, Gus Empek's Associated Miners Union invaded the convention hall to demand a merger with the International Miners Union and representation on the top-echelon committees. There was the moment when Ben Holt faced not only dethronement, but permanent exile from the ranks of the American labor movement. Not alone Gus Empek, but Jack Brady and half a dozen brawny leaders of the Associated Miners joined in a charge up to the platform, to shoulder Mark Golden, union attorney, away from the microphone and seize the attention of the assembled delegates.

At one side of the stage, Ben Holt sat in thoughtful silence, flanked on one hand by veteran Jack Mullen and on the other by his public-relations expert and assistant, Alvin Cutter. No one of the three said anything or appeared in the least disturbed, nor did Ben Holt appear in the least annoyed. Neither did he make any attempt to defend the microphone or regain it. Jack Brady, of the Associated Miners, had begun to introduce Gus Empek and extol his virtues, when Ben Holt arose lazily, stretched, yawned, and then slowly sauntered toward stage center. Jack Brady glanced at him nervously, and suddenly began to claim the right of free speech without interference. The six husky Associated Miners started toward the two men.

Suddenly, Ben Holt reached up to the lapel of Brady's jacket, and, calling into play that extraordinary strength of his, ripped off not only the lapel, but half of Brady's jacket, exposing the shoulder holster and gun that Brady always wore. As the Associated Miners' strong-arm men began their rush toward the microphone, Ben Holt roared out, in a voice that shook the rafters of the auditorium,

"What is this—a miners' convention or a meeting of Chicago hoodlums? Since when are cheap gunmen allowed to address this convention! I took that gun away from Brady four years ago in Pomax, and I'm taking it away again!"

And with that, Ben tore off the holster and flung gun and holster onto the stage. His roaring voice had stopped the muscle men cold in their tracks. Now he turned his back on them and walked to his seat without another word. But even if he had spoken, no one would have heard him. Pandemonium reigned in the hall as the delegates charged up to the stage and forcibly ejected the Associated Miners. Through all that, Ben Holt never moved, only sat there with an expression of utter disgust on his face.

So there is the cutting and the story, Alvin, and were you going to tell it as Kingsley Rowe did, in the same simpering style the *National Post* uses to force any man of stature or individuality into the Madison Avenue mold—even a trade-union leader, safely dead? Or were you going to tell the truth?

Or are you saying to yourself now, that I am on both sides

of the fence, worshiping Ben and hating him, loving him and despising him, and that it makes no sense? But it makes a great deal of sense, my dear Alvin—the only sense in my whole life with Ben. And as for the truth, I do know it, wholly and completely.

You may remember that from Chicago, Ben came to Ringman. By then, the children and I had been at Father's house in Ringman for three weeks, and those three weeks had worked wonders for all of us. Kingsley Rowe's picture of the "pinched" faces of my children, as they "whimpered" with hunger leaves something to be desired in terms of the truth. I have seen hunger and even starvation among miners too often to suggest that my children ever knew either. The worst that ever happened was a flattening of their diet, with perhaps too little good protein and too much starch, oatmeal twice a day and almost no eggs or milk or meat, but that is a far cry from either hunger or starvation.

However, after three weeks of fresh farm milk and eggs, orange juice and all the meat and chicken they could eat—as well as the freedom of the house and the fields—the children glowed, and some of the growing network of lines on my own face were being ironed out. When Ben arrived and saw me, his grin of pleasure was so real and boyish that my equanimity only increased. He was to remain with us in Ringman for a full week, the first real vacation he had taken in years, and I had a wistful hope that somehow we could go back to our first days together in Ringman and make new beginnings. But isn't that always the hope, twice-lived youths and new beginnings?

Father had always liked Ben. My father recognized no virtue as superior to intelligence, and he was ready to forgive a myriad of sins, so long as the sinner was well salted with common sense. Next to boors and hypocrites, he hated fools most, and once he had gotten over the shock of Ben Holt marrying his daughter, he was rather pleased with the notion of having his daughter dedicate her life to what he regarded as a high social service. While he knew a great deal about coal miners and the Miners Union, I don't think he ever had the vaguest notion of how we lived or what life with Ben Holt was. He had noted Ben's increase in salary to five and then eight thousand a year. We had not bothered to inform him or the world that subsequently it shrank back to five thousand, then to four and now to two thousand a year—when there was enough money in the treasury to pay the forty dollars a week.

With Ben's arrival, Father was as excited as a boy at the prospect of having someone at the dinner table each night for seven nights, with whom to discuss politics, history, the situation in labor, the international situation, plus whatever other abstruse subjects might be raised. By now, Norah was nine years old, Sam seven, and little Ben six. Father loved his grandchildren, but there was no denying that they were a trial for an entire summer; he expected to find repayment in Ben and he looked forward impatiently to our first dinner. And when we had finally seated ourselves, Ben already beginning to look like the elder statesman with his graying hair and increasing girth, Father couldn't suppress a smile of delight.

"I've looked forward to this for a long time," he said. "You've been too long away and too far away."

We agreed, and our talk filled in the years and the empty spaces, and that took us through most of the meal. It wasn't until Mrs. Privit's excellent roast had been cleared away that we got to the convention.

"I want to hear all about it," Father said. "The whole story—the inside story, if you don't mind, Ben."

"How do you know there is any inside story?" I wanted to know, a little annoyed with Father's habit of romanticizing things that were not in the least romantic.

"Because there certainly is, Dotty, make no mistake. Am I right, Ben?"

"You could be right."

"There you are. Why, you couldn't read the papers without reading between the lines. They not only had written

245

Ben off; they had printed his obituary. He was finished. He didn't have a chance in the world, and the only question was who would fall heir to the fragments of the union. Would it be Gus Empek? Or would it be Fulton Grove, called back by acclamation?"

Ben's laughter roared his appreciation. Father filled their wineglasses, and said, "And the gun, Ben! My word, that was lovely—that was as gracious and fine as anything."

"And the interesting thing is," said Ben, "that the newspapers were not so far from wrong. So far as we could see, it was the end of everything—and I was there to be the roasted goose. That's the history of the miners, isn't it— break your heart and back for them, and when you're down, they'll stamp on your face."

"That's what they did to Tom Hennesy, who founded the union," Father agreed, "and a saintlier man never lived. They did it to Joe Kempton and they did it to McClellen."

"Miners," Ben sighed. "Hate—suspicion—and mistrust, their definition of any man who leads them. I swear, sir, I had no place to turn, no idea, no notion—only the simple fact that a union which once numbered almost four hundred thousand members was now down to a handful. No one cared to remember that it was a handful when I became president, and that I had built it up to where it was. Oh no —that was nothing anyone wanted to remember. They wanted a victim, and they wanted to tear him into pieces. Empek knew that. Grove knew it. And I knew it too."

"Then you knew that Empek would try to raid you?" Father nodded.

"Not quite," Ben replied. "No, that took a little doing."

"Ben, what on earth do you mean?" I asked him.

"Dotty, Dotty," Ben grinned, "wake up. The bad things happen, no matter what. But when something helps, it's because you make it happen."

"And you engineered that whole thing?" I whispered.

"Myself? No. The truth is, it wasn't even my idea. It came from our own pillar of integrity, Alvin Cutter."

246

"No. I don't believe it."

"Then you'll ask him," Ben said flatly.

"It's your story of what happened that I want to hear, Ben," Father said.

"All right, sir. I tell it from the point of view of hopelessness, sheer hopelessness. We sat there in a hotel room in Chicago—Jack Mullen, Oscar Suzic, Mark Golden—you know who they are?" Father nodded. "There was Lena Kuscow; she's Golden's secretary and a sort of prop for all of us, and Al Cutter—he's the man I met eight years ago down in West Virginia. I believe you know that story. We sat there and beat our brains out and talked around in circles and tried to see some way out, but there wasn't any way out. Then Cutter recalled an incident that had happened some years back in the railroad station at Pomax. I don't want to go into all the details of that, but at that time, Gus Empek and Jack Brady wanted a meeting with me, and they were afraid to show in Pomax, the way feeling there ran against them. So we met in the baggage room at the railroad station. Now Jack Brady is a man with a gun. That's a sickness, like being a rummy, but it takes the form of needing a gun and wearing a gun. I read an article by a doctor, once, who said it was an expression of sexual impotence, and that the gun became a phallic symbol of some sort, but whether that's the case or not, I don't know. I do know that Jack Brady would no more walk around without his gun than walk naked. He never shot anyone, but the gun is his need. That day when we met in the baggage room, Brady lost his head and went for his gun, and I took it away from him—and that was the incident Cutter recalled. He kept harping on it, even though I got annoyed and told him to forget it. Then he said to me, Ben, what would happen if you took that gun away from Brady up there on the stage? I mean, suppose he tried to draw on you, and you took his gun away in front of the whole convention? By golly, wouldn't that take the delegates' minds off you and switch all the irritation to Gus Empek and Jack Brady and maybe Fulton Grove as well?

"I told him that he was crazy, and so did everyone else except Mark, who seemed to be fascinated with the idea. Mark insisted that we pay some attention to Cutter's notion and find out what Cutter had in mind. Cutter didn't have any of the details worked out at that point, only the picture of what should happen up there on the platform, and then the two of them convinced me that maybe it should happen and that there might be a way to make it happen. So we put our heads together and spent half the night hashing it out and putting the pieces together in working order. The result of it was that we worked out a crazy, kid routine that no one in his right mind would fall for, but then greedy men at a convention are not exactly in their right minds."

"Hold on and let me guess," Father chuckled. "You dropped an apple into the lap of the National Confederation of Labor."

"Exactly. They were in the same hotel, and there was nothing in the world they—by they, I mean Fulton Grove and two other members of the executive who were present as observers—nothing in the world they desired more than the demise of Ben Holt and Ben Holt's friends. I was the bone that stuck in their craw—the leader of a union that insisted on being an industrial union in the face of their damn craft unions and didn't play ball in their lousy genteel league. They were wrong, but they had gotten it into their heads that if they could only get rid of me, everything would be on ice for them. Well, we decided that Mark Golden and Al Cutter would go to them and hand them our union. It made sense in a way. Al and Mark were not miners; they hadn't come up the hard way; they held jobs with the union, and what was more natural than for them to look for something else when the union became a sinking ship? So the next day, Al and Mark met with Fulton and his playmates. Fulton's own notion of tactics was as subtle as his Sunday-school mind. He planned to demand time on the platform

248

and to offer the delegates the full support of the National Confederation, providing that they dumped Ben Holt.

"Al and Mark said that this would never work, and that the delegates would not throw me out unless they had someone there ready to replace me. Now Gus Empek and his crowd were already at the convention, and there had been quite a battle in the credentials committee as to whether or not they should be admitted. The fact that they were given observers' credentials was a defeat for me, and this was something Fulton Grove knew. But Fulton had enough sense to know that there was a difference between an observer and a candidate for international leadership. Empek's name still had the stink of Arrowhead all over it, and although that was four years ago, time had not rubbed it clean. It was the job of Mark and Al to talk Fulton into believing that Gus Empek and Jack Brady could make a real bid for leadership —and I guess they were pretty damned eloquent. They worked out the whole approach with Fulton at first, and then subsequently with Brady and Empek.

"And that was the way it happened," Ben finished. "It was staged perfectly. It went through perfectly—and it ended just precisely as we planned for it to end. If we hadn't intervened at the very end, I think the delegates would have killed every last one of those Associated Miners—"

Father was rising now, and he led the way into the parlor, for the brandy and coffee, and cigars for himself and Ben. That harked back to the old days when Ben would dine with us, yet I wondered whether then, a decade and a half ago, Father would have listened to a story like this, nodding and grinning his approval. Ben had to point out that I didn't approve. He read my face more easily than Father did, and perhaps he had his own guilts where I was concerned. Father interpreted this as an expression of my own anxiety over the incident of the gun.

"No," I said. "I don't think Ben was ever in any danger, as far as Jack Brady was concerned. I think Ben described

Brady very well—except for one thing that is perhaps a little clearer to a woman. Brady lives with fear. I don't know about the rest of it, but to me, that's the main reason for the gun. Brady couldn't use it. He's a coward—poor devil."

"There are better candidates for your sympathy than Jack Brady," Ben growled.

"I imagine so. I'd rather not name them."

"Now just what is that supposed to mean?" Ben demanded, angry and hurt that I had taken the wind out of such a fine and clever story. Father was a little upset too, and he hastened to say,

"One moment, Dotty—you can't make a moral judgment of this thing Ben did, because I am not sure you understand it at all."

"What!"

Ben threw up his hands in despair, and let Father know that there was no arguing with me, not when I had made up my mind about anything. Father said,

"Hold on, Dotty—please try to see this thing clearly and calmly."

"I am clear, calm, and also stupid," I replied. "I have just listened to Ben with both ears, but I am obviously too stupid to understand what he was saying."

"That is not what I meant at all, child, and you know it."

"First of all, Father, I am not a child. I am thirty-one years old, the mother of three children, and rubbed raw around the edges. Secondly, I know what you meant. You meant that there are two worlds and two moralities, one for men and one for women. And never the twain shall meet."

"For heaven's sake, Dotty, I only call you a child to delude myself into thinking that I am still fairly young. And furthermore, when you talk that kind of suffragette nonsense, you remind me of your Aunt Alice Aimesley. Now to get back to this other thing, I don't know Cutter but I do know Mark Golden, and I have yet to hear of him mixed up in any kind of dubious business—"

"Nothing is dubious when you do it for the union. Am I right, Ben?"

Ben shook his head wearily. "I don't know what you're talking about, Dotty. At this point, there's not much difference between my leadership and the existence of the union. If the leadership goes, there won't even be scraps for anyone else to pick up and use. It's rotten enough, these days, to be a miner with the union in existence, as weak and shattered as the union is. I hate to think of what the conditions would be if there were no union."

"Be truthful, Ben," I said softly. "What you can't see is the absence of your leadership."

"All right," he nodded. "I can't see that."

"So Mark and Al lie and scheme and degrade themselves in an idiotic little plot and Gus Empek is deflated into an empty sack—a man as decent as any who work with you, made a buffoon and a clown, and you're the man of the hour because you took Jack Brady's gun away again, and—Oh, my God, Ben, why do you do it? Why do you have to do it? Why is the leadership of that union so important to you?"

Both men sat there in silence, a long, long silence, and then Ben said,

"You don't understand, Dotty. Joe is right. You just don't understand."

"Then make me understand."

"How? I've tried. Suppose I told you that if I had lost out there in Chicago, I wouldn't want to live. Would you understand?"

"No."

"Would you believe me?" he asked softly, and it took me a while before I answered,

"Yes, I guess I'd believe you, Ben."

Later that evening, Ben pleaded fatigue from his journey and excused himself to go to bed. Father and I stayed in the parlor for a little while, he with the small end of a brandy and a cigar, and myself with my nostalgic memories of youth.

After we had been sitting in silence for a while, Father said to me,

"I find it disturbing, Dotty."

"What in particular?"

"Nothing in particular and everything. The way you and Ben tear and claw at each other. What has happened to you, and what has happened to Ben—"

"Marriages may be made in heaven, Father. But there's a good deal of hell in working them out. You know that as well as I do."

"Do I, Dotty? Perhaps I had a more fortunate marriage than most. I used to believe that love solved a good many things. Forgive a prying old man if I ask you whether you still love Ben."

"I don't know," I replied slowly.

"How can you not know, Dotty? Isn't this something one knows? Always?"

"I'm not sure. It's harder to love a living person than a dead person."

The reaction, to my surprise, was of a man who had been struck in the face, and he said, "That was cruel and uncalled for, Dotty."

"Of course—I know! I'm so stupid!" I went over to him and put my arms around him from behind. "But I didn't mean what you think, Daddy dear. Sometimes I love Ben, not the way I loved him at the beginning, yet sometimes I love him, and sometimes I hate him. But mostly, there's just a dead, dull feeling that isn't love and isn't hate, and at best, it's pity."

"Pity? Good heavens, girl, how can you pity Ben?"

"What Ben? The Ben you used to know? That great hulking coal miner who walked in here one day and proceeded to instruct us in the realities of war and history and man's destiny? Upstairs, there's a man with graying hair—a man who's getting fat and short-winded and tired, and whose life and dreams are running down the drain like sand. Daddy, you don't know how I prayed for him to lose this election—for him to be free of this curse, this damned need!"

"And do you think for one moment, Dotty, that if Ben lost this election, he'd be free?"

I let go of my father, walked over to the piano, and turned to face this slim, gentle person, who through all of my life had been so wise and understanding—and who now could not begin to comprehend my own situation.

"Daddy," I said, "Ben is sick. It's not like heart trouble or consumption, but it's a sickness all the same. From as far back as I know him, and before that too, he dreamed of only one thing—power. It was bread and butter and meat and drink to him. It was all and everything—power!"

"Dotty—Dotty darling, you're wrong. That's one small part of Ben. I don't deny he wanted power. But what for? That's the important question—what for? So that he could take this devil's curse of mining and turn it into something human and bearable, so that he could feed the hungry and clothe the poor, so that he could ease man's suffering. That's a noble purpose and a noble cause, Dotty—and I know of no one who has ventured his fortune and dedicated his abilities to a higher end. This is the fact. Then how can you say that all Ben lives for is power?"

"Because everything else is subject to the main thing, which is power. That's why he felt that he would rather die than be driven out of the leadership."

"Power over what, Dotty? Ben's fortunes are low. The union has shrunk to a handful, and it grows smaller month by month. You told me that yourself. Everywhere, Ben is cursed and reviled by the men of money and power. No, don't accuse him of what he opposes. Ben carries half the world on his shoulders. Don't make it harder for him, Dotty. Please."

So argument was pointless, and we were a thousand miles apart. I kissed him good night and went upstairs. We had my old room, which had been furnished from the first

253

with twin beds, perhaps in the hope of a sister who never came, but practically for girlhood friends who remained overnight. Nothing in it had been changed since I married and left the house. The same pink wallpaper over the white wainscot, the same Dutch hooked rugs on the floor, the same blue and white furniture, the same brass student lamp, and on the walls, the three Maxfield Parrish prints that I loved so much.

Ben sat on one of the beds, his shoes off, his face contemplative, and he glanced up and smiled as I entered. I said that I thought he would have been asleep by now.

"I've just been sitting here and thinking, Dotty. What a wonderful room this is! Someday, before she gets too old for it, I would want Norah to have a room like this."

"I don't think one is ever too old for it."

"Well—you know what I mean, Dotty. Norah's nine already. A few years more, and she'll have to have a young lady's room, all stiff and polished."

"Did you look in at the children?"

He nodded. "Sound asleep. Good food, sunshine—and kids sleep well, I guess. Who decorated and furnished this room, Dotty?"

"My mother."

"She must have been wonderful. Do you remember her well?"

"Not too well. Sometimes better—well, you know how it is. The years dull things." I had begun to take off my clothes, not facing Ben as he said,

"You're very angry with me, aren't you, Dotty?"

"Not very angry, no. Perhaps a little upset. We're both tired, Ben, and I'd rather not talk about it any more tonight."

"About what happened in Chicago?"

"That. Other things."

"Dotty?"

"What, Ben?"

"Is it because of Al Cutter?"

254

"Ben, what on earth are you talking about?"

"I mean, is it because—I mean because of you and Al Cutter?"

"What? What are you talking about?"

"Oh, Dotty, for Christ's sake, do you love Al Cutter? Is that it?"

"You're not serious, Ben."

"I am."

"Well, I don't love Al Cutter, Ben. I'm not a schoolgirl. I don't look at someone and decide that he's the hero of my dreams. I'm a long-married woman, thirty-one years old and with three children, and I do my own cooking and cleaning. Add it up, Ben. Also, Al Cutter never kissed me, never spoke words of love to me—never even indicated that he had any desire for me."

Suddenly, Ben put his face in his hands, his body wracked with sobs, and through his hands muttered, "Oh, Jesus, Dotty—oh, Jesus God, I've never been so low before in all my life. I didn't win anything there in Chicago. I crawled through on my belly with a few broken pieces in my hands, and I was afraid—oh, I was afraid, and all the time I was thinking, I'll lose here and with Dotty too, and then everything's gone, and I have nothing—nothing." I went over to him, and he looked up at me and said, "Don't leave me, Dotty—please. Never leave me."

Pressing his head to my waist, I stroked his hair and promised that I would never leave him.

Promises are broken, Al, so it was not simply the promise. It was more than that—I think you understand how much more, and it's not simple or easy either, not to be defined in terms of the faithful wife whose love for Ben Holt never faltered, but a complex of things that made it impossible, over all those years, for there to be anything between you and me. That's a part of the truth, isn't it—the complex, snarled truth that any life demands if it is to be explained? And yet short of the truth, for it would also be a lie to say that there

255

was nothing between yourself and me. But it's not the way you write it, Al, obvious and direct, one thing coming properly after the other.

And here this letter has stretched on and on, so that I hardly remember the beginning any more. Was I making a point, Alvin, my dear, that this is a story you can't tell? But that would be true of any story, wouldn't it, and how do you follow a human soul through all of its torment and self-deceit? I don't know. There's too much to explain, and I would not want to have to explain why Ben and I were so lighthearted the following day. We laid the children down for their afternoon nap, and then he and I went out for a long walk, myself in a yellow cotton dress and Ben in blue denims and a miner's shirt. We walked all the way to Belfast Ridge, and up to the top of it, and standing there, we looked down into the valley, through the warm summer haze at the smoke of the collieries, groping for the beginning and praying, I suppose, for some destiny.

Either you accept the fact that people, in and of themselves, have no importance or that they have all importance. If Ben had been written off in the seats of the mighty, I at least felt, at that moment, that we had returned to each other. If it was an illusion, it was a pleasant illusion on that summer afternoon back in Ringman, just as my dreams were pleasant illusions, dreams of Ben not too old to take up the study of law—and the two of us living in the Ringman house. Father would have been happy to have us there, and the children would grow up as I grew up. These are old dreams, recently warmed over.

I paused in this letter to search for something, and now I have found it. Perhaps you remember the interview Fulton Grove gave the press after the convention was over. His reward for his labors was a vice-presidency in the National Confederation of Labor, and he was being questioned on Ben Holt and the Miners Union. Here is the clipping:

"And what do you think of Ben Holt's victory, Mr. Grove?"

"Victory? It was a poor imitation of a victory, if you ask me. Who was it said, 'Another such victory and I am undone'? Or something of that sort. As far as I am concerned, Ben Holt is undone right here and now."

"Then you ascribe no importance to his victory?"

"It was a trick. There isn't an honest bone in Ben Holt's body. It was staged and planned from A to Z."

"Would you care to comment on the future of the International Miners Union?"

"Under Ben Holt, it has no future. Today, it's as fraudulent as Ben Holt. If they quoted true membership figures, they would not show a corporal's guard. It's a splinter, not a union. And the sooner the coal miners wake up to the fact that Ben Holt is leading them to utter disaster, the better off the entire industry will be."

There it was, my dear Alvin, the official point of view, which held that Ben was finished—yet I had the feeling that day of someone renewed, and I think that I was very much in love with my husband as we stood on Belfast Ridge.

So much for my comments, and I hope I have not turned you from the rest of the story. Tell all of it.

2

This letter she signed "Your dear friend, Dorothy Holt," and it summed up our relationship, as it also summed me up, a dry old man, looking backward a long, long distance, and trying to untangle a tangled story.

PART V

1

A liberal acquaintance with the bottom poses the question: "What happens then?" The answer is that nothing very much happens and you remain there—which is nevertheless an enlightenment to many. It's as far as you go. I bought a suit in 1928, and it was still wearable in 1933 when I traveled by bus from Marietta, Ohio, to Pomax, Illinois. It was a gray sharkskin suit, and it had a pleasant shine all over it and it bagged at the knees, and it was also the last suit I had purchased up to this time. When the bus stopped for the passengers to refresh themselves, I bought a ham sandwich for ten cents and a cup of coffee for a nickel. It satisfied my hunger. In any case, my stomach, like the stomachs of so many at that time, appeared not only to have reduced itself in size but to have developed an aversion to rich and nourishing food.

I had been in Marietta attempting to negotiate a contract

259

with a small coal operator named Jack C. Blaine. He was a rather nice, defeated man whose pit was being squeezed to extinction in a one-sided price war with two large railroads. Our negotiations turned into an attempt on my part to persuade him not to close down his colliery, which I finally succeeded in accomplishing. Since the total legitimate union membership in his area consisted of the thirty-seven miners he employed, and since he gave me his word not to force any yellow-dog contract—a contract in which they pledged to leave the union and not to rejoin—the result of our discussion was in the way of being a sort of negative victory.

When we had finished our negotiations, for what they were worth, he said to me,

"Cutter—how does your outfit manage to survive from year to year?"

"How do you manage?" I asked him.

"Hell, I'm a businessman. I have ways. I sign notes, and I still have a few good friends who co-sign them. I deal with factors—I borrow against the coal before it's dug and pay 2 per cent a month on the money. You know what they say, if you operate a pit, save a few miners to dig you out, because sooner or later you'll be in a damn sight deeper than the coal. The little guy is as much a relic as your trade union, Cutter. The railroads and the steel industry are the giants in the coal game today, and when they put the knife into me, I squirm. But I have ways. I have a few pieces of property, and with this and that, I just manage to keep my head up above the water. But I manage. You fellows—"

"We don't have to show a profit," I smiled.

"That's no answer."

"What else?" I shrugged. "In the old days, we rode in Pullmans and ate in the diner. Then it was day coach. I ride Greyhound now—"

"You've gone soft. The old-timers rode the rods."

"They were pretty old timers. But we manage."

But it was an exaggeration to state that we managed. We were at a point where we barely survived, and that took

260

some doing. Before 1929, there were thousands of miners who had left the union, but at least they worked. In the four years of desperate depression since then, fewer and fewer worked.

2

I mentioned the suit, because Ben Holt made a point of it that day when I returned to Pomax and walked into his office. He was sitting behind his desk, smoking one of his foul cigars, a little heavier, a little grayer; and when I dropped into a chair to tell him about my experience in Marietta, he waved my words aside, informing me that he wasn't one damn bit interested in what had happened out there. A week ago, he would have hung on every word, but now he was not one damn bit interested, not at all, and he told me to stand up.

"What?"

"You heard me, Al. Stand up."

Watching him curiously, I stood up.

"Turn around," he said.

"What's this? A fashion show?"

"When did you buy that suit?" he wanted to know.

"Five years ago. Maybe six. What difference does it make—"

"It looks it. It was a lousy, cheap suit to begin with. Also, your collar is frayed. You're a trade-union organizer, not a bum. It makes me sick to see you guys walking around here dressed like bums—"

"I think you got one hell of a nerve. Now see here, just where do you come off to rate me on my clothes! I'm no organizer, which you know damn well. I'm supposed to be research director of this wreckage, and it just happens that I have twenty weeks of back pay coming to me—"

"Take it easy, Al. You got another suit?"

261

"It's worse than this. Who are we going to entertain—the governor?"

Ben grinned, tapped the ash off his cigar, and grinned again, and let me stand there and wait, staring at me, and then put down his cigar, rose and walked around the desk to face me, and told me,

"Tomorrow, Al, at three o'clock in the afternoon, you and I have an appointment with the President of the United States."

I nodded without really understanding what he had said, and made some remark about time and train connections.

"You didn't hear me, did you?"

"I guess I heard you, Ben," I muttered.

"We're going by plane."

"Yes. What does he want to see us about?"

"Coal. But you know something, Al, I want to see *him* about a lot of other things, indeed I do."

3

Today, the kids don't comprehend it, although they comprehend other things that are as bad or worse, things like atom bombs and a world split in two so dangerously; but they don't comprehend how a country can stop, and most of them don't really believe it. They doubt that it ever actually happened, and if it did happen, they're not sure that it happened the way we tell it. Worse, perhaps, is that fact that so many who lived through it then have forgotten that it happened, or washed it out of their minds. It isn't plausible that in 1929, the greatest industrial country on earth found itself with half of its industry idle or soon to be idle. Five million unemployed became ten million and ten million became fifteen million, and the whole country began to be desperately frightened at what had happened to it, at the army of drifting, idle men who inhabited it, at the empty factories and empty houses—and at the whole communities of shacks and shanties and packing cases that sprang up around the old cities where these men and women and children, now broke and disinherited, had once lived. The country was frightened and tense and despairing. In the cities, on almost every corner, a man stood with a box of apples, which he peddled for a nickel each, but vast as this industry was, it didn't serve to take the curse off the great plants and mills that stood idle and empty.

The trade-union movement was, perhaps, worse hit than anything, for there had been little growth over the past decade, and now the respectable and genteel craft unions began to go apart at the seams, the plumbers, carpenters, painters, cigar makers and steamfitters and dressmakers tasting what had been the lot of the coal miners in the most normal of times. The fatted and arrogant National Confederation of Labor was losing its membership at the rate of eight or nine thousand a week, and a desperate industry joined with the economic conditions to hasten the death of the unions. A haphazard, frequently bloody, disorganized and virtually leaderless war between industry and labor spread through the nation. It was without direction and without conclusion, and for three years, we watched its progress with pity and hopelessness—a hopelessness that only slackened when a new president was voted into office. Then, suddenly, hope and direction appeared, not all at once and not very much of it—but a beginning.

In a way, the coal miners were hurt less than others. Not that pits didn't close, but the bottom is the bottom, and what was happening to other workers had been the ordinary lot of the coal miner for a decade. Almost untouched by the prosperity of the 1920s, he was less shaken than others at the disaster of the thirties. Hunger was not new; an empty belly was an empty belly—an empty larder was even more absolute. There could not be less than nothing, and he had lived with nothing for a long, long time. As for our union, the International Miners, it had experienced every conceivable disaster; smashed in lost strikes, ripped to pieces by internal disputes and yellow-dog contracts, reduced to poverty by the poverty of its membership, reduced in numbers until only a loyal, unshakable core of thirty thousand remained, there was little more that could happen to it. Coal had to be mined. Everything else might be dispensed with, but the country itself would perish if coal was not mined—the trains would stop, the lights would go out, the wheels would stop turning, and the cold would freeze the nation's heart into stillness and silence.

It was tragic, awful and hopeless, but by 1933, a bottom of sorts had been reached, and the hopelessness began to reverse itself. The new President of the United States awakened a sort of mystical desire and belief in the poeple, and within days of his taking office, he began to act against the paralyzing depression. His invitation to Ben Holt was only one of a great number of invitations to leaders of labor and industry—his conference with Ben and myself only one of an endless string of conferences, certainly far less important in his mind than his conferences with many others.

In later years, Ben would insist that from the very beginning and from before the beginning—meaning our meeting at the White House—he had planned for and anticipated what would come. I don't think so. I don't think that the President knew or that Ben knew—and certainly, I did not know. I had few anticipations and few hopes, and my dreams had slowed down. The years gave me nothing, and I looked forward to very little. If I didn't enjoy my work, I did not hate it, and my needs were small. Cursed with a good many things, I had at least been spared any real hunger for success or riches; and as the country plunged into the greatest economic crisis of its existence, I lost any feeling of singularity that I might have cherished. My poverty was a very common and widespread disease by the spring of 1933. Mark Golden went with me to buy a new shirt and a new tie. It was an unusual type of draft upon the union's bank account, and I suppose he felt that he should witness the expenditure and at least have something to say in the selection of the tie. We chose a blue tie with thin, diagonal white stripes, dignified and conservative. A suggestion that Ben and I be provided with new suits was vetoed. Not only was there insufficient time for suits to be properly tailored, but it was felt that the President should be aware that he faced representatives of the Miners Union, not the National Confederation of Labor.

4

Jack Mullen drove us to the airport, and Lena and Oscar Suzic came along, less because we were on our way to Washington to see the President than because officials of the Miners Union were going to ride in an airplane. We were pioneering. The increasing popularity of air travel had coincided with the shrinkage of our funds. Neither Ben nor I had ever set foot in a plane before, and in a manner of speaking, we were making precedents.

As I boarded the plane, I shared Ben's excitement—so evident in the way his blue eyes sparkled, in his quick, darting glance which took in all of the airport, the plane's exterior, its interior, the details of the seats, the seat belts, the other passengers, the pretty, smiling hostess, the pilots striding through to their compartment in the front. It was a small plane by today's standards, but large to us.

"While we dig like moles," Ben whispered to me, "they've been opening the skies. Look at this. It's a whole way of life, and we didn't know it existed."

I was leafing through my brief case, making sure that nothing we might need had been forgotten. It was stuffed with the history, the hopes, and the tragedy of coal mining. I had the record of every coal miner killed or injured over half a century, of every inadequate law for the protection of the miners—almost a genealogy of every ton of coal ever dug. I had statistics on employment and unemployment, on coal reserve and coal dug, on working pits and idle pits, working tipples and idle tipples, tunnel mines and strip mines. I knew exactly how many cutting machines were in use in the United States and Canada, how many steam shovels, how many drilling machines, and at least roughly the tonnage of accumulated culm the nation over, practical facts and esoteric facts. I was ready, at the merest suggestion, to locate every deposit of anthracite or semi-anthracite, lignate, sub-bituminous, high-volatile bituminous anywhere in the United States. I had at my finger tips comparative protein content in miners' diets over a period of thirty years, statistics on undernourishment, starvation, police brutality, yellow-dog contracts, union mines and non-union mines. I had reports on hospital beds available, medical care, miners' diseases, life expectancy, childbirth, and childbirth mortality. I had a list of almost every colliery in the country, the facts of ownership and some approximation of the conditions that prevailed there. I had graphs and charts tracing the rise of monopoly control in the coal industry, the enormous and increasing holdings of the railroads and steel mills.

Yet worried that something of key importance had been forgotten, I went through my brief case, asking Ben was there anything he could think of. He didn't hear me.

"Think of it, Al," he said. "Seventeen hours by train— four hours this way. It pulls everything together—Montana to Pennsylvania, a few hours."

"Ben, let's review what we have here."

"The point is to own a plane. That makes sense, doesn't it, the union's own plane, always available to it?"

"Ben, the union can't afford to buy a new car. Will you look at this stuff?"

He glanced at the bulging brief case, and nodded, smiling thoughtfully. We were taking off. "You've got all you need, Al—all and a lot more." He continued to smile. "You know, Al, it's going to be interesting from here on in. Damned interesting. What do you think of him?"

"Who?"

"The President."

266

"I don't know. What can you think of someone who's president? I don't know him. He made a lot of promises."

"They all make promises," Ben said. "You remember, Al, you used to get sore at me when I'd talk about someone being born with a silver spoon in his mouth. Well, this one was born with a gold spoon in his mouth, a fat gold spoon with diamonds all over it. How much do you expect him to care about coal miners?"

"It doesn't necessarily follow. Hoover wasn't born with twenty cents."

"No, it doesn't necessarily follow. But it's going to take some doing."

Then we talked about it and around it, and made this plan and that one. What it all came down to was Ben's decision to play it by ear, look for openings and move carefully. Then we watched the clouds beneath us. We were flying over a strangely motionless and limitless world of white, sun-drenched clouds. We both loved it, I think, and Ben more than myself.

5

We checked into our hotel, washed, shaved, changed shirts, and took a cab to the White House. We did it all most casually, as if an afternoon at the White House were an ordinary affair with us, but underneath we were as excited and pleased as two kids. We had been a long time at the bottom—a long time focused on the bleak and dreary landscape of Pomax—a long time of losing. There was no guarantee that any tide had changed, but there was hope and anticipation.

We were halted at the big iron gates, our names checked, and then told to proceed. When we got out of the cab in front of the White House, we glanced at each other, suppressed our smiles, and approved of where we were and how we looked. I think we made an interesting pair, myself tall, skinny, carrying a bulging brief case, and Ben a massive pile of a man in his fleshiness, the youthful spring in his step not lessened, hatless, his big head crowned with a thick mop of iron-gray hair, his eyes as blue and coldly appraising as ever. He was forty-one then, myself six years younger, and the newspapers had taken to referring to him as the "brooding, wounded lion of the miners." But he was neither brooding nor wounded that day, but confident and very much assured in his manner and bearing. When some newspapermen stopped us and asked for a lead on what line or direction the conference would take, Ben shook his head and replied, "No comment," for all the world like an elder statesman who had been doing nothing else for years. He refused to appear impressed, troubled, or uncertain in any way.

We were rescued from the reporters by Johnson Denny, someone very close to the President, one of a tight circle of presidential assistants, and a man of reputed power and importance. He was just forty at that time, a tall, pipe-smoking man, scholarly in attitude, horn-rimmed glasses, and an air of dedication that was, perhaps, a little overworked at times. He took us into his own office first for a briefing, as he put it. We learned that you did not simply walk in and sit down with the President of the United States. There was a matter of protocol and schedule. He informed us on how the meeting would begin and end, and told us that we had exactly one half hour.

Ben exploded. "The devil you say!" he cried. "I've been waiting fifteen years for this, and you tell me that we have half an hour! We can't even begin to dig into this in half an hour, no, sir, not even a beginning. This is coal, sir! This is something basic to our entire existence!"

"I think the President knows that, Mr. Holt," Denny said calmly.

"Does he? I think not. Let me tell you this, Mr. Denny. It was not worth our coming here for half an hour. And let me tell you something else. Half a million coal miners will not be impressed with the fact that the President of the

United States can't spare more than half an hour for their problems."

I watched Ben in amazement, nervous at first, and then beginning to realize that his manner produced results. If one man was President of the United States, the other was president of the International Miners Union, and from the very beginning, Ben Holt refused to admit that one job was less important than the other. He reminded Denny that he had supported the President, and he wondered how debonairly a man could deal with half a million votes, not to speak of the women—for he made the point then and there that a miner's wife voted as the miner voted.

"We're old-fashioned people, we miners, Mr. Denny," Ben said, "and poor people too. It's not often that we can afford a new broom, but by God, when we buy one, we want to know that it sweeps clean."

"Do you realize that man in there is the busiest man in the world?"

"I do," Ben said, "and that's why we're here to see him. People with time to kill come to see me."

Denny spread his hands and nodded. "All right, Mr. Holt. I'll tell you what I'll do. I'll pass a note to the President, mentioning your request that the meeting be extended. Then it will be up to him. If he wants to extend his time, he will. If he doesn't, there is absolutely nothing you and I can do about it. I can tell you this—if you interest him and he sees your problems as vital, the time question will not enter into it. Now, the procedure is this. We will go into his office in exactly five minutes. Understandably, the President will not rise. He will expect you and Mr. Cutter to shake hands with him, and then we will plunge right into the subject, no formalities, no small talk. You will find him a gracious and charming man, and I think you'll be surprised at the breadth of his knowledge. At the same time, he will not hesitate to question anything that may puzzle him. You may answer him frankly and directly."

"I always do," Ben said.

Denny wrote the note about the time extension, and we went to the President's office. I had seen many pictures of him, but they did poor justice to his strong, sunburned face. He was young then, filled with vigor, and giving one the impression that he delighted in his impossible and over-whelming job. Yet whatever he desired to make of his man-ner, he could not exclude a certain haughtiness. As strongly and as warmly as he shook hands, he somehow managed to maintain a curious curtain of separation between himself and the person he spoke to, and if it parted, it never disap-peared.

"Sit down, please, gentlemen," he said, glancing mean-while at the note Denny had handed him. Then he said to the stenographer, "We'll be off the record until I indicate otherwise. Better that way, I think," he concluded, glancing at Ben, who was watching him thoughtfully and with great interest. The stenographer was well trained, for I was to observe that a nod of the President's head was sufficient to place us on the record, a slight shake of his head enough to halt it. "I expected Mrs. Goodrich," he said to Denny, and at that moment she entered, a brisk, sharp-faced gray-haired woman who was the Secretary of Labor. She nodded at the President, and took a chair next to Denny. They sat at one side of the desk, the stenographer at the other, Ben and I facing it.

"Well, Mr. Holt," the President began, "I've heard a good deal about you. I guess that doesn't surprise you?"

"No, sir, it does not."

The President smiled and said, "We do have this in com-mon. Between the two of us, we've been called everything under the sun. How much of it was deserved, time will tell, but I suspect that in both cases, there is exaggeration. Some-time, we'll talk about that. Right now, we'll talk about coal."

"That's what I am here for," Ben agreed.

"Good. I can see that Mr. Cutter brought a large brief case, so you are probably armed with every fact on coal that one could conceivably require. But let's leave the statistics alone for the moment. If I were to ask you, Mr. Holt, to tell me in very few words what is wrong with the coal industry, how would you reply?"

"The industry is sick," Ben said shortly.

"But isn't that true of almost every industry in America right now?"

"It is, Mr. President, but for other industries, it's a recent sickness. Ours is chronic. The coal industry has been sick for a hundred years"—the President nodded slightly and the stenographer began to put down Ben's words—"and this depression only sharpens the pains."

"Why is coal different?" the President demanded.

"Because, sir, mining is different. The very nature of mining makes it singular, and it's always been that way. The miner digs a hole in the earth and crawls into it, and since the first mines were dug five thousand years ago, it's been a dirty, rotten, and different job."

"That's not to the point," the President said, with a slight show of irritation. "I want to know why you feel that coal mining today is basically different. You were talking about sickness. What is coal's particular sickness?"

"Slave labor," Ben said flatly.

"Just what do you mean by that? I don't want slogans, Mr. Holt. Suppose we talk directly to the point."

"That suits me, sir. The point is this. One of the richest deposits of bituminous coal in the United States, if not in the whole world, lies here in the East. Its northern extremities are the northern borders of western Pennsylvania and eastern Ohio, and from there it runs southward, through Pennsylvania and Ohio, encompassing most of the state of West Virginia, the whole of eastern Kentucky, a small wedge of Virginia, a thick slice of central Tennessee, and more or less the northern half of the state of Alabama. Now you can divide this vast area of bituminous fields by drawing a line parallel with the southern border of Pennsylvania. North of this line, with varying degrees of success, depending upon the time and the circumstances, we have been able to organize the miners into the union. Thereby, we have been able to maintain a certain level of wages, not very high, not very uniform, but enough for miners to live like human beings when they worked.

"South of this line, with a few exceptions, our union does not exist. The last time we made a large-scale effort to organize miners in this vast area, which stretches from Pennsylvania to Alabama, was in 1920. I went into West Virginia then, with a staff of union organizers, and we were met by armed thugs, whole armies of company police, and every imaginable type of violence. Thousands of coal miners were driven out of their homes, terror was resorted to, and finally an army of miners faced an army of company police, the two sides drawn up in what threatened to be an actual war—"

"Are those the facts?" the President said to Mrs. Goodrich.

"More or less. There was provocation on both sides, and finally army units were sent in to prevent an outbreak of what could have been localized warfare."

"And since then, Mr. Holt?" the President asked.

"Since then, Mr. President, we have failed in every attempt to organize in the South. The result is that the southern miner is little better than a slave. The fact that he has been reduced to almost indescribable poverty, that he lives more like an animal than a human being, that he never handles cash but spends his existence in debt to the company store, and that he is the constant victim of undernourishment, pellagra, and beriberi—these facts are in the nature of a personal description and condition. They can be put aside. As far as the industry is concerned—"

"They can't be put aside, Mr. Holt," the President interrupted.

"Sir?"

"I am not used to putting the personal condition of the citizens of this country aside, Mr. Holt."

They were watching each other and measuring each other. In one way at least, in their manner of imperious command

272

and self-assuredness, they were remarkably alike, but in every other way, they were as apart as the two poles, the President precise, restrained, controlled, his speech meticulous and clean as the bare, shining surface of his desk, his emotions as alert and as calculated as his voice, his interest in Holt dulled by a seed of distaste for the big, vital, fleshy man who faced him—and Ben Holt loose, relaxed, and wary at once, bristling inwardly at the closeness of an aristocrat, sensitive, seeking for an insult, a rejection or an innuendo where none was meant, defensive but unafraid, pulling over himself, bit by bit, now and through the time to come, that fierce, frightening cloak of pride that marked the digger from all others.

"Nor am I," Ben answered slowly, his voice deepening, his eyes narrowing. "You asked me for the condition of an industry and an explanation of its sickness. What these miners in the South suffer is a badge of shame this whole nation wears; but the same treatment that turns their lives into hell is destroying the American coal industry. In 1928, when we were able to negotiate a contract under union terms, the miner got seven and a half dollars a day—nothing to write home about for the hardest work man has been able to cook up, but enough to keep body and soul together. Today, there isn't a mine in the country where we can negotiate such a contract. Today, it's a great victory to get four dollars a day, and the last operator who signed a four-dollar-a-day contract with me said, 'Well, Ben, I might as well give you that extra dollar as give it to my creditors. I'll be bankrupt in sixty days anyway.' And he was, Mr. President—bankrupt before the sixty days were up. And why? I will tell you why, sir—because the coal operators in West Virginia and Kentucky and Tennessee and Alabama are paying their miners one dollar and fifty cents a day. Yes, sir, one dollar and fifty cents a day for ten hours of tunnel work. Fifteen cents an hour. There's no colliery in the North that can meet such competition, and within another two years there won't be a northern mine operator who doesn't face bankruptcy."

There was no immediate reaction to this. The President sat there staring at Ben, and Ben met his look. The silence stretched before the President turned to Mrs. Goodrich and asked,

"Does your information bear this out?"

She riffled a folder on her lap, and said that to the best of her knowledge, southern wages ranged from two-fifty to three dollars a day.

"Can you back up your statement?" the President asked Ben.

Ben glanced at me, and I dug into the brief case. I handed a file to the President, explaining, "Here, sir, are a list of southern collieries employing, roughly, some sixty-seven thousand miners. That is, at peak production. At any given moment, employment figures may be less than one quarter of the total, but the operating personnel can be considered in terms of some sixty-seven thousand available miners. For the past twenty-four months, wages at these collieries have averaged from one dollar and twenty cents a day to one dollar and sixty cents a day—for a workday from eight to eleven hours. As far as the individual worker is concerned, monthly wages average in a spread from twelve dollars to seventeen dollars. We use the spread to compute our averages, since it gives a better picture than the single figure. You will find there the names of the collieries, the names of the owners, so far as we can determine, and the numbers of workers at minimum to full employment."

The President's face was like stone as he opened the file and began to examine it. Mrs. Goodrich rose and stood next to him, looking over his shoulder. Denny glanced at his watch, scribbled a note and passed it to the President, who brushed it aside and shook his head angrily. Denny rose and tiptoed out of the room, and as the President and Mrs. Goodrich went over my figures, the silence deepened, broken only by the metallic ticktock of a tall clock in one corner of the room and by our breathing. Ben and I dared to glance at each other, and Ben nodded. Denny returned to the room, glancing at us as if to admit defeat. The half hour had passed.

Suddenly, Mrs. Goodrich snapped at me, "Just how reliable are these figures, Mr. Cutter? I have an instinctive mistrust of statistics."

"So do I, Mrs. Goodrich," I replied. "These figures can be checked. I will leave the file here—we have other copies. I can only say that when I offer something like this to the President of the United States, I do not do so lightly. These are figures gathered by our own organizers and sympathizers, and we believe them sufficiently to stake the unions' reputation on them."

"Then you still attempt to organize in the South?" the President asked, looking up from the file.

"I attempt to," Ben nodded. "I still have to live with myself, Mr. President."

"We all have to live with ourselves, Mr. Holt."

"Yes, Mr. President," Ben replied, as if swallowing his impatience and anger, "but the time element varies. I've lived my entire life with this. The men in my family did not die in bed—they died in the mines."

"Do you have the facts on accidental deaths in the South?" Mrs. Goodrich put in. "Diseases—specifically, I mean?"

As I handed her those files, I said, "And would you like the figures on starvation, Mrs. Goodrich?"

The President glanced at me sharply and said, "Just what do you mean by that, Mr. Cutter? I won't have implications. If you have something, come out with it!"

I handed her the file, adding, "It is naturally incomplete. People have a habit of dying quietly in the mountains of Kentucky and West Virginia. But here are almost eleven hundred case histories, three hundred and twenty men; the rest are women and children. Names, towns, ages, and case history wherever that is possible."

She almost tore open the folder, and she and the President stared at it dumbly. Ben threw me a single glance, but within it such a flicker of appreciation and pride that it wiped out every indignity I remembered from the past.

"You, sir!" The President lashed the words at Ben. "Do you mean to tell me that here in these four states, eleven hundred people died of starvation?"

"Only over the past three years," Ben answered calmly. "There are the names, the facts, and the figures."

"You seem very sure of these facts," Mrs. Goodrich said to me.

"I am. Those facts are my business."

"What I want to know," the President said harshly, choosing Denny for his whipping boy now, "is why these statistics are not available to the government? Or are they lies?" Denny shook his head hopelessly, and the President said to Ben, "I don't think you would dare come here and attempt to hoodwink me, Mr. Holt?"

"I would not."

"Mrs. Goodrich," the President said, his voice icy in his need for control, "I want these facts checked. I don't want them disproven. These damned statisticians of ours can prove or disprove anything. I want them checked. If evidence is left out, I want that too, and I want to know why the Department of Labor has not informed me that during the past three years, eleven hundred coal miners and their dependents died of starvation. In these United States! I want to know where shame begins and where shame ends and how much of it we have to bear. And I want an information service in your department that can bring me as much information as this man Cutter. I don't think that's asking too much. Do you?"

Mrs. Goodrich shook her head. "I can tell you, however, why we haven't informed you of this. We didn't know about it. We've only been in practical operation for a few weeks. There's a lot to learn. Do you have anything else you'd like to show me, Mr. Cutter?"

The President stared at me morosely as I took another file from my brief case. "One more thing, yes, a list of the coal operators in Pennsylvania, Ohio, Illinois, Indiana, Missouri, and Ohio who have filed bankruptcy proceedings. Over twelve hundred during the past year, mostly small operators, family mines, so to speak."

"Small businessmen," Ben nodded. "I know every one of them—either by name or sight. Decent people who believe in this country and our way of life. Their reward for such belief was ruin."

"You'll spare me the preachment, Mr. Holt," the President said thinly, staring at our latest exhibit. "All right, here you are. You've presented your case—"

"Forgive me, only a small part of it."

The President was not used to being interrupted in the middle of a sentence, and I was a little puzzled by the way Ben constantly and deliberately provoked a temper already exacerbated. Afterwards, he told me that his fear was that the President, at each particular moment, would accept our facts, lay them away wrapped in pity or sympathy, and propose a vague assuagement in a vaguer future. Ben's notion was that by provocation and irritation, he could force the President to throw the solution into his lap. Perhaps he was right, for now the President stared at him for a long moment, and then said in a voice of ice,

"A small part of it, yes. But you didn't come here for sympathy, Mr. Holt. You've spelled out the sickness. Now suppose you outline the cure."

"There is only one cure."

"Only one? Modesty appears to be one of your virtues, Mr. Holt."

"No, sir, Mr. President—neither modesty nor immodesty enters into this. Mining is my life, the only thing I've studied and the only thing I know. And I tell you that the only cure for this situation is to make the right to organize workers into a trade union as unbreakable and sacred as the right of free speech. This will equalize the North and the South as producers, save hundreds of operators from bankruptcy, firm prices immediately, establish a uniform minimum wage and minimum price—and establish over-all the trade union

277

as the enforcer of standards of fair price and fair competition. There is no other way to give dignity and the right to a decent existence to coal miners." Ben hesitated a moment, staring directly at the President, then added, "There is no other way to save the industry either."

Now, in silence, the President studied both of us thoughtfully, two men he did not like, two arrogant, almost insufferable men who had presumed to come as teachers instead of pleaders—knowing full well that with any other president they would have been shown the door long before now. He watched Ben curiously, thoughtfully, yet distantly, as if his mind were already elsewhere. He was tiring, I felt, and I also felt that no one in that room, myself included, was inclined toward sentimentalism. Should I except Ben? Mark Golden, in moments of great anger, would define Ben Holt as a "mental slob." It was a filthy, nasty backhanded definition of a man, and you had to know Ben Holt a long time to comprehend the strange truth of it, not a validity in terms of contempt but a furious tag for something soft and gentle inside of Ben Holt, deep inside of him and well hidden. If we had laid eleven hundred corpses dead of starvation upon the desk of the President, only one person in the room truly wept for the dead—that was Ben Holt. An hour later, he would be using those same corpses cheerfully and cunningly, but now he wept for them; and when the President looked at his big, earnest face, he saw the face of an angry if unlovable prophet; and if he never understood this man, Ben Holt, that was not surprising. Few others did.

"You know what you're asking?" the President finally said.

"I imagine others have asked for it. I imagine you've thought of it."

Without any emotion now, the President said, "Have you thought about the power such a law would put in your hands?"

"The world moves with power. Mine or someone else's. Now the southern operators have the power. If you break their power, you must give the power to someone else."

"I think there are other ways," Mrs. Goodrich said.

"There are no other ways."

Denny spoke suddenly, "You can't just write such a law and pass it. There's never been a law like that. It would change every basic concept of America."

The President watched Ben and said nothing.

"It would not," Ben replied, a note of boredom in his voice now, and the thought in my mind of what a consummate actor he could have been, had his ambitions ever turned in that direction. "It changes nothing. We fought it through in the North. We have the right to organize—by common law, if you will, or by our own blood and guts. It will simply apply a civilizing influence in the South."

"And if such a law is not forthcoming?" the President wanted to know.

"All right," Ben nodded. "You leave us two choices. Give up. Let the industry die in the North. Our miners won't become slaves. The union can die, and the industry will die with it—"

"And the other choice?"

"To go into the South with guns. I tried that once. I'll never try it again, so it would have to be someone else's choice. I hate guns. That's not the way I work, and I don't believe in issues that are decided by armies. I don't like to see something like this destroyed. It's easier to pass a law."

"Is it, Mr. Holt? A law has to be enforced."

"Give us the law, and we'll enforce it."

"I don't make the laws, Mr. Holt."

"I think you do, Mr. President—your voice carries."

"Very well, we'll see."

"And that's all you leave me with?"

"Do you want a commitment, Mr. Holt?"

"I do, sir."

The President shook his head. "You know I can't give you such a commitment, Mr. Holt. Let me say this: coal is the food and lifeblood of this nation, and coal will be dug. Of that, you may be sure. And you may also be sure that so long as I have a voice and a will, the men who dig coal will not die of starvation. But I make no commitments. We will both of us do what we can—and make no foolish promises or prognostications. Do you agree?"

Then, to all effects and purposes, the meeting was over. We remained there a little longer, and then we met separately with Mrs. Goodrich, leaving her our charts, statistics, and material. Denny escorted us from the White House, to where an official car waited to take us back to the hotel.

Not until we were in the car and in motion, did Ben permit himself a grin—a grin that seemed to spread all over his face and down through his body.

6

At dinner that evening, Ben asked me what I thought of the President. I replied that I didn't know exactly what I thought, except that here was an unusually complicated man, and Ben brushed this aside with the observation that all human beings were complicated. Since we were taking the morning plane back to Pomax and could now calculate our expenses, we had decided to allow ourselves a good meal at a sea-food place around the corner from the hotel. It was called Jacksons, and was justly celebrated, and for two and a half dollars apiece, we ate all the fish and chowder we could contain. Finished and sitting back with our cigars, I told Ben that it was much more important to know what he thought of us.

"That's no mystery," Ben said. "He hated our guts."

"Wait a minute, Ben—that's a hell of an observation."

"Why? Isn't it true?"

"No. I was there too."

"You've got to get over the beautiful glow of being invited to the White House and being talked at by the President of the United States."

"Well, there's certainly no question of how you feel about him. I grant that."

"What would you like, Al?" Ben shrugged. "You want me to love him? Did he ever do a day's work—I mean with his hands? That kind of Harvard aristocrat cuts no ice with me. He disliked me, and I disliked him. I prefer it that way. It's plain and clean and simple that way, and I don't intend to be loused up in any adoration-of-the-leader movement. As far as he is concerned, I'm a thick-necked coal miner, minus a haircut, wearing a suit five years out of style and a pair of four-dollar shoes. Not in a hundred years would he invite me to his house to do anything but fix the furnace, and I'm damned if I enjoy being at the receiving end of that long nose of his."

"I'm sorry," I said.

"Why?"

"Because it might be easier if you liked him."

"Like hell it would. Let me tell you something, Al—we won the biggest victory there today in the past twenty years of mining, and we won it hands down. And, God damn it, we walked in there like men and we walked out of there like men."

"Then you think we'll get that law?"

"I know we'll get it. We'll get it because he understands coal—and because he realizes that we're both boxed in and there's no other way out."

Ben was right. Three and a half months later, the right of labor to organize and bargain collectively became a part of the law of the land. But in his own mind, there was never any doubt, and he moved ahead with absolute certainty, gambling everything we had on his faith in the way he had assessed the man in the White House. He had meeting after meeting, in Chicago and again in New York, with the leaders of the National Confederation of Labor, swallowing his contempt for them and pleading, shouting, threatening in the cause of a national labor act. We held interviews with the press, gave out stories on the question, testified before Senate and House committees, and finally, in Ben's house one night, took our own first steps in the direction that had become, almost maniacally, Ben's destiny.

7

I remember that night very well, because in the morning of the same day, Andy Lust, the chief of police, arrested a sixteen-year-old boy for theft. The kid's name was Sam Cofferman, and he was one of eleven children of an unemployed miner. He had walked into the grocery, green-goods, and general store that belonged to the Amsterdam Coal Company and had attempted to hold up the owner for the contents of the cash register.

Sam Cofferman was too young, too frightened, and he had a toy gun. Somewhere, he had read that under such circumstances, it did not matter whether the gun was real or not, but the storekeeper had not read the same article, and with the assistance of the clerk, he took the toy gun from Sam and sent for the police. The boy's father, Hank Cofferman, was angry and puzzled—for he was a good father who brought up his kids decently and had attempted to impress upon them that slow death from starvation or undernourishment was better than stolen groceries. Perhaps I have never totally understood this type of reasoning, but it was widespread and it held through the thirties, when it was put to a very severe test. When news of the arrest got to the father, Hank Cofferman came to us. I was with Mark Golden at the time, in Mark's office, and after we heard Cofferman's story, I took the liberty of telling the man that I thought it would come out all right. Mark himself never said a word, only staring at me glumly as I reassured Cofferman about the boy, stating that it would not come to trial and that we could effect his release.

"You understand, Al," Cofferman said to me, "the boy's

got to be punished, but it wouldn't be the right punishment to send him to jail. We've had things pretty bad, not too much to eat, not much of anything, and this damnfool kid decided to take things into his own hands. I don't hold with that, and I'll read him the law, believe me, I will. But if he goes to jail, he's going to come out bad, the way they all do. It would break his ma's heart."

Hank Cofferman was skinny, hollow-cheeked, cough-ridden, and full of weariness and despair. When he walked out, the memory of every meal I had eaten during the past month rose up and turned to ashes in my mouth, and the taste was not improved by Mark Golden's irritation.

"Why did you tell him that, Al?"

"He's got trouble enough."

"Well, he's going to have more trouble. Andy Lust won't release his son."

"What? Is this something new?"

"Andy Lust is a rat who left a sinking ship. I happen to know that the Amsterdam Coal Company is paying him twenty-five dollars a week. It's a cheap price, but everything comes cheap these days."

His prediction turned out to be correct. Ben and I went to see Lust, who, as a pillar of law and order, explained that unless examples were made and the law enforced, Pomax would be the equivalent of a jungle.

"So you're going to start with this poor kid who was half-starved and wanted some groceries for his family?" Ben demanded.

"He broke the law, Ben."

"What law! What did he do, make a bluff with a toy pistol? I hear he was shaking like a leaf all the time."

"Ben, the law's the law. I'm sworn to uphold the law."

"Then you're going to make this stick?"

"That's right, Ben."

"You're forgetting, aren't you, Andy? This is a mining town, a union town."

"You're forgetting, Ben," Lust answered thinly. "What's

left of your union is stuck together with spit and tissue paper, and the first time it rains, that also goes. Don't tell me about union towns. I recognize one when I see it."

"I want that kid released," Ben said softly. "Do you hear me?"

"I don't hear you. I don't even listen to you."

Grabbing Lust by the front of his jacket, Ben pulled the chief of police to him. "You lousy, tinhorn cop—who the hell do you think you're talking to?"

"Just one more word, Ben, and I pull you in for assault and battery and resisting a police officer."

Ben flung him away, and we turned on our heels and walked out. Panting with suppressed anger, Ben said to me, "Al, I don't ever want cops on my side—nothing but grief from these cheap, dirty sellouts. They sell out one, they sell out another. You remember that crazy Jim Flecker down in Clinton?"

"I remember," I nodded.

"Same thing. Brought us nothing but grief and misery. But Andy Lust—well, I'll see him again."

8

That was the day Mark, Lena, and I had dinner at Ben's house, and Ben outlined his plan to Mark and myself. Ben was late because he was with the district attorney. The Cofferman business stuck in his craw, and he would have to spit it out before he could taste food. Mark and Lena and I walked over to Ben's place, and had a drink with Dorothy, waiting for Ben.

Norah Holt opened the door for us. She had grown into a long-legged, sullenly good-looking girl, soon to be fifteen, tall, full-breasted, and already seething with the frustration of a place like Pomax.

If she had been a saint, Norah's role would still have presented difficulties; but she was far from a saint. A combination of Ben's big frame, his drive and burning desires, and Dorothy's beauty, she was trapped, thwarted, and angry. Education in Pomax left much to be desired, and a poor high school of necessity truncated its curriculum to the lowest possible median. Nor was Pomax a place sought out by good teachers. So Dorothy and Ben, but in particular Dorothy, gave their children what they could, tutored them, led them into reading—and on Dorothy's part, if all unwittingly, into desires that could never be realized. It told less on Sam and Ben, Jr., who were younger, but Norah learned to hate and resent all too early. She was torn between contempt for the miners' children and her need for companionship, between hatred of poverty and her mother's dignity and pride in poverty, between the fact of being the daughter of a trade unionist and the dream of upper-class life—or so it seemed to her—that filtered through from Dorothy's memories and the summers at Ringman. At Ringman, she could act out her dreams, but across Belfast Ridge, there were the collieries and pits. Thus, she hated what she was, yet had to take refuge in pride of what she was; and she had enough of Ben, his charm and boldness, to be popular among the miners.

Now, as she opened the door, she wanted to know about Sam Cofferman. Was it true that he was in jail and to be indicted for robbery? It was true, I told her.

Dorothy entered the living room as Norah said to me, "And you allowed it, Al—you and Dad! Because a decent kid couldn't watch his family starve to death, you let him go to jail! Oh, you both make me so ashamed!"

"Norah!" Dorothy exclaimed.

"She's right," I shrugged. "I make her ashamed. I'm ashamed too."

"No! You don't talk to Al like that, Norah."

"Now wait a minute," Mark said. "This thing isn't over by a long shot. Ben is with the district attorney right now. It's not as open and shut as you might think, Norah."

"I know one thing," Norah cried, "that if anyone belongs in jail, it's Andy Lust!"

Tight-lipped, Dorothy said to her, "That's enough, Norah. That's quite enough. Come with me."

They went into the kitchen, and Lena followed them. Mark stood there, regarding me moodily. I asked him whether the Cofferman boy would get off. "No, he won't get off," Mark said, and then he went to the window and stared out at the darkening street. "I hate this lousy place," he said slowly. "I hate myself, and I am beginning to hate every day I spend here. I was fifty-five years old last week. You know, Al"—he turned to me—"I never said anything like this before. I never felt this way before."

I nodded. There was nothing I could think of to say, and a half hour later, when Ben came home, Mark's prediction was confirmed. The district attorney went along with Andy Lust, and the Cofferman boy was to serve as an example of a basic shift in the balance of forces at Pomax. But at dinner, Ben said,

"You know, they're wrong."

He brought that out of the air, apropos of nothing. We had been praising Dorothy's food, something we did uneasily, for the truth is that she was not a very good cook. I think that on this night, we had a stew of some kind. The children had eaten, and it must be said of Lena that she lightened Dorothy's load. She was an easy kind of a guest, helping and never pushing, as if she found in the Holt house in Pomax all that she had ever desired. Like so many women, single and past the age of her best dreams and hopes, she played house.

Now we were relaxed, eating the stew and praising it when Ben made his remark, and Mark asked him who was wrong.

"Lust and Jerry." Jerry Hurst was the district attorney in Pomax County.

"About what?"

"About the union," Ben said between mouthfuls, chewing as he spoke. "About us being finished. That's a damn-

286

fool kind of judgment. A year from now, we'll have half a million members."

"Why don't you whistle that?" Mark smiled.

"I can't, I'm eating." He chewed and said, "Look here, Mark—what about the treasury? How much money have we got?"

"Don't you know?"

"I never could keep track of money worth a damn," Ben replied.

Mark had barely tasted his food. He had a small appetite and ulcers. Now he looked at Ben rather strangely, a trace of amusement on his face, as he said,

"I love you, Ben. So help me God, I do. What do you want money for?"

"I want to hire two hundred organizers," Ben replied mildly, still eating and talking through the food as he chewed. "I'm going to organize this damned industry from top to bottom. I'm going into every damned state where there's a single pit, and I'm going to tell the miners, 'The President says, organize. It's the law of the land!'"

"And when do you intend to do this?" Mark asked, a trace of his smile still with him.

"Al," Ben said to me, "how long do you think it has to take to find two hundred organizers?"

"A month."

"A month?" Ben frowned.

"It's not the law of the land yet."

"It will be," Ben said.

"Maybe not."

"I'll gamble on it," Ben said.

"I wish to hell you wouldn't eat and talk at the same time!" Mark snapped at him. "How much do you need to satisfy that appetite of yours?"

"I always had a good appetite," Ben said. "What about the money, Mark?"

"You're out of your mind."

"Maybe. The money?"

"You can't just put your hands on the money," Mark said with sudden irritation. "We got a little over eleven thousand dollars; we also have bills and debts to fifteen thousand dollars."

"Don't pay any bills or debts. Let them wait."

"Ben, try to understand me. We pay our bills. We always have. That's why our credit is good. One thing this union's always had is a sound financial structure and reputation. You can't just dip into the treasury and clean it out for some harebrained scheme."

Ben finished eating, wiped his mouth, and said, "If our credit is that good, go out and borrow, Mark. We'll need about twenty thousand dollars for the first big push."

Suddenly all three of them—Mark, Lena, and Dorothy —realized that Ben was quite serious. Ben looked from face to face. Then he grinned and said,

"That poor, stupid bastard, Andy Lust. I won't forget him. Indeed I won't."

9

When I walked over to the desk to get my key, back at the Pomax House, Abner Gross said to me, "Evening, sonny. How was the food over at Ben's?" The old man was eighty-three, and this was just a few months before he died. We had become good friends, and when Abner died, he left me a hundred dollars in his will, "to buy a decent set of clothes with." He had no one in the whole world; they had all died, even the ancient, profane bellhop had passed away, and a pimply-faced seventeen-year-old had taken his place.

I told him that food was food.

"And that counts now," Abner nodded. "Good heavens, eighty-three years, Alvin, and I never seen such a hungry time as this. Sometimes, I just close my eyes and dream about the passenger pigeons, as if dreaming about them would bring them back."

"Passenger pigeons?"

"You wouldn't know about them, sonny." He licked his lips. "But them was tasty, believe me, and succulent, and no one had to go hungry. Back in the sixties and seventies, round about this time of the year, they come swarming in, maybe ten, fifteen, twenty million birds right here in the delta country. They'd be so thick you couldn't see the sky and they'd make a noise like a storm on the lakes. Then they'd settle down in the woods outside Pomax, and the miners would go out with sticks and just knock them over and fill their bags with them, and it was the kind of a slaughter you wouldn't even dream about, maybe four or five hundred birds to a man. But no one went hungry then, you can be sure. But each year there was fewer and fewer of them passenger pigeons—Lord, no one ever considered that they would run out. But run out they did. Just disappeared, every last one of them killed by the greed and hungriness of man. Well, that's the way it goes."

"That's the way it goes, Abner," I nodded, and I went on up to bed.

10

About a week later, I was sitting in my office in the Union Building at Pomax, when the door opened and Gus Empek walked in. It was years since the last time I had seen him— the time of the 1928 convention in Chicago—but he had not changed much. People built like Gus Empek don't. He had a little more girth and his hair had thinned and he looked tired, but otherwise no different; and he put out his hand without too much confidence as he said,

"Hello, Al."

I shook hands with him. I had never learned to dislike Gus Empek. There was something direct and uncomplaining about him; his round, heavily fleshed face was without guile, and his permanent sadness pulled at you and frustrated annoyance. Also, I had no illusions about how we had used him that time in Chicago. A man shouldn't be used that way.

"I hear you've broken with the Associated bunch. What are you doing these days, Gus?"

He shrugged. "The best I can. I dig when there's work. There ain't much work, Al. You know that."

"I know." I pulled over a chair for him, and offered him a cigarette, which he accepted gratefully. "I smoke on my friends now," he acknowledged. "It's a terrible feeling to feel that you're one step away from being a bum."

My hand went into my pocket, and he said, "No—no, please, Al. I didn't come here to make a touch. How's Ben?"

"You haven't seen him?"

"No. I walked straight into your office before anyone could spot me and throw me out."

"No one's going to throw you out, Gus. That's no way to talk. About Ben—well, Ben's Ben."

"I know. Son of a bitch, he's still the best man we ever had in this rotten industry. Tell me something, Al—" He leaned toward me, staring at me eagerly. "Is it true, what the boys say about you and Ben?"

"What do they say?"

He crossed his stubby fingers. "That you're like this with the President! That he gave you the go-ahead signal—and that Ben's going out to organize the industry?"

"More or less. We're going out on an organizing drive— a big one. Ben's aim is the whole industry, half a million members. I think we'll do something, but whether we'll end up with that many—well, who the hell can say!"

"You will," Empek nodded. "The time's ripe. Al, it's so ripe it stinks. There never was a better time than this. When they think you're done and finished, then they're not looking your way—no, sir."

"It's as good a time as any," I agreed.

"Al—Al, tell me, you hiring organizers?"

I stared at him for a while, before I nodded and agreed that we were taking on organizers.

"Al, give me a job. I'm through with the Associated—I split with Brady and that bunch. Al, I'll work for fifteen dollars a week, smokes and food, that's all I need—Jesus Christ, I'll work for nothing, if it comes down to that. You know what this industry means to me—I spent my life with it. Al, I'm forty-seven years old—what have I got left? Ten years ago, my wife walked out on me. The hell with it, she said. She's not married to a man, she's married to a union. I need this, Al. I'm a good organizer, you know that, and I know coal from A to Z. So give me a break—"

"Wait a minute—wait a minute, Gus," I broke in. "You know I can't hire you. Let's go in and talk to Ben."

"He'll blow his top," Empek said hopelessly. "He'll see me, and he'll come at me screaming."

"Maybe he will maybe he won't. But I can't hire anyone without Ben's approval. If you're going to work here," I said flatly, "you might as well know how this union is run. We got an executive board and we hold elections, but it's Ben Holt's union, and it moves the way Ben Holt wants it to."

"Don't I know that, Al?"

"All right. Let's go in and see Ben."

I went to the door and held it open, and Gus walked through. Lena and Mullen had just come into the outer office, and they stared at Empek as I led him through to Ben's office. We had just taken on another girl, a young kid called Ruth McClosky, to help Lena set up the organization patterns and to take care of Ben's correspondence. She had a new push-button arrangement on her desk to call Ben with, but when she moved to use it, I pushed her hand away and walked in, herding Empek in front of me and closing the door behind me. Ben looked up from where he sat at his desk, stared at Empek moodily for a moment, and then said,

"Sit down, Gus—tell me how you've been."

Empek sat slowly, watching Ben. "Well, you know, Ben. It goes this way and it goes that way."

"I heard how you broke with Brady and the others."

"I had to, Ben," Empek said, turning his hat in his hands, staring at the floor. "I had to. A man's got to do some things for his self-respect."

Ben nodded and waited.

"I hear you're going out and organize?" Empek said. Ben nodded again.

"I'm a good organizer," Empek said.

"The best," Ben agreed.

"Give me a job, Ben," Empek said suddenly. "For Christ's sake, Ben, give me a job. I'll work for nothing. I'll work for cigarette money."

"You make me sick," Ben said. "You talk about self-respect, and then you come in here and plead with me and tell me you're going to work for nothing. What the hell kind of self-respect is that?"

"I was afraid you'd throw me out, Ben."

"Then I'd throw you out. Where you been eating, Gus?"

"Soup kitchens."

Ben went into his pocket for his wallet and pulled out a ten-dollar bill. "Here, take this and get something to eat that will stay with you. We're paying twenty-five a week, and this is against your first week's pay. Talk to Lena outside, and she'll tell you where you can find a room. It'll be maybe a week or ten days until we get moving, but there'll be something to do until then."

Empek remained seated, staring at the floor.

"Well, what is it? You want the job, don't you?"

When Empek looked up, his face was wrinkled and quivering, his little eyes red and wet. He tried to talk, but he couldn't. Ben rose, walked around to him, and gripped his shoulder. "O.K., Gus," Ben said, "sit a while and take it easy."

"Thanks, Ben," Empek managed.

"What in hell are you thanking me for? You'll get your neck broken and your hide beat off. So help me God, I could never figure diggers—a lot of crazy bastards." And then he motioned to me, and we walked out, leaving Empek alone.

11

When we began, after that dinner at Ben's house, and fought it out on the executive board—giving it to Ben his way, as always—I would have said that it would take months to set up a complete organization pattern, hire over a hundred organizers, and set out to organize coal fields in twenty states of the country. But Ben laid out a schedule of three weeks, and actually we were ready to move in nineteen days. I have no clear memory of how it happened—except that after months and years of defeat and despair and frustration, we suddenly had a job and a goal. We worked day and night. I had wondered where organizers would come from—and to this day I don't know how the word got around; but it got around, and suddenly it was known in Chicago and Pittsburgh and Scranton and Denver and in a hundred towns and villages, and just as suddenly, for ourselves and our purpose, Pomax became the center of the country. Men poured in—men we had not seen for years and men we had never seen before, old men, bent, work-twisted, with thirty years in the pits behind them, young men without jobs or hope of jobs, diggers, trade unionists whose unions had died in the depression, steelworkers, auto workers, college students full of working-class dreams and socialist ideals, socialists, anarchists, old wobblies, and tough, organization-skilled communists.

We asked for only two qualifications, that a man should know something about mining and be able to organize. If he had that and was willing to be sent anywhere under any conditions, he was our man. If he was willing to be distrusted by the workers he went to, beaten up by the local police, threatened, hounded, and ready to work for twenty-five dollars a week, no expenses paid, he was our man. And it was surprising how many came, ready, willing, and eager.

A number of them were communists. Ben hated communists. "They are controlled," he would say, but it went deeper than that, and basic to the matter was the fact that he could not control them. They were also useful, even when they were non-existent, for he could blame them, as he had, through the mouth of Fulton Grove, at the Arrowhead affair. They were the most useful of scapegoats for anything and everything that might happen, and they were also good organizers, often the best. About what they preached and stood for, Ben knew little or nothing, but loathed it without knowing it. It was the one religion, the single folklore that he could be openly and violently against, and since they were most often against him, the situation never improved.

But during our preparations at Pomax, a curious truce was declared. We needed enthusiasts, dedicated men, idealists, miners, professional trade unionists—but above all, we needed skilled, trained organizers, and without the communists there were simply not enough. Ben hired them, but he made his conditions plain. I remember one of the communists whose name was Lou Broderick, a man in his late twenties and a miner from western Pennsylvania. He had been active in his own local since he was a kid, and when he walked into the building at Pomax, we all knew him and who he was. He made no secret of it.

"You know what I think of you and your goddamn organization," Ben said.

He nodded. "And you know what I think of you, Ben."

"All right. That's clear. When you finish this job, you're through. I wash my hands of you."

"If that's the way you want it, Ben."

"That's the way I want it. Take it or leave it."

He took it. Ben didn't understand why any more than I did. It was like a tool you took and used, without ever knowing what made it work; but in all justice it should be said that communists were not the only men Ben used and cast

294

aside when he had no more need for them. He was in motion now, and nothing could turn him from his goal. He had only one measure, one yardstick—would it advance the process of organization?—and by that measure he gauged everything. His temper grew shorter, his manner more demanding, more imperious than ever before. Often, a certain sullenness took hold of him. He would not talk about anything but the organizing drive. When other matters were discussed, he remained silent. He was nervous and fretful, ate huge amounts of food rapidly and without any evidence of discrimination or appreciation, stuffed himself. Once, discovering that Jack Mullen had hired a man he despised, he turned on Jack and snarled,

"You fool! You goddamned horse's ass, can't you ever use your brains!"

No one talked to Mullen like that, and for a moment, watching them stand face to face, I thought they would destroy each other. But it passed. Mullen walked out of it in silence, and an hour later Ben was apologizing to him.

There was one night I walked over to Ben's house at about nine in the evening, taking some letters for him to sign that had to be posted the same evening. Lena Kuscow opened the door, motioning for me to be silent. From inside, I heard the sound of a violin accompanied by a piano, and when I walked into the living room, there was Mark Golden playing on the violin, and Dorothy at the piano. Dorothy had brought the piano with her when she married Ben, but I had never heard her play. Mark Golden with a violin was a complete surprise to me. Entranced, I stood there and listened, the whole audience Lena and myself. Ben was not there.

When they finished, we applauded, and Dorothy turned to me, smiling and delighted. "Do you like it, Al?" she wanted to know.

"It's wonderful. I just didn't know, Dotty—not about you, nor about Mark."

"Neither did I," Dorothy said. "Or if I did, I've forgotten. And Mark is very good, don't you think?"

Mark disclaimed the praise, and there was some talk about this and that, when I remembered the letters for Ben. They told me that he was up in the bedroom. As I went upstairs, they began another duet. In the bedroom, door and windows closed, Ben sprawled on his bed, in a rank haze, smoking a cigar and reading a newspaper. I knew better than to comment on the scene downstairs. I gave him the letters, and after he had read them through, he signed them.

"We got to get moving, Al," he said. "We can't sit around on our collective ass."

"We're getting there, Ben. As of tonight, we've hired over a hundred organizers."

"It's enough. I want to get moving. I can't stand this place. It stinks. It's the asshole of all creation."

"Take it easy, Ben. It's no worse today than it was a year ago."

"It's worse—it's a year worse. Hell, this is no place for a union like ours to have its headquarters anyway. There's only one place for a national union to have its headquarters, Washington."

"We couldn't afford to ship the furniture to Washington, Ben," I said.

When I came downstairs, finally, Mark and Lena were leaving. I walked with them for a while. Lena said to me, "You should have stayed and talked to Dotty."

I shrugged.

"You give me a bitter pain, Cutter," she said.

"Let him be," Mark told her. "Don't push trouble, Lena. Just wait for it, and it will come." And to me, "What do you think, Al—are we going to be the proud employees of the biggest, richest union in these United States a year from now?"

"Sooner than that," I replied. "I'm beginning to understand Ben Holt—a little."

12

There is neither space nor need here to detail the endless hours of meeting we spent working out the blueprint of the organizing drive of 1933. Sufficient to say that again and again and again, we sat through half the night, planning our campaign as, I suspect, few battles in history have been planned—and slowly, steadily, if reluctantly, my respect for Ben Holt increased. His knowledge of coal mining was enormous, encyclopedic, and constantly surprising. I would guess that there were at least two hundred collieries he was familiar with out of direct, personal knowledge, and twice that many he knew by reputation. He knew the character, capability, and dependability of dozens of local leaders. He knew a hundred operators, how they should be approached, what their weaknesses were, what action they would take against organization. When, with him, we pooled our knowledge, we comprised an extraordinary picture and grasp of the industry— and we tried to leave little to chance.

The allocation of area was Ben's. He spelled it out at a meeting where the core of the organizing process were present—a young miner called Fred Soames, twenty-five, dark, serious, and the most likely successor to old Dan Jessup, who led the Pomax organization; Gus Empek; Jack Mullen; Oscar Suzic; Mark Golden; Lena Kuscow; Dan Jessup, sixty-nine now, but still vigorous; and myself. Ben explained to us that he had broken down the areas of coal production in terms of the number of pits and the difficulties to be encountered—and that in each case, we would have varying degrees of local assistance to call upon.

"First of all," he said, "we'll take the Rocky Mountain area. Geographically, it's large, but in terms of production, it's the smallest area we have to deal with. That doesn't make it less dangerous or difficult—and it cannot be thought of for a moment in terms of any second-class citizenship.

Now what I'm doing here now is tentative. I'm assigning Oscar to head up the drive there, and I'm going to give him fifteen men." He turned to Suzic. "How does that sound, Oscar?"

"Pretty good, Ben. I want to think about it."

"In some ways, that's the worst area," Mullen observed. "You got half a continent out there, and some very nasty operators. That's a big chunk for Oscar alone."

"Then he'll grow up out there," Ben smiled. "What else? We use what we got. Some day we'll have a headquarters out there and a staff and half a dozen broads for Oscar to play with. Until then, he'll do it himself. But you, Jack"—he thrust a thick finger at Mullen—"you get the pivot of the whole thing, Illinois, Indiana, western Kentucky, Missouri, and Iowa, but the friggen heart of it is Illinois, right here, and going out from here. Here's the backbone. Everything else is flesh, but you give me a backbone like an iron ramrod shoved up this industry's ass, and I'll put the flesh on it."

"How many organizers?" Mullen demanded.

"I'll give you thirty to start, more if you need them. Dan Jessup will work with you, and you can use this building and whatever staff is left here as your working headquarters. Lena turned over her old Model T to the union. It runs, but not so good, but it runs. You also have the Chevy and the old pickup, so you'll have three cars at your disposal. Except for Pennsylvania, you'll have the biggest budget. You'll have Ruth as a working secretary, and you can hire another girl. You'll get all your printing here in Pomax on credit, and the mimeograph room in the building is at your disposal. I think that's a nice setup."

"It's all right," Mullen grunted.

"It's better than all right. What do you want, the sky?"

"What about Pennsylvania?" Mullen demanded.

"I think Mark knows Pennsylvania better than any of us."

Never one to trouble about another's feelings, Mullen observed bluntly that Mark was anything but young. "Mark's tired," he said. "He's a good lawyer but he's not a miner."

"Thanks for everything," Mark said sourly. "There's no need to be nasty, Jack. Try a little, and you can be a thoroughgoing louse."

"Will you cut that!" Ben roared. "What are you—kids? Are we playing games? Just live a little, Jack, and you'll know as much as Mark does about mining and diggers. As for being a miner, who the hell is there in this room who put his hand to a pick in the past ten years? Soames—he's too young to have the belly fat of a pro yet, and Gus Empek. Not you, Jack, and not me."

"Knock it off," Mullen said.

"All right. Mark takes Pennsylvania. I'm giving him Fred Soames because you, Freddy"—he turned to Soames now—"you got the youth and energy, and some brains too. Lena will head up the staff in Pittsburgh, and we'll use local headquarters there and all the local staff that's left. There are good people there, and they'll give you whatever help they can."

"How many organizers will we have, Ben?" Lena asked.

"About forty. More if we can spare them. You'll want a concentration in Scranton as well as the West, because there's no reason why we can't sign every damn digger in anthracite. You can make a secondary base at Ringman— what in hell am I going into this now for? I told you all that Mark knows Pennsylvania better than I do." He turned abruptly to Empek. "Gus—you still want to thank me?"

"Where do you want me to go, Ben?" Empek asked softly.

"You ever been to Alabama and Tennessee?"

"I been there," Empek nodded, smiling slightly.

"There never was a union there," Ben sighed. "Not even a lousy little organization for them to break. But they tell me the climate's nice and the scenery's good. I want you to take twenty men down there and organize it."

Empek nodded thoughtfully, and then he sat for a little while, turning it over in his mind. I have wondered sometimes whether he wasn't the only person in that room who truly knew Ben, understood him and loved him. In later

299

years, when it was forgotten how much came out of a handful of organizers who set out to build a union in the coal fields, it was acknowledged that a good many persons in high places owed a good deal to Ben Holt. It was noted that they respected Ben, honored him, admired him, and all that goes with it, but it was never specified that they loved Ben. I think Gus Empek loved him. I think that even in the worst of times, when the name Associated Miners was the equivalent of scab in every town in Egypt, Gus Empek loved Ben. It has often been held that Empek was just a boob, and others said that from the very beginning he was Ben's boy and that Ben paid him to do his antics with the Associated Miners, the point being that he was Ben's foil and presented various opportunities for Ben to shine.

But Empek was neither a boob nor a cheap hired hand nor a traitor of any kind; and that kind of thinking was as specious as the thinking that Ben sent him down south in the hope that Empek would be knocked around or jailed or maybe beaten to death. The plain truth was that Ben had something of the same feeling about Empek as Empek had about him, and he sent Empek to the South because he knew that Empek had good sense and guts and that nothing on earth would stop him from doing what he had to do.

Empek knew this, and it was a consideration as he thought the thing through and finally said to Ben, "I got no complaints about that part of the country, Ben—but it's only half the job. Who's going to back me up in West Virginia and Kentucky?"

"I saved that for Al and me," Ben said. "We both cherish old memories about West Virginia."

13

It was no surprise to me that Ben had selected West Virginia as the state in which to begin the drive, and I would have staked my life on the fact that the town would be Clinton. Ben's memory was as long as his life, and the simple if primitive credo, "Reward your friends, punish your enemies," could have served as a definition of a good part of his philosophy. He had been driven out of West Virginia. He had never been driven out of another place.

We had twenty organizers with us, and we rode to Clinton by day coach, sleeping in our seats through the night. We were now operating on the ultimate financial resources of the union with a foreseeable dead end; at such a point, unless we succeeded, bankruptcy would envelop us and the union with us.

So we rode day coach, ate sandwiches, and lived in our shirts. I never heard Ben Holt complain. He was indifferent to poverty, just as he was indifferent to the physical conditions that surrounded him at a given moment. In his mind, it was all flux, it was all motion. The very concept of standing still, of building in a single place, of permanence and security, did not exist for him. He was both driven and the driver, and chained to both conditions.

The evening before we arrived at Clinton, we sat together in the coach and Ben talked about old times and remembered the people he had known and still knew in West Virginia. He told me that he had telephoned Max Macintosh and wired him a retainer as our legal counsel, and that Max had arranged for us to have headquarters in the old Traveler's Mountainside Hotel.

"Funny about Macintosh," Ben said. "We never got along and we never had any trouble working together. There's too much miner in him. He doesn't trust me. You been with me a few years now, Al—do you trust me?"

"I don't have to trust you," I said. "I got nothing to lose."

"That's a hell of a way to put it. Do you think I'm honest, Al?"

"That's an original question."

"I don't know. It's almost fourteen years since we met. It's just a personal question, and I think I'm entitled to an answer."

For a minute or so, I didn't answer, staring out of the window at lights moving past, at more stationary lights in the distance, at the dark, reflecting surface of the train window, thinking of all the train windows I had stared out of, just like this, through so many years, listening to the click-click-click of the wheels passing from rail to rail, counting my years against them, Alvin Cutter, thirty-five years old, worldly goods, none, worldly achievements, none—and then, at last, I replied to Ben.

"I think you're honest, Ben, as much as I know what honesty means."

"Stupid question, stupid answer," he shrugged. "Funny thing, Al, here we are, going back to West Virginia, and you never say a word about your wife. I don't think I heard you mention her half a dozen times these past ten years—"

"No, I don't talk about her."

"Why don't you get married, Al?"

"On what your lousy union pays me?" I snorted.

"That will change," Ben nodded. "You're good at arithmetic. Try adding up the dues from half a million members."

The next morning, when we arrived at the Traveler's Mountainside Hotel, there was a telegram from Mark Golden waiting for us. Mark had gone to Washington a few days early, leaving Lena and Soames to bring the organizers into Pennsylvania and begin the operation there. Now Mark wired: BILL PASSED BOTH HOUSES MAKING RIGHT TO JOIN UNION LAW OF THE LAND.

14

Almost ten years since I had seen Max Macintosh, and the years were gone and nothing. Ten years are long only when they're in front of you; when they are behind you, they are no account of time at all. The wind blows, and you feel it brush your face. Time spins like one of those twisted paper toys you buy for children, and the summer was over in the

West Virginia valleys, the maples turning red, the oaks browning and the birch full of yellow. It had been no more time for Max Macintosh than for us, but Macintosh had stayed there in Clinton, where he was born and where he would live out his whole life and die. It sometimes seems to me that there is someone like Macintosh in every town in America, clear-minded and sensible and not taken in by the big lie and all the small lies that spin around it, but engaged in the observation of reality and curious about truth.

He had fattened around the girth. Poverty doesn't supply a reducing diet; you eat bread and corn-meal mush and fat back instead of meat. His hair was all gray now, going white in places, and what teeth remained in his mouth were yellow where they held his pipe. But he was pleased to see us, and he shook hands eagerly with Ben and me. He said a few words about Sarah McGrady, my mother-in-law, who had died in 1930; he remembered the old times a little, and he made some observations about the organizers we had brought with us. "They're good men," Ben said, and Macintosh agreed that they would have to be. We all walked slowly through the town, toward the hotel, a small army in civilian clothes in a town not unfamiliar with armies in civilian clothes.

But word was ahead of us, and the people in Clinton knew who we were. You don't need a wire service; I don't think there was a coal town in America that didn't know that Ben Holt was in it for the big try, all out and the stops be damned, kill or be killed, dig coal like men or go and live and die somewhere else. So, although this was still before eight o'clock in the morning, there were people on the streets, a great many people, diggers and their wives and kids, people in patched denim, wash-bleached cotton and mended gingham, diggers barefoot and their wives barefoot and the kids barefoot, not cheering or yelling or whooping it up for us, but calm-faced, silent, and deeply intent on our progress through the town to the hotel.

We were bringing something, but we weren't coming with

gifts, and it was a big question what we were bringing, maybe death, maybe misery beyond even what misery they knew, and maybe some realistic hope. They didn't know, and they waited.

The storekeepers, opening their shops, stood and watched us. A handful of diggers on their way to work stopped to watch us. The sheriff—we learned that his name was Jack Cavanaugh—along with his deputy, came out of his office to watch us, and the railroad people left the station to stand in the street looking after us.

It was a cold, sweet day in October.

15

At breakfast with Ben and myself, Macintosh said, "It's a funny thing, Ben, but the way I feel it is this. Either it's going to begin right and go right, or it's going to be the worst trouble either of us ever saw; and believe me, I have seen a little trouble in my time. I'll tell you something else. I feel this. The time is right. Everything's right, and if it goes here, you're going to be like a fire all over the damned state. Nothing will stop it then."

Ben said, "Nothing will stop it, Mac."

"Sure. I know that. It just happens that right at this minute there's a warrant out for your arrest."

Ben nodded and went on eating.

"That doesn't bother you?"

"Sure I'm bothered," Ben said. "I'm also hungry. Who's serving the warrant?"

"Jack Cavanaugh, the sheriff, and Paul Tillman, his deputy. You saw them standing in front of their office as we came down the street."

"Why didn't they arrest me then?" Ben demanded.

"Good God, can't you wait? I had a long talk with Cavanaugh about this. You remember Fulton Oswick?"

"The big coal operator? I remember him," Ben nodded, signaling for the waiter to come and fill his coffee cup.

"He's the biggest man in these valleys," Macintosh said. "He has something to do with the warrant—perhaps he preferred the charges. Anyway, he's driving down from White Sulphur Springs, and he won't be here until ten o'clock. He's bringing one of the officials of the state police with him, and he sent word to Will Stevenson, our mayor, to hold up the arrest until he arrives. That might indicate that he's afraid it won't stick."

"The mayor's in this too?"

"Ben, we're a small town. Ten years ago, we were a busted town. Now we're just used to it and maybe worse. I talked to Cavanaugh and I talked to the mayor, and I got them to agree to exercise the warrant in my office. I said that we'd be there, waiting for them, at half past ten."

Finished with his ham and eggs and grits, Ben buttered a roll and asked Macintosh why he didn't have them swear him, Macintosh, in as a deputy, and save everyone a lot of trouble.

"Use your head, Ben. We're not going to run."

"Who in hell said anything about running?" Ben growled.

"Then act like a client and I'll try to act like a halfway smart lawyer. If they're going to arrest you, the sooner the better. Last night, I called old Judge Kingsford. He burns when they start stacking the cards against the miners, and he promised bail on the same day. The point is to keep active, not to sit in some lousy can. I don't want to avoid this. It's got to come to a head, and the sooner the better."

"All right," Ben agreed. "Now tell me something about Fulton Oswick. Are his collieries working?"

"Some of them."

"Why not all of them?"

"The market's rotten. You know that."

"I also know that he can undersell Pennsylvania and Illinois soft coal."

305

"But maybe you didn't know that Kentucky's underselling him?" Macintosh smiled.

"No?"

"Sure as God. They're paying one dollar, twenty cents a day down in Kentucky. Oswick pays low wages, but not like that. One-eighty a day is rock bottom for him. He's a pillar of the community—big church man, gifts to the university—and he moves in fancy circles. He and his wife have all kinds of social ambitions, and he just can't afford to be tagged as a slave operator."

"Well, what do you know," Ben muttered thoughtfully. He swallowed the rest of his roll and said, "How does it go, Mac—great fleas have little fleas, upon their backs to bite them, and little fleas have littler fleas, and so ad infinitum—something like that? Funny, the things you remember. Did you get the band?"

"Well, sort of. I got some kind of brass combination of four pieces. High school kids. They're coming over from Beckley. This is West Virginia, Ben, and it's 1933. Everything is not easy."

"Good enough," Ben grinned. "We still have an hour and a half before I get arrested. Let's get the banner up."

The banner was four feet high, and it stretched all the way across Main Street. One end of it was anchored to the window of my room in the Traveler's Mountainside Hotel and the other end was fastened to the window of Max Macintosh's office. In three-foot-high letters of red, the banner screamed: THE PRESIDENT SAYS: JOIN YOUR UNION! THE LAW SAYS: IT IS YOUR SACRED, CONSTITUTIONAL RIGHT! A row of blue stars bound it top and bottom, and when it was drawn tight, stretching full across the street, it could be seen the whole length of the town. It had been made for us in Pomax, and if it quoted the President a little less than accurately, the President was in no position to issue a disclaimer. The fact that it was Ben's gamble and had anticipated the passage of the law by at least three weeks did not lessen its effectiveness or Ben's reputation for political prognostication.

The banner had been purchased on credit, the same credit that brought us a million leaflets and throwaways bearing identical slogans, and even now being read wherever coal was mined in America.

While we were raising the banner and putting up a flag-draped stand on the street, Sheriff Cavanaugh came by and expressed his indignation. Macintosh convinced him that it would do no harm to wait until ten-thirty. If the banner had to come down, it might as well be at the same time Ben was marched off to jail.

16

At half past ten, Ben and I were waiting with Macintosh in the lawyer's office. We were talking about the old days, when Macintosh was mayor and Jim Flecker was sheriff and about the great gunfight in the streets of Clinton, and how different it was, the way it had happened, from the gunfights we saw in Western films. Macintosh and I kept the talk far off and down the lane of the years because we did not want to contemplate the fact that Ben would be arrested in a few minutes, but Ben was not unduly disturbed. He sat loosely and comfortably in a chair, the way large, heavy men do, and occasionally he would glance at the clock on the wall of Macintosh's office. At twenty to eleven, Ben said,

"Now isn't this the damndest thing—to keep a man sitting here, waiting to be picked up! You know, Mac, this will make eleven times I've been arrested." He took out a cigar. "You don't mind if I smoke?"

"Go ahead. By golly, you still smoke those rotten weeds, don't you? Tell me, Ben, did you ever do any time with those arrests?"

"Five times overnight. Once, thirty days in the Iron City jail. That's a rough place."

"I just bet it is," Macintosh nodded. "Funny thing, Ben, we got us a little jailhouse behind the sheriff's office, but there's practically no crime in a town like this. Killings—yes. People fill up to the brim and burst, and then they go crazy and kill someone, but that's not crime. I mean it's different from city crime. No one steals anything here—true, there ain't a hell of a lot to steal—" He was interrupted by a discordant blare of horns and drums. "The band's here. What do you know!"

I went to the window and leaned out. Four scrawny kids were on the hastily erected platform, one with traps, two with cornets, and a fourth with a French horn; and they were trying to get together on a single version of a Sousa march. From all over, people were drifting toward the bandstand, attracted by the music and the big, garish banner overhead. Then a long black car pulled up next to our building, and two men got out. Fulton Oswick was one of them, and I seemed to recognize the other. It turned out that he was Captain Sedge of the state police.

"The company's here," I told Ben.

Sheriff Cavanaugh and his deputy must have been waiting in the hallway downstairs, and a few moments later, the four of them entered the room, Cavanaugh tall, stringy, sour-visaged, his deputy a boy in his twenties. Oswick's hair had whitened and he had put on weight; I don't think I would have recognized him. With Captain Sedge, the uniform told the story. I had no clear memory of the man.

We were introduced, but there was no handshaking. Ben didn't rise. He sat sprawled in his chair, puffing slowly and comfortably on his foul-smelling cigar, and he regarded the four men with almost detached interest and a certain amount of sympathy. "I can understand why they're here, Mr. Oswick," he said, pointing at the law officers, "but I don't know why you're here. I do feel honored by your presence, however." His voice was so gentle and ingratiating that it took them aback. Macintosh watched Ben sharply.

"I'll tell you why I'm here, Holt—I'm a deeply interested party."

"That makes sense," Ben nodded.

308

"I'm a coal man. I want to dig coal, break it, and ship it. That's all I want, and I don't want either interference or trouble. When you came here ten years ago, all hell broke loose. We remember that, and we don't want it to happen again."

"I don't want it to happen again," Ben said seriously.

"Then we see eye to eye, Holt. Sheriff Cavanaugh here has a warrant for your arrest. I don't want him to execute it, but if he must he will."

"I don't want him to execute it, either," Ben smiled. "This is the last moment in the world I want to be in jail. We've just started the biggest organizational drive in the history of this industry. A year from now, we'll have half a million miners in our union. Wouldn't I look like a damn fool if I sat in jail while others did the work?"

"You don't impress me, Holt. We're giving you a fair choice. Take your men and pack up and get out of the state on the next train, or you go to jail. One or the other."

"Did you see our banner, Mr. Oswick?" Ben asked.

"I think you got one hell of a nerve," Captain Sedge put in. "Do you really think you can come in here and pull something as raw as this?"

Ben took Mark's telegram out of his pocket and handed it to Oswick. Sedge read it over Oswick's shoulder. "It was waiting for me this morning," Ben said mildly. "I didn't fake it. My word, would I fake something like that? All you have to do is pick up the phone and verify it."

Oswick dropped the telegram to Macintosh's desk. "It changes nothing, Holt. You still have the same choice."

"Would you let me see the warrant, Sheriff?" Ben asked Cavanaugh. "I think I have that right. Do I, Mac?" Macintosh nodded, and Cavanaugh, interested and puzzled by what was going on, handed the warrant to Ben. At that moment, Stevenson, the mayor, entered. He owned the gas station at the end of Main Street, and he and Macintosh were old friends. There were introductions and a summary of the situation while Ben studied the warrant. Then Ben handed the warrant to Macintosh.

"Incitement to riot," Ben said. "Can anyone else execute this except Sheriff Cavanaugh?"

Macintosh shook his head slowly. "Only the sheriff."

"The sheriff's enough," Oswick said.

Ben picked the telegram off the desk and handed it to Cavanaugh. "Read this, Sheriff—you too, Mayor. It's the truth. There's no legal power in this state that can prevent us from organizing the miners here. You may delay it, but you can't prevent it. Put me in jail, and you'll still have a union town in thirty days. But what about you? Comes the next election—Sedge and Oswick don't vote in Clinton. You can vote for each other, but that's about as far as it goes."

"I'll be damned if I'll listen to any more of this—" Sedge began, but Ben continued, as if Sedge were not present at all.

"Hell, I'm no stranger here, Sheriff." His voice deepened, hardened. "There isn't a miner in West Virginia or Kentucky doesn't know the name Ben Holt. We're not playing games. We're in here to organize this state, and so help me God, no force on earth is going to stop us! So if you want to arrest me, Sheriff, go ahead and get to it!"

"Cavanaugh, execute that warrant!" Sedge snapped.

"Just take it easy, Captain Sedge," Cavanaugh drawled. "Just one small pea-picking moment, and let me think about this."

"I told you to execute that warrant!"

"You told me?" Cavanaugh's brows went up. "And since when have I been working for the state police, mister? You're not telling me anything, just don't you ever forget that!" Stevenson nodded his agreement.

"Captain Sedge," Oswick burst out, "is that true—what Macintosh said? You can't arrest Holt?"

Sedge took a deep breath, swallowed, and nodded. "He's right. It's a county charge under a county statute. The sheriff or the local constable has to make the arrest. In twenty-four hours, however—"

310

"Twenty-four hours!" Oswick said disgustedly. "You couldn't anticipate this, Captain—not at all! Believe me, my respect for you is at a low point—a low point, sir, believe me." He turned to Cavanaugh. "Sheriff, you're building a pile of trouble."

"Maybe. Maybe not."

"I'm going to ask you once more to execute that warrant and make the arrest."

"I said I want to think about it, Mr. Oswick."

"Then just let me tell you this, Cavanaugh. There have been sheriffs here in the past who played the role of hoodlums. There was a time when Jim Flecker thought he could flout—"

"Now, Mr. Oswick," Cavanaugh broke in, "I won't have you comparing me with any member of the Flecker family in any particular, I won't! Hell no! I been sheriff here five years and I think I know my job, and I got a record behind me. So just don't you go talking to me about any Jim Flecker."

"Good heavens, Mr. Oswick," Ben said amiably, "here I sit listening to an argument about whether I should or shouldn't be arrested, and damned if it doesn't listen like a scene out of *Alice in Wonderland*. You and I may look pretty much the same after almost fifteen years, but the world doesn't. The open-shop colliery down here is finished. That's a plain fact that nothing in the world is going to change. Why don't you face it?"

"Don't tell me what to face, Holt!"

Ben shrugged. "O.K., leave it the way it is. You pay a dollar-eighty a day. Kentucky pays a dollar-twenty. You can't stay in business that way. Six months from now, there'll be a uniform union rate—four dollars a day here, four dollars a day in Kentucky. The dollar-eighty days are over, and you might as well face it. Maybe you won't take out of the pits the kind of money you're taking now, but you'll stay in business, and if this lousy depression ends,

311

you won't have your heart broken with competition from Alabama and Kentucky. Why not think about it?"

"I'll see you in hell first, Holt!" Oswick roared. "Come on, Sedge, we're wasting our time!"

They stormed out. Ben puffed on his cigar. It was out. He lit it again, drew a long breath of smoke, and allowed it to float gently from his mouth.

"What now?" Stevenson asked worriedly.

"No private armies," Ben said thoughtfully. "No wars, no evictions, no lockouts—no, sir—I don't think so. Things have changed. That's a hard conclusion for reasonable people to accept, and harder for unreasonable people, but it's a fact. Things have changed. Don't you think so, Sheriff?" he asked Cavanaugh.

"I been turning it over in my mind."

"Four dollars a day should have a nice, comfortable effect in Clinton, considering the times we live in," Macintosh said.

Cavanaugh stared at the warrant in his hand. "Tell you something, Mac," he said to the lawyer. "I don't say I changed my mind. I want to think about this. I never liked these incitement charges, and Judge Kingsford, he don't like them no better. So I'll just hang onto this for a little while. I'll have to advise Mr. Holt here that I hold him responsible for his actions and for the actions of them organizers he brought into town. First thing, he's got to have a permit for that platform out on the street."

"Sheriff," Ben said gravely, "I wouldn't respect you if you didn't hold me responsible for my actions. And that goes for your deputy, Mr. Tillman."

Tillman blushed and swelled. All through it, he hadn't been able to take his eyes off Ben. I've seen a good many men try their hand at the role of a hero, but the only one I knew to bring it off every time was Ben Holt.

Then Macintosh reached into a drawer of his desk and brought out a bottle of local corn and six small glasses. We all drank to the President of the United States.

17

We held our first outdoor meeting in Clinton that afternoon at five o'clock, while there was still daylight. By this time, the kids who constituted our four-piece brass section were exhausted. They had been playing on and off all day since eleven in the morning. None of that day was wasted. We had hired three cars. Macintosh took one, Ben took the second, and I had the third. Ben and I had local unemployed miners to guide us, and we loaded the cars with as many organizers as we could carry. This was to be the only time we concentrated all our forces in one place; subsequently, we broke up into groups and spread out, but this day we covered almost every pit within ten miles of Clinton. We gave out our leaflets, held short, impromptu meetings, and swept on from place to place in a heady surge of confidence that nothing could dampen, and were back in Clinton in a few hours.

The word was in the air. By five o'clock, half the people in the Clinton area knew, in one version or another, what had gone on between Ben and Oswick in Macintosh's office. At collieries that worked a ten-hour day until sunset, the miners laid down their tools and walked out. There was no violence, no terror, no intimidation—but rather a strange meeting of knowledge and consent, as if the place, the time, and the motion had been miraculously blended, and, starting at about three o'clock that afternoon, miners, employed and unemployed, began to stream into the town and gather around the bandstand.

Meanwhile, the organizers who had remained in Clinton had turned Macintosh's office into temporary union headquarters. There were three empty rooms in that building, and we rented them immediately. (Eventually, the same building became the union headquarters for the entire state.) By the time I returned to Clinton, at three o'clock, two girls who could type had been found, engaged, and installed with two battered typewriters. The October wind was blowing cool, so we set up a hot-drink stand alongside the bandstand, bringing big pots of coffee from the hotel across the street and purchasing, at one clip, the town's entire supply of doughnuts and packaged cake, an act which awakened among the local merchants fond memories of a time when real money had actually circulated in Clinton.

Framed by the high, sloping mountains, gaudy and unreal in their brilliant fall colors, the town took on a carnival air. Not in all the memory of the people of Clinton had there been a day as carefree and triumphant as this one—Main Street thronged with men and women and children, an increasing crowd around the bandstand, where the kids were proudly blowing their hearts out, coffee and cake passed out until the supplies were exhausted, our own men struggling with the components of a loud-speaker system we had brought with us from Pomax, talking to miners, holding impromptu meetings here and there on the street, and passing out leaflets everywhere.

By five o'clock, when we were ready to begin our main meeting, there must have been almost five thousand men, women, and children packed into the area between the hotel and our platform. There was an increasing chill in the crisp mountain air, yet half of the crowd were barefoot, women with no other covering than their shapeless, patched gingham dresses, men in faded work shirts and ancient overalls, children huddled against the legs of their parents, infants cradled in the arms of their mothers, old, toothless crones, and miners wearing their lamps and carrying lunch pails. The musicians had stopped playing and were satisfying their thirst with soda pop.

Max Macintosh climbed up on the platform and spread his arms for silence. A hush settled over the crowd.

"Good friends," Macintosh said, "this is a festive moment, but it is also a solemn moment. That is why I have asked the Reverend Arthur Boone to give the invocation at the opening of the meeting and the Reverend Clement Harper to give us his blessing at the close of it."

Boone was the Methodist minister and Harper was the Baptist minister. Macintosh had picked up both of them on his way back from the pits, and between them, they covered most of the religious persuasion of the crowd. It was the first time a public-address system had ever been heard in Clinton, and the force of the amplification sent the speaker's voice echoing through the valley. It had a fine effect, and there was a good deal of whispering about it. Then the whispers quieted as Boone, old and thin and shivering a bit in the cold breeze, said,

"Brothers and sisters, we are met here in peace not in rancor, and we ask the Lord God to look kindly upon our efforts. Too long have we been afflicted with poverty and privation—" He paused, taken somewhat aback at the majestic echo of his voice, cocked his head to listen, and then said, with the simplicity of a child, "We have given thee our faith, oh Lord, and we beseech thee to give us back our hope."

Standing next to the platform, I found that my eyes were wet, and I wanted only to get away somewhere into a dark place and put my face in my hands and weep. All the years came to nothing, and in some peculiar way that was past my understanding, I was home, the only place that was anything of home in all truth, weeping inside of myself for the one woman I had been able to love, my heart going out dumbly and futilely to these skinny, stoic, almost animal-like people, who had squeezed everything human inside their skinny bodies and out of sight, so that they might suffer silently according to their own long tradition of suffering.

Ben Holt, standing next to me, put his hand on my shoulder and said, "How about that, Al? Mac's a genius when it comes to these little touches. He knows these people—by God, he does!"

On the platform, Macintosh said, "I don't have to tell you about Johnny Clarke. He's been digging coal in these hills

315

just about half a century—and there was never a day he didn't cry out, 'Give us a union!'"

Clarke, a big, rawboned man in his sixties, climbed onto the platform—only an arrangement of planks and crates—looked suspiciously at the microphone, and then boomed into it,

"By golly, I don't expect you to applaud a preacher, but right now I feel like a stranger up here. I must have a few neighbors in this here crowd."

Slow at first, the clapping and shouting began, then swelling up to a roar. It was a new way. They had to learn about it, it was so long since they had had anything to applaud.

"Thank you kindly, then. Mac should have taken out of those fifty years the past nineteen weeks I ain't set foot in a pit. My condition ain't so strange. It's called unemployment when I don't work and starvation wages when I do. Back in 1920 or so, a man come into these valleys to do something about that. I think maybe some of you knew him then. Well, they run him out, but it took an army of gunmen and the United States Army to do it. He said then that he'd be back to see us again, and that took a little time, but here he is—and this time the United States Army is on our side, not on theirs. Brothers and sisters, I want you to listen to some words from Benjamin Renwell Holt!"

This time they had learned, and a roar went up that echoed and re-echoed through the dusky valleys. I learned later that just about at this moment, two cars of state police drove into Clinton. But they parked at the railroad station and stayed in their cars and listened.

The sun dropped behind the hills as Ben climbed onto the platform, and as he spoke, the shadows crept on us and the air chilled. But no one moved, not one soul in all that crowd. The edge of the long shadow touched the platform, but from his waist up, Ben was still in the sunlight, the golden-red light striking him at an angle, setting his great shock of gray hair aglow and softening the folds of his big, fleshy face, washing away the ravages of time and physical neglect and overeating.

316

Bathed in the golden glow, Ben loomed like a giant, spread his arms for silence, and then let his deep, resonant voice beat at the microphone with all the portent and rhythm of some old prophet. A thing electrical and magical happened, a transmutation I had observed to one degree or another every time Ben Holt stepped onto a platform and spoke. He transcended himself. From somewhere deep inside of him, somewhere lost and unremembered by his day-to-day self, there was awakened a beat and pulse of ancient music, an eloquence that gripped his audience utterly and made of them a single instrument upon which he played with consummate skill.

In any case, he would have been a fine speaker. Practice, plus his intelligence and his rich voice, had given him a great deal of skill; but this was something beyond professional ability, and even I, knowing him so long and well, responded emotionally as he cried,

"What are we, my brothers and sisters? Are we strangers in this rich and fruitful land? Are we cursed that in a place so bountiful, we must starve? Are we interlopers?

"Or was it our own fathers who opened this land, who came across the passes with their long rifles, and trod where no white man had ever trod before? They fought the red men and made a road through the wilderness, and then they opened their arms and their hearts to all the people, and said to them, Come because we have made a road and opened the way! Come through the wilderness because it is wilderness no longer! We have made it safe! We have opened the way to the rich pastures and the boundless plains!

"Is this fanciful, brothers and sisters? Then I give you the thought to comfort you when you work ten hours in the tunnel's darkness for fifteen cents an hour! I give you the thought to comfort you when your children tell you that they are hungry! I give you the thought for those long winter days, when the snow lies four feet deep on the ground, and because your children's feet are naked, they cannot set foot out of doors or go to school!

317

"No! No, enough of that! I am not here to enumerate your miseries, to catalogue your suffering, to recollect your hunger. You know me better than that. I came here once to build a union. I have come back to build a union, and so help me God and in His holy name, I take an oath that I will not leave here alive until a union exists! I will not leave here alive until every digger in these valleys locks arms with his brother and cries out in a voice they can hear a thousand miles away, I STAND BY MY BROTHER AND I WILL DIG NO COAL UNTIL I AM PAID FOUR DOLLARS FOR AN EIGHT-HOUR DAY!"

The last lines exploded from him. He threw up his arms as he cried it out, and from the people facing him, the people conditioned by years to silence, there came a wild, angry roar, a roar that thundered up and smashed from hillside to hillside.

He called them to silence, his big hands over them like the hands of a giant at a giant piano. There is a maxim in the labor movement that you do not call an important mass meeting with a few hours' notice, but rather prepare for it days and sometimes weeks in advance. But we had come into Clinton less than twelve hours before, and here the street was packed from side to side and backed up at each end with a solid mass of people, stretching from the railroad station to the outskirts of the town, and still more arriving, men and women on foot, in ancient trucks, crowded onto hay wagons, on bicycles and in old buggies. From how many miles away they came, I don't know, any more than I know exactly what curious network of information brought them, but come they did until it seemed to us that half the miners in West Virginia were packed into the narrow street in front of the hotel. And Ben stretched his arms over them and quieted them until the hush was as meaningful as the roar had been.

"I went into the White House," Ben said. "There it stood, so proud and pretty, enough to make you want to weep, and I walked into it because I was invited there. I, Ben Holt, a digger, with a digger's hands"—holding his big hands out to them—"and a digger's mind, in these same clothes I wear today. I walked into the White House because the President of the United States had asked me to come there and talk to him about the miners. I talked to him, and I told him about the miners. I told him the truth. I held nothing back. And as it says in the Book that the truth shall make you free, so this truth faced him and he faced it. He said to me, Well, Mr. Holt, what is there to do? And I said to him, Mr. President, give us a law that will give the miners the right to organize into a trade union. But who can enforce such a law? he asked me, and I said to him, Mr. President, give us the law—only give us the law, and we will enforce it! The miners will enforce it!"

Again he quieted the swelling roar of the crowd, and when the hush came, his voice exploded it,

"And he gave us the law! Yesterday, the law was passed! The right to organize is the law of the land! Organize! the President says to you! It is your holy, sacred, inalienable right! Organize!"

The last bit of the sun passed across Ben Holt's face as the crowd went wild, a roar of sound that rocked back and forth until it seemed to become the substance of the space that filled the darkening valley.

18

We had not planned what happened. We had not anticipated that it would happen or even in our wildest dreams imagined that it might happen, but it was happening, not only to us, but at the same time in Alabama, in Pennsylvania, in Pomax, and in the Rocky Mountains—not always the same, differing in the specific nature and conditions of each place, yet also the same everywhere our organizers were.

There was no sleeping that night. We took over the Traveler's Mountainside Hotel and the little wooden office building, and still hundreds had to wait shivering in the street but would not leave until they were a part of the International Miners Union.

We enlisted volunteers until we had over fifty men and women filling in questionnaires and issuing union books. We ran out of union books—a shipment had been mailed but not yet arrived—and bought out the entire stock of school supplies in every store in town. The hotel kitchen was set to cooking huge pots of stew, and by midnight, we had served stew, bread, and tea to over a thousand people. We had issued over fifteen hundred union books then, and by dawn, still working, the number of books issued passed the three-thousand mark. We set up locals. We appointed temporary executive committees and turned our hotel rooms into committee meeting rooms, where they caucused and elected their own temporary local leadership. A whole structure, a whole state-wide union came into being that night in Clinton, a miracle that could not properly be explained, only witnessed and noted.

And strangely enough, at least half of the miners insisted on paying their first dues. Facing the necessity of creating a whole slate of officers immediately, Ben appointed Max Macintosh state treasurer. He sat in his office all night, with three helpers, a set of books, a cigar box, and all the miners the room could hold, and hour after hour, out of these poverty-stricken people, the money poured in, old, worn dollar bills, treasured silver dollars, jars of pennies, disability checks, Liberty bonds, postage stamps, and even dues in kind, sacks of potatoes and corn and turnips, a side of bacon, and two lean chickens. The dues in kind went into the stew pots. The manager of the hotel, torn between avarice and anxiety, complained that we were turning his hotel into a shambles, and Ben told him to go soak his head and come back next year and the local would buy his lousy hotel.

As dawn was breaking, we began to see the end of that first day of organization. I checked off the last union book in the dining room, facing one of our men who dozed and mumbled as he tried to make up his totals. The lobby was full of recumbent forms, people asleep on the couch, the chairs, and sprawled out on the carpet, while the defeated manager slept with his head on the hotel desk.

I went out into the crisp, clean morning air, time frozen in that moment when the edge of the sun sends its first shaft of light over the black lip of a mountain. Ben stood on the veranda, his legs spread, his face dark with beard, a cigar clenched between his teeth. "Hello, Al," he said to me, and reached into his jacket pocket to offer me a cigar.

"Why do you keep pushing those rotten weeds at me?" I asked him morosely. "My stomach's sour enough. I feel like hell."

"I feel great," he said, drawing his lungs full of air. "I feel wonderful—by God, to see something like this happen! What did you think when we came down here, Al? What were you expecting?"

"Anything. To be beat up, shot, mauled a little—maybe thrown in the can."

"Not this."

"No, not this."

"You know, Al, I feel it, but I don't understand it. So help me God, I don't. I will bet my last dollar that it's happening everywhere—because that's the kind of a feeling I have. Something has happened to this whole country." He turned to me suddenly. "You know, Al, we're going to come out of this with one hell of a union. We never had a union before. We never knew what a union was—only a bunch of piss-catting locals, whining about their autonomy and trying to get two cents more than the diggers in the next county. But that's gone. That's over. We had to be shamed. We had to sit bare-ass on the bottom and start it clean, but by God Almighty, we are going to have a union—a union like this country never saw before!"

19

I went down to Kentucky with six organizers, while Ben worked out of Clinton, fanning out through the coal counties of West Virginia. It wasn't easy in Kentucky, and when I returned to Clinton three weeks later, the memberships were rolling in by the thousands. We remained in Clinton a few more days after that, and by the time we left, we had negotiated contracts with eleven operators, Fulton Oswick among them. That was a moment of historical and particular pleasure for me, even more, I think, than for Ben.

Macintosh, Ben, and I met with Oswick in his beautiful home near Charleston, a fine Georgian house that stood among thirty acres of rolling lawn, gardens, and broad shade trees. He greeted us himself, politely if unenthusiastically, and led us into his study, where his lawyer and his general manager were waiting. As the discussions began, Ben automatically took out a cigar and started to light it. Before the match reached its mark, Oswick was offering Ben his own humidor.

"Try one of mine," he begged Ben.

Ben looked at the humidor coldly and said, "I knew an operator once, Mr. Oswick, who claimed he could buy a union man with a fifty-cent cigar."

"These are dollar cigars," Oswick replied hastily. "I'm sure you'll enjoy smoking it, Mr. Holt. They're put up for me in Havana. Try one."

"Evidently, you didn't hear me," Ben said, striking another match and lighting his own.

That story has been told a good deal and blown up out of size, but it happened.

When we left West Virginia, we left a union behind us, a powerful union of men tempered by such years of poverty and struggle as few knew ever existed in these United States. Kentucky was more difficult, but the organization was set up, and in Tennessee and Alabama, Gus Empek was fantastically successful.

We met in Pittsburgh with Mark and Lena and Jack Mullen, who had come in from Pomax to join us. It was snowing as Ben and I entered the union's offices there, snowing and late at night, but every window in the building blazed with light and the rooms and corridors teemed with office workers, miners, organizers, and volunteers. We felt like provincials as we were greeted by big, burly Dan Gratinski, the district president, and ushered into his office where the others were waiting for us. They had known that we would not have time to eat. A table was spread with a cloth, and on it a tray piled with succulent roast-beef and corned-beef sandwiches, bottles of beer, a pot of coffee, and in a decanter, a magnum of champagne. After the greetings were over, Gratinski explained that it was in the way of a little celebration. He began to open the champagne as Mark told us,

"And I think we have something to celebrate. Lena learned to use an adding machine, so we have some tabulations. Like they say at election time, not all the returns are in, but we estimate that we have at least 80 per cent of what the final total out of this drive will be." Almost apologetically, he added, "I could have told you that on the telephone the other day, Ben, but I wanted to save it until you were here. You don't mind?"

"Mind? I ought to break your arm," Ben said.

The champagne popped and poured over onto the floor as Gratinski filled tumblers for us. Mark's voice thickened. He was very moved, keyed up emotionally. Ben was in a good mood, swelling with anticipation and pleasure.

Mark cleared his throat and said quietly, "The total membership, dues-paying, of the International Miners Union at this moment is three hundred and seventy-six thousand, eight hundred and nineteen. We have negotiated one hundred and five contracts, begun negotiations on twice that number, and paid off all our debts. At this time, the International's bank balance stands at exactly two hundred and twelve thousand, six hundred and twenty-two dollars and eighteen cents." He paused and nodded. "That's it, Ben—that's just it." Then he sat down, shaking his head and wiping his eyes, and Ben whispered,

"Mark." He repeated it louder, "Mark!"

Golden got up, stood uncertainly for a moment, and then walked over to Ben. He appeared small, shriveled, insignificant against Ben's great bulk, and I thought his ribs would crack as Ben embraced him in a bear hug. Then Lena began to cry.

"Jesus God," Mullen burst out, "what is this—a lousy wake? Here I am with a glass of champagne in my hand for the first time in forty lean years I've lived and I'm boxed in with tears!"

20

In January, at the Union Building in Pomax, I was sitting in Ben's office, going over some statistics with him, when Lena told us that Milton Humber, the mayor of Pomax, was outside and asking to see Ben. Ben looked at her thoughtfully for a moment, then nodded and said to send him in. Humber was a pudgy, carefully dressed man in his fifties who had served three terms as mayor of Pomax and who itched with the frustration of a dead-end job in an insignificant coal town and nursed ambitions to be the party's candidate for Congress.

He entered pompously and asked—trying to make a poor joke out of it—why Ben didn't come to see him any more. When Ben did not invite him to sit down, or to remove his coat, he took a chair of his own accord, sitting there in his heavy overcoat, with his hat on his knees. The room was warm, and we were both in our shirt sleeves.

"I didn't know I was in the habit of coming to see you,"

Ben replied, reading a paper on his desk and not raising his eyes.

"Well, Ben—you know what I mean. You used to drop in every once in a while. There used to be something now and then that City Hall could do for you."

"City Hall?"

"You know. The administration."

"Election's coming up next year, Milton—isn't that right."

"That's not why I'm here, Ben. You know me better than that."

"Do I? I don't think I know you one damn bit, Milton. We sort of lost touch with each other while the union was on its uppers." He glanced up, then went back to his reading, and said, "So don't come sucking around now."

"That's a hell of a way to talk, Ben."

"I talk as I please. You should know that by now."

"What's eating you, Ben?"

Ben pushed the papers aside and stared at the mayor. "You know what's eating me, Milton."

"That Cofferman business—the kid Andy sent to jail? That's old hat, Ben. That's over and forgotten."

"You didn't forget it, Milton. I didn't forget it. As a matter of fact, I forget very little. You'd like to go to Congress —always wanted that, didn't you? Out of this district? A fat chance, Milton."

The mayor was sweating in his overcoat. He found a handkerchief and wiped the sweat from his brow. "O.K.," he said, "O.K.—let's stop beating about the bush. What do you want me to do?"

"Not one blessed thing," Ben said. "Next year, there'll be another mayor."

"Sure. Enjoy yourself. Have your fun. I can sit here and ask you what you want. You can at least give me a fair answer."

Ben thought about it for a moment, then nodded. "All right. Two things. Fire Andy Lust and get the Cofferman kid out of jail."

"Oh no. No, Ben. You know I can't do that. Andy's been here a long time. By God, if it wasn't for the way he cooperated during that Arrowhead scandal, there would have been plain hell to pay. Andy always did right by your crowd. You know that. And how can I get the kid out of jail?"

"Don't plead for Andy," Ben said with disgust. "Get him out. Fire him—frame him—but get him out. I want him out —do you understand?"

Humber nodded slowly.

"And now. I'll give you thirty days and you give us a new chief of police. I don't care who. Anyone. But get rid of Lust!"

"All right, Ben. But I can't get the kid out of jail."

"You can," Ben said, softly and dangerously. "You can, or you're washed up in this county. And when I say washed up, I mean permanently."

"How? Just tell me how."

"There are ways. See the parole board. See the governor. Have him pardoned. What in hell do you belong to a party for? Let the party do something for a change. Just do it. Now, I'm busy." When the mayor left, Ben said, "Pompous little son of a bitch!"

"Still, he had the guts to come here, Ben."

"You're right. I suppose it took something to come here."

Two weeks later, Pomax had a new chief of police, and the following month, Sam Cofferman's sentence was suspended and he was released on probation.

21

"How does it feel?" people would ask me, and I would tell them that it felt good. Why shouldn't it feel good? We had gone through the hard years, the long, dirty dry years, the years of starvation and retreat and defeat, and here it was 1934, and our membership passed the four-hundred-thousand mark, and the newspapers and magazines were full of the "Miracle of the Miners Union," and Benjamin Renwell Holt was the most important, respected, and feared leader in a hundred years of American labor history. You couldn't pick up a newspaper without reading his name, or go into a movie house and watch the Pathé News without hearing Ben's voice or seeing his face.

I no longer had to face the reporters, but could delegate the job. I had a staff now. My assistant was a young fellow out of the Columbia School of Journalism, dedicated to the labor movement and burning to erase inequity, and my personal secretary was a plain-faced girl with dark hair, a Miss Claire Schwartz. Suzic and Mullen were both annoyed at my choice. They considered her to be without sex appeal or charm, and they felt that to have someone like her working in the same building was a shameful waste of space and opportunity. But they had the solace of their own staffs. We were possessed of a treasury now.

The Union Building on Lincoln Street underwent a face lifting. Although Ben was fretting to deed it over to the local and to establish national headquarters in Washington, D.C., it had to serve for the time being, and there was no question but that its condition required improvement. We had the brickwork washed, the trim painted, and the inside modestly redecorated. We even took an old front storeroom, cleaned it out, furnished it, called it the press room, and established my new assistant, Richard Henty, there.

In February, Ben was invited to meet with the executive board of the National Confederation of Labor at the Carmine Plaza Hotel in Miami, Florida. He had been holding back, playing dead, so to speak—but looking forward to an invitation. Since the completion and success of the organizing drive, he had been so full of a new idea that had taken hold of him that he could talk of nothing else, and the invitation to Florida appeared to be the ideal opportunity to present it. He decided that Mark and I should go with him, and the day after the invitation came, we were on a plane for Miami.

The quick transition from winter to summer was a new

experience for us, and we walked into the Carmine Plaza, carrying our heavy overcoats on our arms. The hotel was an enormous, sprawling affair, covered with pink stucco, adorned with Moorish columns and mosaic floors, and possessed of its own private beach and an oversized swimming pool for any contingency that might cause the ocean to run dry. When Ben discovered that a two-room suite would cost us forty-five dollars a day without meals, he was ready to explode, drop the whole thing, and return to Pomax. Mark calmed him, and we went up to our rooms, where Mark said to him, pointedly,

"As far as we're concerned, Ben, there is no moral issue involved here. I know exactly what you are thinking, but we are here for a purpose, and if we had to carry out that purpose in a Turkish bath or a cathouse, the end result would remain."

"I know, I know," Ben muttered. "I just hate this stinking place. I hate the whole notion of trade-union officials coming down to a place like this and lying around in the sun on their fat asses and ordering the run of three drinks and a twelve-dollar meal to follow, and all of it out of the union funds. Do you know where that money comes from? Do you know how long a miner works to pay out a dollar in dues?"

"Ben—I know and you know, and that's what matters. We know exactly what these so-called 'leaders of labor' are. We don't have to instruct ourselves and we don't have to instruct them or reform them. We're here for a purpose, and we stick to that. Will you promise me?"

Like a boy reprimanded gently by an indulgent father, Ben nodded. It was late afternoon now, and as we cleaned up, Mark told us that in all probability, we would be meeting with a sub-committee of four: Fulton Grove, who was a vice-president in line for the presidency at the next convention; Myron Stillman, whom the newspapers fondly referred to as "the grand old man of the labor movement" and who was seventy-six and bordering on senility and asked no more of life than to be permitted to sun himself at Miami for six months out of every year and play cards in his poshy New York apartment for the other six months; Joe Briggs, the oversized and not too bright president of the Woodworkers Union, who was reputed to be the richest man in labor if not the most honest and who was roundly despised by most of his membership; and finally, Arnold Clement, shrewd, calculating and tactically brilliant.

Stillman was the president of the Confederation, the other three were vice-presidents. Clement would have been in line for the presidency when Stillman retired—as he did at the coming convention—but since Clement had been mixed up with the Left a quarter of a century back, putting him outside the pale of the Confederation's requirements of respectability, and since Joe Briggs was as short on brains as he was long on size, Fulton Grove remained with aspirations and the best possibilities.

Mark held that Clement was the one to be convinced, Grove the one to be mollified. Briggs would go as the other two led, and Stillman, at worst, would fall into a patter of nonsense, which Ben was not to take umbrage at.

"Mark, stop worrying. I know that old idiot twenty years. He once said I was like a son to him."

"He's a nice old gaffer, Ben, if you don't get him started worrying about his bonus and retirement pay. He believes he's going to live forever, and he doesn't want the organization defaulting on any of his pension checks. Fulton Grove, on the other hand, is something else indeed. You always considered Fulton a stupid prick—"

"Just a prick," Ben shrugged.

"He's not stupid, and he has a sharp eye on the presidency. He's going to play everything safe and careful, and he won't want to play ball with us. So don't rile him, Ben."

But when we met them, an hour later, on the terrace for cocktails, I could see that control was going to be a problem for Ben. It began well enough, and the introductions were pleasant, and each one of the four went out of his way to praise Ben's conduct of the organizational drive and to express his amazement at the results. Old Stillman said that he had known all along that Ben was destined to be a great labor leader, and he said that Ben was just like a son to him. But when Ben tried to get started on the business of the meeting, they pushed it aside and said that now was the time for relaxation. Business could come later. Then they ordered drinks.

The repeal of Prohibition the year before had not changed Ben's drinking habits. He had never been a heavy drinker, usually satisfied with a single drink before dinner except on those rare occasions when he tied on a load because at the moment he happened to hate the world too much to face it sober, and when he chose his drinks, he preferred bourbon. I had seen him drink everything from sugar alcohol to cut scotch, but he always returned to corn whisky. Now they ordered scotch for him, explaining that it was the thing to train his taste, since we no longer lived with cheap bootleg hooch. It was bad enough to order Ben's drink; when they talked about training his taste, I thought it was all over. But Mark leaped into the gap, and I kicked Ben and said a lot of quick, foolish things.

At dinner in the hotel dining room, they started the meal with cold lobster, with prime T-bone steaks to follow. Ben, who had built his shell of diamond-in-the-rough over a very solid core of education, experience, and sophistication, was sufficiently amused by the pretensions at work to suppress any comments on gluttony or extravagance. Clement considered himself a connoisseur of wines, basing his talent on three trips to Europe to attend international conventions, and he ordered champagne with the lobster and sparkling burgundy with the meat, three bottles of each at about ten dollars a bottle. Stillman did not enjoy the wine; he said it tasted like bad soda pop, but Joe Briggs poured it down a glass at a gulp, his great, sagging paunch apparently bottomless. Mark Golden, always in middling health and always watching his ulcers, only sipped at the wine. When Clement had urged him several times, Mark admitted that he had never faced just this combination of wines before, and that it took a while to come up to it. Clement said that Prohibition had robbed Americans of any real taste for wines. Europeans would no more sit down to a meal without wines than a meal without bread.

"I don't know," old Stillman sighed, covering his mouth as the gas erupted. "I like this hotel, but the food is too rich, I think." He belched again. "My doctor tells me to stay away from rich food, but a funny thing about getting on with the years, it don't do nothing to my appetite. How is your appetite?" he asked Ben.

"It stands up," Ben said.

"If anything, I think I get a little more appetite with age."

"My idea," Joe Briggs said, "is to hold the next convention down here. I'm fed up with Atlantic City—up to the neck with it. Compared with this place, it's a monastery. I mean that I've had a bellyful of those run-down middle-aged broads who hang out at Atlantic City. I'll tell you something, Ben, this here place is a quail run. Just stand in the lobby and hold out a twenty-dollar bill, and they'll fall over each other as they come running. Beautiful. They got broads here that are the nicest things you ever laid eyes on. They got broads you wouldn't be ashamed to say was your own daughter—"

"Shut up," Clement said wearily.

"What the hell is eating you?"

"One thing, no fights at dinner," old Stillman told them. "No fights, no business, no arguments. Dinner is to be enjoyed. Relax. You'll live as long as me."

For dessert, we had baked Alaska as big as a watermelon, and then brandy. I watched Mark Golden staring glumly at the parade of courses. His face was drawn, the hollows under his eyes darker than ever. His strength was limited enough, and he had used it all during the organizing drive, and now there was no resiliency. It happened with age. The trade-union movement could be a place where you lived forever, as Myron Stillman intended to do, or a place where you were old and used up all too quickly. I tried to remember how old Mark was—fifty-six, fifty-seven—he couldn't be that old, I told myself, not so quickly. By contrast, it was a fairly youthful man I remembered from the days when I first came to Pomax.

Finally, it was decided that we would go up to Stillman's suite and talk. I don't think Ben could have stood it much longer. Usually possessed of a very substantial appetite, he had eaten little and left the drinks almost untasted. That was not good. Food calmed his nerves. I would have felt better if he had stuffed himself.

We went up to Stillman's suite. He had a bedroom and a living room. Fulton Grove explained to me that because of the old man's age, they felt that he ought to be comfortable. A sort of tribute to his years of service at seventy-five dollars a day, with windows overlooking the ocean and a carpet on the floor an inch thick. He turned on the radio for us—a cabinet set that came with the room for only four dollars a day extra—so that we might appreciate its fine tone, while Carlton phoned down for setups. Joe Briggs pulled big armchairs up to the couch; as he said, we could talk better if we were not seated hard on the ass. When Ben took out one of his five-cent miner's consolations, they set up a howl and pressed a box of fifty-cent pure Havanas on him. He could hardly refuse. As Myron Stillman said,

"In a brotherly gesture, Ben, we share things. We sit here like brothers. Isn't it better we should discuss things like this, here in comfort, our stomachs full, our brains rested, with a fine environment like this around us? What could your heart desire now?"

"Only a good heart-to-heart talk," Ben agreed, as he lit the cigar. He was working every muscle in his body to be amiable and gracious.

"And that's exactly what we're here for. Suppose we let Brother Arnold Clement tell you what we have in mind."

We all knew exactly what they had in mind, but Ben

nodded pleasantly, and we sat back as Brother Arnold Clement said to us,

"It's no secret to anyone here that we've had our differences in the past. My word, you couldn't run a movement like this without differences cropping up every day. But that's in the past. I say, forget the past, bury the hatchet. If you and Fulton haven't always seen eye to eye, well, that's over and done with. If you and I have had our arguments, well, we're both a little older, a little wiser. The past is done. Do you agree?"

"You couldn't say anything to make me happier," Ben smiled.

Stillman said, "What did I tell you? Ben is like a son to me. He always has been like a son to me."

"The long and short of it is this," Clement continued. "You've performed a major miracle, Ben. You took a union that was written off and built it into one of the strongest unions in America. Our collective hat is off to you for that, and we could think of only one practical way of expressing our admiration. We're here to extend a hearty invitation to you to bring the International Miners Union into the National Confederation of Labor. What do you say to that?"

"You know what I say," Ben replied. "My position has never changed. I stood for unity twenty-five years ago. I stand for unity today. For fifteen years, I fought tooth and nail against the principle of autonomy in the Miners Union, and I saw that principle tear our union to shreds and bring it to its knees. I rebuilt it—as a united union, and it will remain united. So when you talk to me about unity, I hear you and I agree."

"Then we take it that speaking for your union, you consent?"

Ben took a deep puff on his cigar and then let the smoke flow slowly from his mouth. "Yes and no," he answered.

"Yes and no?" Clement smiled. "That's a hell of a note when a straightforward proposal is made."

"We'll let Ben explain," Stillman said. "Don't push him.

This is no small thing. This is a historic decision Ben is called upon to make."

"I'm not trying to push Ben," Clement told the old man. "Hell, anyone who's dealt with Ben Holt knows that you don't push him around."

Ben leaned forward and said to them, calmly and directly, "I'll tell you exactly what I mean. Mark here, and Al and myself, well, we talked this over pretty thoroughly. We'd have to be kids not to know why you invited us down here; and the fact that we came—and we're still not out of our organizational difficulties, believe me—but the fact that we put everything else aside to fly down here indicates how seriously we take your proposition. But before we can give you a clear answer, I must lay some cards on the table. I don't want anything held back. I want to spread out the dirty wash and identify it. Right?"

Clement studied Ben narrowly, warily, but Stillman said, "Ben, if there's dirty wash, spread it out. I want to look at it."

"Very well," Ben nodded. "Let's get down to facts. Your Confederation consists of twenty-two craft unions with a total membership of about three million. Apart from the Miners Union, that's the bulk of organized labor in the United States. You have what amounts to an association of skilled mechanics—using the word in its old sense. You have unions and guilds that consist of plumbers, carpenters, woodworkers, steamfitters, cigar makers—skilled workers who form bits and pieces of an industry. In a shop where ten thousand men are employed under one roof, you might have no more than a hundred who belong to your unions—but the shop itself remains an open shop—"

"We know what a craft union is, Ben," Fulton Grove said shortly, speaking for the first time.

"Of course you do, but I'm spreading out the dirty wash, as Myron asked me to do."

"That's your dirty wash?" Clement demanded.

"Let's examine it. Maybe it's clean, but let's take a long, hard look at it. Your Confederation consists of twenty-two

334

craft unions and only craft unions. But the International Miners Union is not a craft union. We include anyone and everyone who sets foot in the mine or the tipple or the breaker, no matter what his job is, no matter how skilled or unskilled he is. The mine is the union and the union is the mine."

"Ben, Ben," Clement said with controlled patience, "we've been through this industrial-union argument a hundred times. Why do we have to go through it again? It's not to the point here. You can't organize unskilled labor. You can't organize factory hands. You can't organize the men on an assembly line. They're laborers. You made the distinction yourself, mechanics on the one hand, laborers on the other."

"And what are diggers?" Ben demanded, his voice hardening.

"You mean miners?"

"I mean diggers," Ben said. "I mean men who crawl into a black tunnel every day, two, three miles underground, and then with their two hands they load ten tons of coal—"

"They're skilled craftsmen, Ben."

"Horseshit!" Ben exploded. "That's horseshit, and you know it!"

"Ben, Ben," Stillman begged, "I said no fights, no arguments. Here, we're trade-union brothers."

"All right, Ben," Mark Golden said comfortably and easily, "give yourself a rest and enjoy a good cigar for a change. My life mission," he explained to the others, "is to ride herd on Ben Holt's temper. And it's a beauty. I earn my dollar, believe me—"

The cigar clenched between his teeth, Ben listened and remained silent. I breathed a quiet sigh of relief as Mark went on. "But there's still a good deal in what Ben says. The Miners Union is an industrial union, and if we argued all night, it wouldn't change the fact. We're not interested in dynamiters who work in oil fields or marble quarries—if dynamiters work in those places. We're interested in dynamiters who work in coal mines because they're members of our union, and if you were to organize a dynamiters' union, we'd fight you tooth and nail before we'd let you set foot in the coal fields. The same with steam shovels and bulldozers. There's a craft union to cover those operators, but when a man operates a steam shovel in a strip mine, he's got to be a member of the Miners Union or he doesn't work. The same with the mechanics who operate the breakers—they hold their books in the Miners Union. So the plain fact of the matter is that we have an industrial union and it works. So if you take us in, you take in an industrial union."

"Now is there any argument about that?" Clement smiled. "If you set up a straw man, you got to knock him over. I say forget about straw men and let's get down to business."

"Mark didn't finish," Ben said.

They looked at Mark, who said, "That's part of it. It doesn't end there. Ben has an idea, and it's been driving him. I think it's the biggest idea in the world, but let him tell it."

We all looked at Ben, who put down his cigar now and composed himself to be amiable, simple, and winning. It was not easy, but he did it and told them, "It's an idea, and it's big. It's not new—no idea this big is new, but it sticks up on the horizon now, and it's inescapable. Here it is. Today, in the United States, there are twenty million unorganized workers. I say organize them—into industrial unions like our union, the automobile workers into one great auto union, the rubber workers into a rubber union, the steelworkers into a steel union. Each industry into one great union cutting across every craft in that industry. The steel industry in particular is a life-and-death matter to us. You know how many coal mines the big steel companies own. It cripples us to try to negotiate with an industry that's half union and half open shop. But think of what happens when they're organized, unions so big that nothing on earth could shake them—packing-house workers, agricultural workers, glass-workers—great God Almighty, we'd have a labor movement then like nothing the world ever dreamed of! That's the idea I came here with. I can't do it—no one can do it except you. But you can. You have the resources, the money, the trained organizers, the prestige, and by golly, if you play your cards right, you'll have the President of the United States behind you. What do they say—that there's nothing as powerful as an idea whose time has arrived? Something like that. I tell you, you can do it—we can do it! Just agree to do it, and I bring the International Miners Union into the Confederation. Four hundred and fifty thousand miners. Men with a record of struggle that goes back a hundred years. A year from today, we'll have a million dollars in our treasury—five years from today a strike and organizational fund of ten million dollars and a union that's like an iron-ribbed ship. Will you do it? Will you shake hands on that?"

I had never heard Ben talk more simply, more directly, more eloquently. If ever he spoke from his heart and to the single point he believed in, it was then. He opened himself. He dropped his defenses. You forgot the girth, the sagging cheeks, the gray hair, and you listened to a young man on fire with his dreams.

You did and you didn't. They didn't. They listened to him. They heard him through, and then they sat in a silence that stretched on and on, until finally Fulton Grove cleared his throat and said, "I know him. I told you those would be his conditions."

Myron Stillman sighed deeply. "Ben," he said tiredly, "you knew what we would ask you. We knew what you would ask us. Why do you make things so difficult? Here, we're union brothers. We don't have to make things difficult for each other. We want you and your union in the Confederation. You belong to us. Come to us. That's all." He belched and apologized. "I ate too much. It was the spirit of the evening."

But the spirit, as he called it, had fled. Arnold Clement tried to ease the tension and prove to Ben that you could not organize factory workers. "We'll end up broke, Ben— all of us, you, us—all of us."

"Broke! Arnold, for Christ's sake, you've got fifty million dollars in your treasury, and you tell me that you'll end up broke!"

"That fifty million dollars—and it's only forty-five million, not fifty—it's the heartblood of our organization. We're not the owners of that money. We are trustees, in a manner of speaking. And what is that kind of money, Ben, when you set out on a national organizational drive? How far will it go with twenty million workers? A few national strikes—"

"I organized the miners with twenty cents!" Ben said.

"Miners, Ben, miners. An auto worker is something else—hillbillies out of West Virginia and Kentucky who decided to get jobs in Detroit instead of starving in their scrubby hills—that's what your auto worker is. Are you going to organize some dumb Polack who hits a cow over the head with a hammer in a slaughterhouse? Is that your idea of trade-union material? I wasn't born yesterday, Ben. I've been around. I've worked with the lumberjacks up in the Northwest—crazy, wild-eyed bums—you going to make unions there? Or those niggers they're taking on in steel? You going to take some big, black ignorant buck out of Georgia or Alabama and make him into a trade unionist? Ben, you're dreaming. We can't afford dreams. We're practical men—labor leaders. That's why we are where we are. That's why we have three and a half million members. We have a lifetime of experience at this kind of thing, we're no mavericks. Myron here has put fifty years of his life into this organization—that's experience, Ben. That talks."

"You wanted an answer," Ben said thinly. "Now give me an answer. Do we have anything to discuss?"

"Not unless you change your conditions, Ben."

"They don't change. Not so long as I'm alive."

"There's no hurry, Ben. This is a nice place. Why don't you boys make up your minds to join us here for a week or two? Let the sun loosen the tensions. Live a little. We can take our time, and after a few weeks of relaxation here, you'll see things differently, believe me. You'll be our guests.

It won't cost you a nickel. I'm no chaser, but it never hurts to vary the diet a little. There are some broads down here you'll feel absolutely no pain with. Then we talk easy instead of trying to decide everything in one night. What about it, Ben?"

Ben was sitting on the couch. Now he rose, towering over them. "Mark, Al," he said, "let's get out of here. Let's get out of here before I say something to these pricks that I'm likely to regret."

As we rose, Joe Briggs stumbled to his feet and advanced on Ben, yelling that no one was going to call him a prick and get away with it. Ben hit him. I know that Ben had some rough times when he was young, but this was the only time I ever saw Ben hit a man in all the years I was with him. Briggs collapsed onto the floor and sat there, a dazed expression on his face, his nose bleeding all over the inch-thick Carmine Plaza carpet.

We left Miami the following morning, after being awakened by the Associated Press at 5 A.M. I declined to make any statement and refused to let them speak to Ben. To get free of the hotel, we had to push our way through a bank of reporters. How the story got out, I don't know, but the morning papers carried the headline: BEN HOLT BELTS JOE BRIGGS. LABOR SPLIT BY ONE-PUNCH KNOCKOUT. Like most headlines, it was somewhat less than accurate. You have to join something to split from it.

22

For the first hour on the plane, Ben sat and brooded in silence. Then, suddenly, he said, "They patronized us. Those lousy bastards patronized us."

"So they patronized us," Mark agreed. "The hell with it! Forget it."

"How old is that suit you're wearing?" Ben asked me. "I told you that once before."

"We look like slobs—all of us."

"Ben, knock it off," Mark said wearily. "So we look like slobs."

"There's no use telling ourselves we don't live in the same world they live in," Ben reflected. "We do. Maybe nothing could have changed the way it ended, but if you ask me, we got Pomax written all over us. We think like Pomax and we act like Pomax."

"What are you telling me, Ben?" Mark asked mildly. "That we have to think big?"

"We're not small-town boys, Mark. That's what I'm telling you."

"All right. We're not small-town boys. We're important. We're a lot more important than those creeps at the Carmine Plaza. They're dead, and they don't know it."

"Maybe we're alive and we don't know it," Ben said.

"Maybe."

"What have you got on your mind, Ben?" I asked him.

"We've got to get out of Pomax and we've got to act like what we are."

"How do you do that?"

"We can pay ourselves what we're worth, for one thing. It's time we did."

"All right," Mark nodded. "How much are we worth?"

"I'm going to take fifteen thousand a year," Ben said. "You take ten. We'll give Al eight."

There was no response to that, and after a while, Ben said, "Well—what about it?"

"You're doubling your pay, Ben," Mark said.

"So I'm doubling it. Am I worth it?"

"You're worth it," Mark said. "I'm not worth ten thousand a year. I don't want it."

"You're out of your mind. If I went to any big-time firm of lawyers, they'd ask for a retainer of twenty thousand dollars before they touched our business."

"I suppose so. But I'm not a big-time firm of lawyers. I

make five thousand dollars a year now, and I'm paid each week. It's enough. I'll tell you when I need more."

"Al, what do you think?"

"I'm not thinking, Ben," I shrugged. "You want fifteen thousand a year, that's your problem and you solve it."

He solved it. In March, a month later, he raised his pay to fifteen thousand dollars a year. The following year, he increased it to twenty-five thousand dollars a year.

PART VI

1

On a cold, bleak December afternoon, in 1937 in Washington, D.C., I met Mark Golden and Lena Kuscow at the offices of Kollman and Watts, a real-estate firm. Mark and Lena had been in Washington for the past week, trying to find and buy a building to house the headquarters of the International Miners Union. Failing in that, Mark made arrangements to rent a building as our temporary headquarters. A year later, plans were drawn for a new building, the one which today houses the union.

Kollman and Watts were the real-estate brokers through whom Mark had been working. We met there because I had been sent on an errand to Washington to buy Dorothy Holt a house. This was almost, but not entirely, as bald as it sounds.

Nineteen thirty-seven had been a tumultuous year. The country was still in the grasp of the great depression, and from coast to coast there had been an endless series of violent strikes against falling wages and bad working conditions. Almost all of these strikes had been wildcat affairs in non-union industries, and now they had culminated in an enormous sit-down movement in the auto industry in Detroit. Thousands of workers in the biggest plant in the industry had laid down their tools, stopped the assembly line, declared a strike, and refused to leave the plant. Other auto workers, who had put together a thin skeleton of a union, sent a desperate plea to Ben to come and give them the benefit of his leadership and experience. Nine days before Christmas, he left for Detroit, telling me,

"Al, there's no way out of this and there's no way to make up to Dotty for the fact that I won't be spending Christmas with her and the kids. But there's one thing I want to do if it's humanly possible. For years now, I've been talking to Dorothy about moving the International from Pomax to Washington. Mark's down there now trying to find a building. Tell him to wind that up just as soon as he can, because I want him and you too in Detroit with me. This thing in Detroit is the biggest thing in the history of labor in this country, and if we come out of it on top, we've got what I always dreamed of—the beginning of a new kind of an association of industrial unions. But I must have Mark there with me—I need him, do you understand?"

I said that I understood. I understood better than he imagined.

"All right. Now here's what you do. Take a plane to Washington, and find a house for Dotty and me and the kids. A good house, useful, pretty, in the kind of a neighborhood Dotty would like. You have good taste, and you know what I mean."

"You're not serious," I said.

"I'm serious, Al. I don't mean for you to go ahead and buy the house. Just select one and get a good, large photo of it, so that I can give the photo to Dorothy for Christmas. Maybe she won't like it—"

"Ben, would any woman want a house someone else had picked out without even consulting her?"

"You're making too much of it. It's a gesture—a thought. If she doesn't want it, she'll find another house. We have plenty of time. But I want the picture—and then I want you and Mark in Detroit."

Thereby, I was in Washington, sitting with Mark and Lena in the offices of Kollman and Watts, and going through a stack of glossy photographs of houses for sale, disgusted with myself, and not unaware of what we might expect from Dorothy Holt when the harebrained scheme was revealed to her. She would be infuriated, hurt, and bewildered, angry at Ben and despising me. I decided that I would deserve her contempt.

Lena made no bones about her own feelings on the matter. "My opinion of Ben Holt does not bear expression," she said. "But at least it was an opinion I always held. As far as Al Cutter is concerned—"

"Let Al be," Mark said wearily. "He's doing something that Ben asked him to do, and to Ben it's important. Maybe it's the most important thing in the world to Ben."

"Then why doesn't he do it himself?"

"Because he's in Detroit and he must be in Detroit. Try for one minute to understand that Ben is in a special category. Right now, the whole world is sitting on his shoulders."

"The whole world is not sitting on his shoulders," Lena protested. "You're like a kid, Mark."

"Sure, I'm like a kid."

"Yes, like a kid. Ben Holt is a hero. Ben Holt is a man on a white horse. That's never changed for you, has it? Never. You can see through anyone else, but not Ben. Ben is it. Ben is God."

"God damn it, Lena, you know that's not true. I take Ben as he is, and I know him for exactly what he is. But I don't confuse the man with his achievements."

"I do."

I pushed the photographs away. "Enough of that back-

345

biting," I told them. "There's nothing here that makes me want to live in it. I'll look at more tomorrow. Now suppose we eat."

Mark rose slowly and wearily. "Age and a man's back," he commented. He tried to smile. "Lena says I'm a kid. That's a laugh, Al. I'm going to be sixty years old, and I feel like a hundred."

"Are you all right?" I asked him.

"I'm all right. I'm fine."

2

At the restaurant, Mark sat stiffly and looked at his food without touching it.

"Why don't you eat something?" Lena asked him.

"I don't know. I don't seem to be very hungry."

"You had no lunch either," Lena said. "Are you all right, Mark?"

"I don't know," he replied strangely. "I think I'll be all right. Don't worry about my eating, Lena. I'll have coffee and a piece of pie later. That's enough to carry me through. The truth is, I don't require much food." He began to tell me about the building he had made arrangements to rent. It was four blocks from the White House. "I thought you and Ben would like that, Al." He tried to smile, and instead he grimaced with pain.

"Mark, what is it?" Lena whispered.

"I don't know. I don't feel so good."

I called the waiter and asked whether I could see the manager. When the manager came, Mark was leaning over the table, supporting his head with his hands. "My friend here is ill," I said. "Do you have a place where he can lie down?" He said that there was a couch in his office that we could use, and I asked him to try to get a doctor. Lena and I supported Mark as we led him into the manager's office and then helped him to lie down on the couch. His face was

346

gray, his breathing heavy and labored. I loosened his tie and shirt collar and opened his vest.

"Should I take off his shoes?" Lena asked me.

I nodded. Then I asked Mark how he felt. His eyes were closed and he didn't respond. His hoarse, heavy breathing continued.

Meanwhile, the manager had telephoned for an ambulance. We sat helplessly next to Mark until the ambulance arrived. The intern who examined him wasn't certain what was wrong with Mark, but he felt that it could be a heart attack. They carried Mark out into the ambulance, and then Lena and I took a cab to the hospital. When we arrived there, Mark was dead. He had suffered a coronary thrombosis, and he had died in the ambulance.

3

Lena sat in the waiting room, dry-eyed, her hands clasped in her lap, her eyes focused across the room on nothing and witnessing nothing, her sight perhaps turned inward and witnessing more than I knew. Did she want anything? No. Was there anything that I could do? No, there was nothing that I could do, and would I please leave her alone for a little while and then she would be all right. Anyway, the world was a place where you were all right or you were not all right, and there was not a great deal more to it than that. "Rotten, stinking way to die," she had whispered, but I wasn't sure that there was any other way to die. "Do you want a drink? A glass of water?"

"Al, I don't want a goddam thing."

An intern with a clip board asked me about the body. They wanted to do an autopsy. It was procedure when there was any question at all about the cause of death, and I said that there was no reason why they should not perform an autopsy. "It's usual to have the signature of some close kin, a wife or relative."

"I don't know that there is any."

"Isn't she his wife?" nodding at Lena.

"No, just a friend."

"He must have some relative," the intern insisted. "Someone has to assume custody of the body and arrange for the burial."

"I'll take care of that," I assured him.

"But the autopsy?"

I went over to Lena, and he followed me, and I told her what the question was. She said that Mark had been through enough, and why did they have to cut him up now.

"They have to find out the exact cause of his death."

"He died. What difference does it make now?"

"It's a district ordinance," the intern explained. "Aren't there any relatives?"

"He had a wife once," Lena said dully. "They were divorced years ago. I don't know her name or where she is. He had a sister who died last year. His mother and father are dead."

"No children?"

There were no children. There were only the two of us, sitting in a bleak waiting room, while outside big, wet flakes of snow levitated and turned over and over and plastered themselves against the windowpanes. As an official of the organization he had worked for, I signed the papers. The intern was a decent young man who had probably seen too much death of this kind to allow himself to become emotionally involved in it, but who desired to be helpful, and he said that downstairs in the hospital office they would assist me in making arrangements with a local undertaker, either to have Mark buried in a local cemetery or to undertake a cremation. Myself, I favored a cremation, and when the intern had left, I told Lena what we would have to do.

"I don't want to do that," she said to me. "I want to take the body back to Pomax and bury it there."

"What?"

"That's what I want to do, Al. I want to take the body back to Pomax."

"But why?"

"Why? You have to ask, Al? It was the only place he had —the only place that meant anything to him—yes, that lousy, stinking miserable town was the only place that meant anything to him. You want to burn him up and get a pot of ashes? I don't. I want to put him back where he spent his life, whatever there was of his life that made any sense."

"Lena, that doesn't make any sense," I argued. "In the first place, Mark was Jewish."

"What the hell difference does that make?"

"It makes this difference. As far as I know, you can't bury a Jew in a Catholic or Protestant cemetery."

"Who says you can't? Is Mark going to object?"

"The people who operate the cemeteries won't permit it, believe me, honey. Here in Washington, we can find a Jewish cemetery—"

"You make me sick," she said. "I'm Greek Orthodox, and there's an Orthodox cemetery in Pomax, and if anyone tries to stop me from burying Mark there, I'll burn down their lousy church. So stop this kind of thing, Al, just stop it!"

I nodded, and we went down to the hospital office and made the arrangements that were necessary. The undertaker agreed that he would pick up the body at the hospital, embalm it, and ship it to Pomax the same day. They had a Western Union service there, and I sent a wire to Ben, telling him what had happened, and another one to Oscar Suzic, at the Union Building. Then I took Lena back to the hotel. It was about nine o'clock in the evening now.

We went to Mark's room. I would have felt better if Lena had been able to weep or go through some kind of an outburst, and I think she would have felt better too. It would have lessened the effect of whatever was building up inside of her, but evidently tears or hysterics were impossible. "I can't cry," she said to me. "I didn't love Mark, that's the terrible shame of it. You only cry for yourself. It's a lie that we weep for others." I tried to tell her that we weep for others, each in our own way, but she informed me that I could keep the platitudes. In Mark's room, we gathered together his clothes, an extra suit, a few shirts, underwear, handkerchiefs, some shaving stuff, and packed it into his grip.

I said to Lena that unless she had some other idea, we could take it back with us and give it, along with the rest of Mark's clothing, to the Miners' Relief. She smiled for the first time since dinner, a wan, drawn smile that reminded me of how beautiful she had once been, and, indeed, considering what had happened, still was, the strong, sculptured bones of her face defying the pressure of time and misery, her skin pale and clear, her eyes bright and bitter.

"The rest of Mark's clothes," she shrugged. "These are his wardrobe, Al. Practically all of it. Did you ever see the place where he lived?"

I shook my head.

"You knew him fourteen years and you never saw the place where he lived," Lena said. "What a rich, warm world we live in! Well, he had a little room with the Kovacs—just a plain miner's family in Pomax. Like a monk's room in a monastery. He had a bed and a chair and a little chest of drawers in that room. He didn't even need a will. If he had any money left over at the end of the week, he gave it to the Miners' Relief. Since he was the supervisor of the fund, no one ever knew—not even Ben. I knew, but no one else. Sometimes, he used the money for food or for toys for kids. Never saved anything, never wanted anything. You think I admired that? Like hell I did! I hate saints. He gave away his own life—and that's even more selfish than hanging onto it tooth and nail. He had to be Jesus Christ!" She choked up suddenly, her breast heaving. "Lousy, damn Jews—what do they want from us? Wasn't one Christ enough? Al, why did he have to do it that way? Why?"

350

"I don't know, honey," I said. "I don't know one damn thing about people, so help me God, I don't."

"Buy me a drink, Al," she whispered. "Please buy me a drink."

"All you want."

"Stay with me. Oh, Jesus, I'm so frightened, Al. He was my father and my mother and he made the whole world right for me even when he tore my heart out, because he could give me nothing—but nothing, Al. Don't leave me alone, Al."

4

In the cocktail room in the hotel, we took a little table in the corner and we each of us put down a double whisky, and then we felt a little better, not much better but a little. We ordered double whiskies again.

"Cold son of a bitch," Lena said to me. "You could put down ten of these and you wouldn't even be high. Al Cutter. A cold son of a bitch."

"I don't get drunk easily. I wish I could, but I don't."

"With me, it's easy, but not tonight. I won't get drunk tonight. I'll just sit here in this fancy cocktail lounge—that's a good word, lounge—we're lounging here, Al, right on top of the world, you and me, two trade-union functionaries in Washington to pick up a couple of buildings for Ben Holt. Sweet Benny. Mark, run down to Washington and buy me an office building. Al, run down to Washington and buy Dotty a house. Buy Dotty a pretty house. You always adored Dotty, so you'll know just the kind of a house that would make her happy."

"That doesn't help, Lena."

"Sure it helps, Al. It makes me feel good to know that everyone's doing what Ben wants him to do. Except you and me right now. We're sitting in a cocktail lounge. Ben always hated cocktail lounges. A worker should get drunk in a saloon. None of the frivolous stuff for Ben. No hundred-dollar-a-night whores—not for Ben. No twenty-dollar dinners, no night clubs. Just substantial stuff, like office buildings and Georgian houses. Isn't that what he wanted, Al, a fine Georgian house with a red brick front and maybe a porch of white pillars? It surprises you, doesn't it—that a trade-union slut, a cheap convention lay like me should know all about Georgian houses? Thank Mark Golden, who taught me to read good books. Good books and good conversation. We used to talk for hours—hours. Once we talked all night long. I could mention a different kind—look, baby, shut up and screw. I'm here for the pleasure not for the conversation. Buy me another drink, please, Al. Please put up with me. Don't get angry with me."

"I won't be angry with you."

"I know. I know. Al Cutter takes any kind of crud. I would ask Mark why, and do you know what he said?"

"What did he say, Lena?"

"Because he believes in something, but he isn't sure what he believes in but he believes in it very strongly. Does that make sense, Al."

"No, not much sense, Lena."

"Mark didn't say it. I said it. I don't know why I said it. Sometimes I love you and sometimes I hate you."

"That's normal."

"Like hell it is. What's normal about me, Al? Mark ran out on me, and I feel like I'm sitting here naked. Where is my life, Al? You know what a woman's career in the trade-union movement is, Al? It's an Indian wrestle, a Japanese wrestle—what do they call them, kabookie, kaboochie? We're brother and sister, baby, so let's screw. This is a struggle for the deepest and most basic rights of man, so let's screw. You been brought up in it, baby, you know the working class from A to Z and nobody has to tell you what it suffers and what we're trying to do in this movement, so let's screw—how about it, what are you waiting for, what's a convention for? What's a convention for, Al?"

"I think you've had enough to drink, Lena."

"Don't tell me that, Al. Nobody tells me that, Al."

I shrugged and ordered another drink for her.

"Now you're sore at me again."

"I'm not," I wasn't; I was too filled with grief. I think that it was grief for myself, and that Lena was right when she said that we weep for ourselves and not for others.

"Poor Al," she whispered. "Poor Al, poor Mark, poor Ben. It's a lousy sleigh ride. I wish Dotty was here. She's good to me. She's good to everyone, a stinking saint, like Mark. Why don't you marry her, Al? Why don't you ask her to go away with you? Why don't you give her a chance? I never gave Mark a chance, but I didn't love Mark. You love Dotty, don't you?"

"No," I replied. "I don't."

"Ah, that's a lie. We're all liars—you, me, everyone. We keep telling ourselves that there's something noble and worthwhile, and when we get afraid, we turn to Mark and look at him. No more Mark. No more nothing."

Later, I helped her up to her room. I took off her shoes and covered her, turned out the lights, and went to my own room. The undertaker had called and left word to call him back, no matter how late it was. When I phoned him, he told me that we had never settled what kind of embalming Mark was to have. The undertaker pointed out that usually he hesitated to recommend the most expensive type of embalming, because it was about twice the cost of the ordinary kind. But since then, he had probably checked the credit of the International Miners Union, and now he was certain that it would not be safe to put the body in transit without the expensive embalming. I told him to go ahead and spare no cost. After all, the union could afford it, just as the union could afford my five whiskies and Lena's seven whiskies.

I took off my jacket and vest and tie, and then kicked off my shoes and sat on the edge of my bed. I looked around the standardly equipped hotel room, with its ivory walls and its Renoir reproductions, its twin beds and its two overstuffed chairs—and I tried to recollect how many times I had inhabited such rooms and where they were and whether there was any essential difference in the bleakness of each. The small adventure into memory was fruitless, as most such adventures are. I was tired, yet I had no desire to sleep. As they say, I attempted to compose my thoughts, and reflected that somewhere I had read or heard that the first requisite for composure is a man's decent respect for himself. I lacked the first requisite. I had no respect for myself. I had no respect for what I was, what I did, or for what I ever might be. I could not even be properly sorry for Mark Golden, for in some way that was entirely beyond my understanding, Mark Golden had fulfilled himself. I blamed the five whiskies for the notion that he had come to earth, done his work, and departed. Aloud, I said, "That is pure, unadulterated horseshit, and if it's the best you can do, then it's time that you departed." But I had no inclination toward departure. Without any strong or principled desire to live, I was possessed of no pressing need to die. I was possessed of nothing. I was just a little bit drunk and possessed of nothing when the telephone rang. It was Ben Holt calling from Detroit.

"I tried to reach you before," he said. "This is a hell of a note about Mark. It knocked me over. I never expected anything like this."

"He was run-down," I said. I didn't know what else to say.

"I guess so. Where did it happen?"

"In a restaurant." I told him the details about where it had happened and how it had happened.

"Did he have much pain?"

"I don't know. Not much, I guess."

"I'm glad there wasn't much pain. My God, Al, I never expected anything like this. It couldn't have happened at a worse time—a more crucial time."

"That was thoughtless of Mark."

"Don't be such a goddamned wise guy. Mark never did a thoughtless thing in his life. Do you know what I'm into up here? Ten thousand workers are holed up in the biggest

354

automobile plant in these United States. Did you hear me, Al? Ten thousand workers."

"I heard you."

"Do you wonder that I need Mark?"

"Mark's dead."

"I know that, God damn it, that's it. Try to understand my position, Al. Just listen to me and try to understand it. This is a sit-down strike. The workers in the largest factory in the world under one roof just laid down their tools and sat down. Closed the plant and locked themselves in, and they're going to stay there until the company gives them a proper union contract. There's never been a real union in this rotten industry—and suddenly these auto workers take the most militant action in the whole history of the labor movement. And so help me God, no one knows exactly what is happening. Should management break into the plant? There'll be a blood bath if they do. Should the governor take over? Should he use the militia? Every goddamn one of these questions, and they call me in here to lead the thing. Al, I'm blind. For twenty years, I never took a step without Mark putting the go-ahead signal on it, and now he leaves me here with this—"

"It's a damn shame," I agreed.

"Are you drunk?"

"A little, yes."

"I can understand that," Ben said sympathetically. "How do you feel right now?"

"Lousy."

"Did you make all the arrangements? I mean the body and what to do with it?"

"I made them."

"All right. Al, I got to have you here—now. Get a good night's sleep, and take the first plane in the morning for Detroit."

"I can't, Ben."

"What do you mean, you can't. Al, I tell you it's absolutely necessary."

"We're taking Mark's body back to Pomax, and I'm going to Pomax for the funeral."

"Of all the crazy notions! Mark has no family in Pomax."

"He has no family anywhere else."

"Whose idea was this?"

"Lena's."

"Yes—Lena," Ben said, and then he hesitated for a moment before he asked, "How is she?"

"Rotten."

"She took it hard?"

"How do you suppose she took it?"

"All right. If she wants the body shipped back to Pomax, there's nothing wrong with that. But I want you here in Detroit tomorrow."

"No," I said. "I'm going with Lena, Ben. I can't leave her alone."

"Look, Al—this is Ben. Don't make sentimental speeches to me. The whole world is exploding here in Detroit. Doesn't that mean anything to you? A week from now, we can be out of business or have the beginning of the biggest labor movement in the world. This is everything we ever dreamed of."

"I know that, Ben," I agreed wearily. "I know that. But I have to go back to Pomax with Lena."

Finally, he agreed. I would meet him in Detroit a day or two later. But he couldn't forgive Mark for dying at a time like this. And apparently, he had forgotten all about the house he had sent me to Washington to buy, or at least a picture of the same.

5

The day they buried Mark Golden in Pomax was clear as crystal and cold as ice, the sky a burnished blue and the wind pouring down out of the north and sighing through the crisp, bare branches of the birches. Jack Mullen had gone to Detroit with Ben, leaving Oscar Suzic and Gus Empek at Pomax.

Of their own accord, they had called a day's stoppage, and two thousand diggers turned out for Mark's funeral. They followed the casket down the street to the edge of town, to the Orthodox cemetery where Mark was buried. There was no difficulty about that. A priest in Pomax could hardly hew to the hard edge of rule or prejudice, and when the union contributed two hundred dollars to the Church fund, a small corner was found where, by stretching a point, the ground could be considered a little less than hallowed. We sent a car to Cairo for a rabbi, and he read the Hebrew prayers while the bearded Orthodox priest stood by and watched. Altogether, it was more thoughtful care and consideration than we had ever shown for Mark while he was alive, and a scrupulous attention to detail that was alien to all he believed in. But the dead do not argue these things.

The rabbi was impressed. As he and the Orthodox priest shared a drink, he wondered whether there was any precedent for this kind of thing and said that it had a symbolic meaning beyond the fact of the burial. I couldn't see any symbolism in it, and as it was very cold, we soon left to go our separate ways.

Dorothy took Lena home with her, and since there was no other place in which to pay our respects, Gus and Oscar and old Dan Jessup and one or two of the older miners came to Dorothy's house for a little while. They had a few drinks and tried to express something of the very real feeling they had had for Mark, and then they left. I remained there with Lena and Dorothy. Norah was away at college this year, and Sam and Ben, Jr., oversized, pimply-faced boys of sixteen and fifteen respectively, uncomfortable and somber in the presence of death, excused themselves and hid in their rooms. We three sat in the living room, drinking tea and trying to remember Mark with conversation, simply in terms of our own need for self-respect.

At forty, Dorothy Holt was still an attractive and desirable woman, somewhat subdued, her hair beginning to streak with gray, but slim and tight-skinned. She had been deeply disturbed at Mark's passing, perhaps more deeply, in a manner, than either Lena or myself; for here in Pomax, Mark had been a pillar of support and sustenance to her. The rare moments when they had played together, Mark on his violin and Dorothy at the piano, had been very rich and much anticipated events, breaking an otherwise unexciting existence. Mark had also played the role of confidant and father confessor, and had seemed to impart in her at least an illusion of security. The illusion was gone now, and suddenly Dorothy seemed utterly bereft.

I spoke about the funeral, and said that Mark would have liked it—only miners, and no one else, to mourn him. Lena said that when you are dead, it makes little difference what you like or dislike. She was very tired, and Dorothy persuaded her to go upstairs and lie down for a little while. I remained in the living room, while Dorothy took Lena to the bedroom. When Dorothy returned, she said that she had never seen Lena this way before.

"She's never been this way before. She's never been without Mark before."

"I suppose not," Dorothy agreed. "Did she take it very badly when Mark—when he died?"

"She took it badly."

"I never thought she really loved Mark. I thought—"

"Mark loved her," I said.

"Yes. I suppose that meant a great deal."

"I don't know. Maybe it did, maybe it didn't. Sometimes I feel that Lena's like myself—"

"How?" Dorothy asked me after a long moment. "How do you mean that, Al?"

"Waste. You look back, and it seems that it's all wasted. You try to understand why it should have been that way, and it's blurred and unclear, and none of it makes very much sense."

"For God's sake, Al," Dorothy cried, "how much sense does anyone's life make? The waste is everywhere you look. Do you think you and Lena are so exceptional? We live in a time when the whole world's a wasteland—last spring a million cabbages dumped into the river, a thousand tons of corn burned while people starve, apples rotting on trees because it's not worthwhile to pick them and ten million men rotting in hopelessness and idleness. Or the waste in Spain now, with this filthy war started and Franco riding in there on his white horse, or the waste in Germany with that terrible man, Hitler! At least you made something and Lena made something and Mark made something."

"What?"

"The union. Hope and life for half a million men who lived for so long without it."

"Not me or Lena or Mark. Ben did that."

"Really? Do you think so?"

"He did it. I know—I watched. That's all I did, I watched. Like he's doing it now in Detroit."

"You're a fool, Al!" she cried.

"Thank you."

"Stop that! Look at yourself for once, Al!"

"I've looked."

"Don't you want anything? Haven't you ever wanted anything?"

"I've wanted," I nodded. "But I never really knew what I wanted, and if I had, I wouldn't have known how to take it."

"You gave it all to Ben," she said, smiling ruefully. "You, Gus Empek, Oscar, Jack—oh, it's such a long list—and Mark too. Mark did it in his own, peculiar Jewish way. Let me suffer for the sins that others have visited upon my fellow man. His whole existence was a passage of guilt. I never knew what he atoned for, but his life was an endless act of atonement—"

"For being present in the company of human beings," I said sourly.

"Al!"

"I'm sorry, Dotty."

"Al, why don't you take Lena and get away from here?

Go away for a month, both of you, and give something to each other. God knows, you have it coming to you."

"Two reasons, Dotty. One, Ben needs me in Detroit."

"Ben needs you in Detroit," she repeated scathingly. "What a fool you are, Al!"

"You said that before."

"Then it wants saying again. Ben doesn't need—he takes. There's a difference, or don't you know that there is?"

"Needing and taking—"

"There are people who need and can't take. And there are people who take without any need."

"There's another reason," I said dully. "I'm not in love with Lena. She's not in love with me."

"Who are you in love with, Al? Do you think you're in love with me?"

"I don't know. If I did, I'd ask you to go away with me."

"I wouldn't go," Dorothy smiled. "You know that."

"Naturally. Ben wouldn't want you to."

"Go to hell," she said.

"I've been there—there and back. Why don't you leave me alone? Go up and see how Lena is."

"Lena's all right. I want to talk to you."

"All right—talk."

"I know why Lena and Mark went to Washington. Why did you go there?"

"Ben sent me."

"What did he send you there for, Al?"

"Ask him."

"I'm asking you."

"Oh, the hell with it. It's small and nothing. It's a part of nothing."

"Good old Al. Loyal to Ben. He worships Dorothy, but loyal to her—oh no."

"I'm loyal to no one, not even Al," I said morosely. "I don't want to play any games. I don't even want to weep for Mark Golden, or to remember fourteen years I spent near him and never heard a harsh word from him or a nasty com-

360

ment, or to remember when I first came to this lousy, mis-
begotten place and found just one person to make me feel
that I was wanted or welcomed."

"Why did you come here at all, Al?" she asked softly.

"That's the big question. I never asked myself that one,
Dotty, no, not at all."

"Do you know?"

"I know. Of course I know. It wasn't the hardest thing to
figure out. There are men who can just live. There are other
men who can't just live, because life makes no sense at all
to them. Then they spend their lives trying to find a sensible
reason for their own existence."

"As simple as that?"

"It's not so simple, Dorothy Holt," I answered sadly. "Not
one goddamn bit so simple, because no one ever finds the
reason, not Mark or Lena or myself—"

"Or Ben?"

I shrugged.

"So you're going to Detroit after all?"

"Yes, Dotty, I'm going to Detroit."

"A sensible reason for your own existence, Al?"

"More or less."

"What about Lena? Don't you know one damn thing
about women, Al?"

"Very little," I shrugged.

But I knew enough to know that Dorothy Holt was
drained more empty than I, that if I told her about Ben and
the picture of a house, it would have tipped her over the
edge of something. I didn't want to, mostly because I no
longer cared.

6

"I'm going to Detroit with you," Lena said, and I said
that was all right, if that was what she wanted—or anything
else that she wanted. But she didn't believe me, except about

361

Detroit. "Ben is there," she said, "so we'll both go to Detroit, Al. I don't want to stretch it any further than that."

"Don't jump on Ben," I said, and she said, the hell with Ben, and she didn't give a damn. "Then why are you going to Detroit?" I asked her.

"I hate Pomax."

That made sense. The following morning, we drove to Cairo and took a plane, and a few hours later we were in Detroit. The struck plant was a few miles outside of metropolitan Detroit, in a suburb called Blent, and the cab driver who took us out there explained that as far as he was concerned, this was his last trip. I asked him why, and he said,

"Because any minute now that sonovabitch place is going to be the worst bloody sonovabitch battlefield on this continent."

He drove slowly and carefully on a slush-covered road between endless rows of drab houses, dumps, and car graveyards. A few leafless trees; a few wretched farms. Then army tents, row upon row of brown army tents. Tanks, mortars, and a pool of trucks. The town itself swarmed with men in uniform and men out of uniform, and National Guardsmen detoured us around the plant, but in the line of the cross streets, we could see the machine-gun emplacements, and there was one street filled with men in civilian clothes, carrying clubs, picks, and improvised spears. We circled, always with the plant in the distance, like a beleaguered fortress in some strange, silent war.

The hotel was full. They directed us to the Auto Union headquarters. We circled the plant again, back now along the opposite side of it. There were two armies, strangely intermingled, clusters of workers armed with improvised weapons and clusters of National Guardsmen, armed with rifles, bayonets, and machine guns, each apart from the other, tight, suspicious, shivering with the cold and the tension. We passed a tank, jockeying from tread to tread, grinding and twisting as it shifted its position to cover a cross street.

"You see what I mean," the cab driver said.

"I see what you mean."

At the Auto Union headquarters, the cab driver announced the end of his services. "Pay me off, mister," he said. "I want to get to hell out of here." I paid him off, and, carrying our suitcases, I pushed my way through a mass of people into what was once, many years ago, a luxurious mansion. Lena followed me, and my insistence on seeing Ben Holt brought us finally to a room on the second floor. I left Lena with the suitcases and went in. There were about fifteen men in the room, among them Ben. Half of them were talking, and the other half were trying to get some silence and to begin talking themselves; and through it, I could hear Ben's voice as he argued with one of them,

"Hell, no! Don't give me that crap about all that flesh and blood can stand! Sure it's cold in that plant. Sure they're hungry. Half of this stinking country is hungry. But if they don't settle down and make up their minds to hold on for another twenty-four hours, they'll be a lot hungrier and a lot sorrier-looking."

Someone said something about one of the leaders of the Auto Union, who was evidently ready to give up and capitulate to any set of terms.

"Get that sonovabitch out of town!" Ben roared. "Lose him somewhere!"

Suppose they promised the strikers in the plant that it would end in another twenty-four hours, and suppose it didn't end?

"What am I, God?" Ben yelled. "I told you that I'm seeing the governor tonight! How many times do I have to tell you that? I spoke to the President of the United States! I spoke to the governor—and I'm speaking to him again! All I'm asking is that you sit tight in that plant for another twenty-four hours. That's all I'm asking. Is that so much to ask?"

Some of them left then, and Ben saw me. "Al—for Christ's sake, it's about time! Come over here!" Then he said to one of the men in the room, "I got to have an hour alone with Al Cutter, here. Will you clear this room?"

"An hour, Ben?"

"Make it a half hour. Give us fifteen minutes. The world isn't coming to an end. You can yell at each other outside as well as in here."

They got out finally, and I sat there with Ben, who stared at me and grinned and lit a cigar and pushed one toward me. I shook my head. "Ever seen the like of it?" he asked. I shook my head again. "What do you think's going to happen?"

"God knows," I said. "I don't."

"I do," he nodded. "So help me God, I do. In the next twenty-four hours, it's going to wind up and finish, and it's going to be the biggest, fattest labor victory there ever was. That's what I'm telling you, Al."

"How do you know, Ben?"

"How do I know? Because it's in the cards—written all over every card. You saw what's going on outside?"

"I saw it."

"It's a siege, ten thousand workers in that big plant—the biggest single plant of its kind in the world—and they been sitting in there, day after day, just sitting there with the stipulation that the company recognizes their trade union or they sit there forever. And the hell of it is that it came out of themselves. There's no real union in this industry, just a kind of spit-and-paper organization that a bunch of kids threw together, and these kids are trying to play it by ear— just as the bunch in the plant are trying to play it by ear— and every day the company gets another injunction and another regiment of the National Guard, and every day the ten thousand men in that plant get hungrier and colder and more frightened. So just to look at it that way, you'd think it was pretty damn hopeless, wouldn't you?"

"I might."

"Sure you might," Ben grinned. "But you've been around and you've seen one or two things. Like hell it's hopeless!

They begged me to come up here because they got scared —who in hell wouldn't, this thing is so big, and day after day, I been fighting them to sit tight. I been pushing it up to the edge, and right now it's as close to the edge as anything can get. The men in the plant were frightened at first, real frightened, but fear's a funny thing, it rubs off. Now they insist that they're going to die to the last man, and all that really bothers them is that they're cold and hungry. On the other hand, the soldier boys were all set to bust into the plant, but now they have had a chance to think about a slaughter of unarmed men, and they're not sure they want to bust into anything. I spoke to the President, and he's like a man on a rail riding this, but he can't stand to think about a plant full of dead workers either, and the company itself is raging all over the place, but they keep wondering how many cars they'll sell if they tell the soldiers to fight their way in there, and meanwhile their competitors are selling cars a mile a minute and their own place is cold and quiet— and might even get all smashed up and burnt down if they force the issue. That's the way it stands, Al—and that's why it's going to be settled tonight—because there's no other place for it to go. I'm meeting with the governor tonight and with the president of the company and with the vice-president of the company, and so help me, I'll come out of there with an agreement! Do you know what that means?"

I nodded. "You've been waiting for it a long time, Ben."

"But haven't I! You remember that day in Florida, Al? Can you imagine, that sonovabitch Arnold Clement, that lousy little prick had the effrontery to telephone me here and beg me to call this sit-down off. Promised me everything under the sun, if only I'd call it off."

"He'd think that way."

"Al, you know what I'm going to ask you?"

I waited.

"Al," he said, "right now, this thing is confusion from the word go—sheer hell and confusion. No one knows who is who or what is what. I dreamed of this kind of industrial-union setup for years. I planned for it when everyone else said that I was out of my mind. Now it's here, and a year from now, we'll have fifteen million workers in the biggest and best trade-union organization the world ever knew. I said that about coal, and I was right. I'm saying it here, and I am just as right. And, Al, I'm going to lead it."

I listened and said nothing.

"You understand me, Al? I want you to be at the meeting tonight. We're meeting at the Prince George Hotel in Detroit. And I want you to write the story of this. I want it to be written officially as the statement of our own union concerning its national leader, Ben Holt. I'm not asking this for myself. I'm asking it for the whole labor movement. If there was anyone else beside me, I'd say what the hell, let the chips fall where they may. But I can't do that. I'm playing a role here, and I want it made plain. Do you understand me?"

"I understand you, Ben," I said.

"Do you think I'm wrong?"

"You think you're right," I said. "That's all."

"I'm holding a room for you at the Prince George. Don't think that was easy. There isn't a bed in Detroit that's for hire."

7

The time was up. They were pushing into the room again, and I left and went outside, to where Lena waited with our luggage. Jack Mullen was talking to her, big red-faced, white-haired Jack Mullen who was Ben Holt's right-hand man, and who said,

"Well, if it ain't Al! Maybe you can convince her—I been telling her that she might as well stay with me. There's no other place to stay."

"You make me tired, Jack," Lena said. "Why don't you go away?"

366

"You hear that, Al? She comes here and tells me to go away."

"We're going into Detroit, Jack," I told him. "Do you suppose you could find us someone to drive us in?"

"You name it, we got it," he grinned. "We rate here. No one ever saw Ben Holt in action until they watched him work here these five days. Between you and me, Al, this would not have lasted two days if they hadn't brought Ben in."

"So I understand," I said.

Jack found us a car, and we were driven back to Detroit. As we drove in, I put my arm around Lena. She was shivering. "That louse," she whispered, and I said to her, "The hell with him. He doesn't matter. Ben doesn't matter." It had taken me a long, long time to say it that simply and even to understand it a little. We saw the plant in the distance, the huge, sprawling length of it speechless, gaunt, expressive only in what one knew or understood of its present, its past, and its future. I pointed to it, and said to Lena,

"That matters. It's all there."

"I wish I had a home," Lena whispered. "I wish to hell I had a home, Al. I want to go home, and there's no place to go. Do you have a home, Al?"

"Not to speak of."

"Where'd you come from, Al? I think you told me once —someplace near Rochester, New York?"

"Someplace near there."

It was cold in the car, and she pressed against me. The car was an old Buick. The driver sat in front, with a friend who had come along for the ride and the ride back. I sat in back with Lena.

"Funny, Al," she said. "I feel comfortable with you. Like I've known you forever."

"Almost forever, when you think about it."

"I don't like to think about it. I'm thirty-six years old, Al. It frightens me to think about it."

Then she was silent, until we came to the hotel. We didn't

have to register, since the room was held and paid for in the union's name. It had twin beds. "It'll do for us," I said to Lena.

"Brother and sister." She stared at me hopelessly, then walked around the room as if it caged her, long strides, a tall, long-boned, beautiful woman. "Al," she said, wheeling to face me, "didn't you ever want me—ever once in all those damned years?"

"I wanted you," I said. "I still do."

"Why in hell do I always feel sorry for you?"

I shook my head. She came over to me, and I took her in my arms. "Oh, Jesus, Al," she whispered, "feel a little sorry for me now. I was right at the end of the rope. If you hadn't done that—"

But I didn't do it because she was at the end of a rope. I did it because something had happened to me or begun to happen, and because what I felt for her was more than I had felt for any woman in a very long time.

8

Ben had phoned to say that he would join me for dinner, the conference with the governor and the company people to follow. Lena and I had a drink in the bar just before dinner. She didn't want to meet Ben. She said that she would have a sandwich in the room.

"Try to get a typewriter up in the room," I said to her. "Ben wants me to do the release on this tonight if it winds up tonight."

"Will it?"

"He thinks so," I said. "Take a nap, just in case you're up half the night."

"You understand why I don't want to see Ben, don't you, Al?"

"I understand."

368

"What did he say about Mark? People think of themselves—there's nothing wrong with that. But I know how it must be for Ben without Mark. Was he terribly upset?"

There was no point in lying to her. "He never mentioned Mark," I replied.

"No. I can't believe that."

"He was full of a great many things," I told her. "We both know Ben. We know him a long, long time."

"I suppose we do," Lena said slowly.

I took her up to the room and left her there. It was a half hour past midnight when I returned, and she was sprawled on one of the beds, asleep. Gently, I awakened her, and she was able to smile when she saw me. "Hello, Al," she said. "My dear Al—"

I asked her how she felt.

"Good enough. You want to work?"

"I'll dictate. You're not too tired for dictation?"

"Let me wash up. Some cold water, and I'll be all right."

A few minutes later, she had seated herself with a pad on her knee, and I began:

"Last night, December 23, 1937, Benjamin Renwell Holt, president of the International Miners Union, met with the governor of Michigan and with the representatives of the largest automobile manufacturer in the world. They met on the twelfth day of the sit-down strike of the auto workers of Blent, Michigan—a strike whose drama and spirit has captured the attention and has stimulated the imagination of the entire world.

"Each day of this strange and original strike, during which ten thousand workers occupied the plant in which they worked and held it in ransom for a union contract, has supplied increasingly tense drama—a drama which culminated in a battle of giants in a room of the Prince George Hotel in Detroit—"

"That last is awkward," Lena said. "It might be better simply to say that the last act took place here in the hotel."

"It's all right if you want to change it. Now I'll continue.

"Three parties entered the room, each determined to wring concessions from the others. But of the three, only Ben Holt knew that so long as he lived and breathed, there could be no concessions concerning that which was basic to his existence—the right of workers to organize into unions and to bargain collectively. He went into this historic meeting determined to win that right for the auto workers, just as he had won it through his years of struggle for the coal miners."

Lena looked up at me now. "Do you want it that way, Al?"

"Do you think it's a lie?"

"I wasn't at the conference, Al."

"You don't have to be there to know whether that's a lie or not."

"Then you tell me, Al."

"Honey, I'm not writing history or rewriting history. Ben asked me to do this. I haven't quit my job yet, so I'm doing it."

"What really happened in that room, Al?"

I thought about it for a while, before I said, "What had to happen. The time was ripe. You remember 1924?"

"I remember it," Lena nodded.

"You remember how we went out to the Arrowhead Pit? Ben had gone to Cairo. Things moved. Things happened. You couldn't change anything and I couldn't. Do you think Ben could have?"

"I've often wondered," Lena said.

"I doubt it. We lost the strike. Ben couldn't stop that. Then the union crumbled—could Ben or anyone have stopped it?"

"I don't know, Al."

"When we came into the conference tonight, I knew what had to happen. So did Ben. It's a chain of things, and God knows where the beginning is. The auto workers took the plant. Thousands of other workers supported them, and all over the country people prayed for them and supported them too. Some of the National Guardsmen were auto work-

370

ers and some of them were rubber workers and other kinds of workers, and none of them knew what they would do if they were ordered to take that plant by force. Ben knew that. The president of the company knew that. The governor knew it. And in Washington, the President of the United States knew it. So whatever they might have hedged with, they knew when they walked into that room with Ben tonight that an agreement would be signed. There was no other way out of it for any of them."

"Is that what you're going to write?" Lena asked.

"No, that's not what I am going to write. It's also late. Do you mind if I continue?"

"Go ahead," Lena said. "That's what I'm here for."

A half hour later, I came to the end of the piece:

"Thus, one man emerges as the giant the American labor movement has waited for, hoped for, prayed for—a man called Benjamin Renwell Holt. The undisputed leader of American labor today, a man dedicated to the creation of a mighty federation of industrial unions, he stands erect and triumphant, the eyes of the whole nation upon him—"

I sprawled on my bed, smoking, watching Lena as she typed it out.

9

There was a party going on in Ben's suite, and he had asked me to come down there the moment the release was finished. He asked me to bring Lena when I told him that she was in Detroit with me. The party was in the way of a victory celebration, and there would be people from Blent there and people from other places too, and it was likely to go on all night.

Lena said that she wouldn't come with me, to Ben's suite, but would stay in the room and pack, if I didn't mind. "You're not tired?" I wondered. But she had slept for three hours and was more worried about me. I told her that I could sleep on a train or a plane or anywhere, which was more or less true.

The suite was packed. Counting newspapermen, there must have been almost a hundred people jammed in there, and I imagine that the noise kept half the hotel awake. If the hotel had objections, they didn't voice them. The Miners Union was picking up the tab, and a steady stream of waiters brought mountains of sandwiches and crates of champagne, whisky, gin, or whatever your fancy turned to. As more and more people poured in, the hotel made an adjoining suite available. It was not enough. The party poured out into the corridors.

I fought my way in and finally managed to break through the press of people to where Ben was. He greeted me with a bear hug, and pulled me with him into a washroom, locking the door behind him. "Isn't this a hell of a note?" he grinned. "That we got to lock ourselves into a can to get a few words in private. Where's Lena?"

I gave him the release instead of answering his question, and immediately he began to read it. While he read, I watched him. He was in a condition of high excitement, reward, and achievement—and more than anything else at that moment, he desired to read the picture of himself on the typewritten sheets. When he had finished, he said,

"That's it! Al, how do you do it, every time?"

"What do I do with it now?"

"I'll take it," he said, putting it in his pocket. "I'll get the local boys here to turn it out immediately—but, by God, if it comes to the press, I'll read them this myself. To hell with modesty. I don't feel modest tonight. I'm sitting right on top of the world tonight."

"I'm glad you feel that way, Ben," I said.

"Sure you are! I wish Mark was here with us—all of us together to see this happen. That's how it should be."

"Well, I'm glad I'm here tonight, anyway, Ben, because I'm leaving you."

"What? You mean you're going back to Pomax? Al, you can't do that. I need you here with me."

"I don't mean Pomax, Ben," I said carefully. "I'm leaving the union for good. I'm quitting."

"Al, are you out of your mind?"

"No—no, I'm quitting, Ben."

"Al, you're crazy or you're drunk! Which is it?"

"I'm sober, Ben."

"Then what in hell are you talking about? This is no time to talk like that. This is a victory celebration. You want to cry on my shoulder, do it tomorrow. I've had a long day, Al, and I've had it."

"I know, Ben. It just works out that way. I'm sorry, but I can't help it."

"Why? All I'm asking is why?"

"It's no use trying to explain."

"Al, you son of a bitch—Al, do you know what I made up my mind to do? I made up my mind that when we shift our operations to Washington, I'd put you on the payroll for fifteen thousand a year. That's a promise. Al, this is only the beginning. We're going to have something so big and powerful I don't even dare to dream about it—and you, you son of a bitch, telling me you're quitting! The hell with that now! You want to talk to me, talk to me tomorrow. Get drunk now! Live a little! Quitting! You bastard!"

He put an arm around me and swept me back into the suite with him. He was immediately surrounded by people, and I was able to fight my way out of there unnoticed.

When I returned to the room, Lena had our suitcases packed. She told me that she had been able to make reservations on the first plane to New York, at six o'clock in the morning. Since it was after 3 A.M. already, we had time for breakfast before we left for the airport, and then not too long a wait there.

"Did you tell him?" Lena wanted to know.

"I tried."

"He wouldn't believe you?"

"No, he wouldn't believe me," I said.

"I didn't think he would," Lena said. "It couldn't make any sense to him."

10

Lena and I were married in New York. We never returned to Pomax again. Lena had nothing there that she wanted, and the few things of my own that remained there were mailed to me by Oscar Suzic. Ben sent me a check of a thousand dollars for severance pay and a check for half that amount to Lena. The letter that came with it said:

Dear Al:

I had to let my anger cool down before I could write this at all. It has always seemed to me that there is a right way and a wrong way of doing things, and I don't mind saying that you chose the wrong way. There were only two people in my life that I trusted completely and felt close to—as close as to blood brothers. Those two were yourself and Mark Golden. Mark died, and you walked out. I'm not going to ask you why, because at this moment, I just don't give a damn.

In appreciation of your loyalty during the past years, I am enclosing this check. I wish you and Lena the best for the future.

I did not hear from Ben Holt again, until I saw him for the last time in 1954. The years between that time and the time we had left Detroit were spent by Lena and myself in upstate New York, where I took over my father's weekly, paid off the debts, and managed to operate a fairly successful small-town newspaper. For the first time in our lives, Lena and I were reasonably content, reasonably happy. I would note an Associated Press piece on occasion, such as the item which told that Benjamin Renwell Holt of the Miners Union had raised his pay to fifty thousand dollars a year, or the item that told of the purchase of the new Union

374

Building in Washington, or the item that spoke of the first great coal strike after Pearl Harbor—of the beginning of the violent feud between the President of the United States and Benjamin Holt.

Lena and I talked about these things, but not to distraction. Time blurs the edges of everything.

In the spring of 1954, Lena and I took a much needed holiday in New York City. The years had been kind to both of us, and if Lena's hair was white, her figure was still slim and firm, her eyes as blue and exciting as ever. There was an afternoon when I left her at a matinee that she wanted to see and I wanted to avoid; and since the day was bright and pleasant, I walked uptown along Madison Avenue. I was passing the street entrance of a brokerage house, when a man emerged who looked familiar, and a moment later, I was shaking hands with Oscar Suzic—a heavier, older Oscar Suzic, but still the man I had known and liked.

With a mixture of pleasure and embarrassment, pleasure at seeing me, embarrassment at emerging from the brokerage house, he explained that he had a few shares of stock that required some attention. "We all begin to think about our old age, don't we, Al?" I agreed that we did, and said that I wished I had a few decent stocks. "Ben is the one to advise you on that," Oscar said. "You know the way Ben is—anything he touches he has to learn from A to Z."

Ben was that way, I agreed.

"He began investing about eight years ago," Oscar said. "He's a very wealthy man now," he added with respect. "But it hasn't changed him, Al. His principles still stand."

"How is Ben?"

"Al," he said, "why don't you come along with me? They're giving a little reception for Ben at the Astor, nothing very big, cocktails and so on, just an opportunity for him to pass the time of day with the local labor leaders here in town. I'm on my way there now."

"You think it would be all right, Oscar? No warning— just to drop me in there?"

"Of course it would be all right. Ben always speaks of you. I know he'd like to see you."

"I'd like to see him," I agreed.

When we came into the room at the Astor, I saw Ben immediately, looming over the circle that surrounded him. At sixty-two, his hair was white but unthinned, still a great mop and more the lion's mane than ever. His girth had increased, his neck had thickened, but he remained a big man rather than a fat man. He spotted me over the heads of the people around him, fixed his eyes on me, and then pushed through toward me, rolling on like some implacable machine, until he reached me and threw his arms around me in that bear hug that I remembered so well.

"Al Cutter!" he cried. "Son of a bitch, it's Al Cutter!" And he turned to the men near him and roared, "Union men, you call yourselves—Al Cutter here could teach the lot of you what a real trade-union man is! And on twenty cents a day!" And to me, "Maybe we both could—hey, Al?"

"It's good to see you, Ben."

"Good to see you! Wait until I tell Dotty that I ran into Al Cutter in New York!"

"How is she, Ben?"

"Great. You know, some woman's trouble, none of us are getting younger, but that's over now. She's fine. We moved into our new house last year, and she still hasn't finished decorating. You know the way women are about fixing up a place, Al."

"I know."

"What have you been doing with yourself, Al?"

"Running a little country weekly upstate."

"I heard something about that. How are you making out?"

"We manage."

"You and Lena. How is she?"

"Beautiful as ever."

"I'll bet. You know something, Al," Ben said, his voice dropping, "for your sake, I'm sorry we ever split. You'd have done well if you had stuck with me. Take Jack Mullen

for example. He's one of the biggest independent coal operators in western Pennsylvania today. Gives us a little trouble
at contract time because he knows all the answers, but we
work it out. I know that kind of thing wouldn't be for you,
but I would have had you on the payroll for twenty-five
thousand a year by now. Take Oscar here—he's become a
very shrewd investor. He's worth a hundred thousand if he's
worth a nickel. Well, things are different, easier some ways,
harder other ways. You have to have both points of view.
The whole country's different today, Al—and a damn sight
better, if you ask me."

"It couldn't be much worse than in the old days, Ben," I
agreed.

"Isn't that the truth. You remember those days, Al? By
golly, we ought to sit down with a bottle and have a good
talk. You know, we got a union weekly now too, half a
million copies each edition. It's a big enterprise. Our advertis-
ing revenue alone is over a million a year. I'll bet that tops
your sheet."

"It certainly does," I said.

"Well, what do they say—the old order changeth and so
forth. It would be a hell of a world if it didn't. Now, let me
buy you a drink."

I had the drink and I left. It was still a bright and lovely
afternoon as I walked back to the hotel, but when I got up
to our room, I was drowsy, and I lay down on the bed. I
must have dozed, for I seem to remember a dream of Pomax
with the cold rain falling, and the miners' kids, all indifferent
to the weather, running barefoot through the rain as they
floated sticks in the gutters.

Lena awakened me, and I asked her how the matinee
had been.

"Delicious. There's this charming French gentleman who's
a *couturier*—that's a dress designer to you—and he has the
most famous establishment in Paris. Or at least it was. Now
he's going broke, but he's too proud to admit it to anyone,
and he has this model who falls in love with him. Well, any-

one would. He's just beautiful—I fell in love with him my-self, the way you keep me penned up like a prisoner out there in the sticks. Anyway, it turns out that this model is the daughter of an American millionaire, and the question is will she bring her friends, all millionaires, of course, in to bail him out, which will make him as proud and snobbish as he was before—he belongs to the nobility, did I tell you?—or will she let him go broke? He's nicer when he's broke."

"Well, which does she choose?" I asked her.

"See it yourself and find out. What did you do all after-noon?"

"I took a walk."

"Was it fun?"

"I met someone I used to know," I said.

"Anyone I know?"

"No," I said. "No one you know."